DEVELOPMENTS IN SEDIMENTOLOGY 40

CLAY MINERALS

A Physico-Chemical Explanation of their Occurrence

DEVELOPMENTS IN SEDIMENTOLOGY 40

CLAY MINERALS

A Physico-Chemical Explanation of their Occurrence

B. VELDE

Ecole Normale Supérieure, Laboratoire de Géologie, 46 Rue d'Ulm, 75230 Paris Cédex (France)

ELSEVIER
Amsterdam — Oxford — New York — Tokyo   1985

ELSEVIER SCIENCE PUBLISHERS B.V.
1 Molenwerf
P.O. Box 211, 1000 AE Amsterdam, The Netherlands

Distributors for the United States and Canada:

ELSEVIER SCIENCE PUBLISHING COMPANY INC.
52, Vanderbilt Avenue
New York, N.Y. 10017

Library of Congress Cataloging in Publication Data

Velde, B.
    Clay minerals.

    (Developments in sedimentology ; 40)
    Bibliography: p.
    Includes index.
    1. Clay minerals.   I. Title.   II. Series.
QE389.625.V43 1985   549'.6   84-21204
ISBN 0-444-42423-7 (U.S.)

ISBN 0-444-42423-7 (Vol. 40)
ISBN 0-444-41238-7 (Series)

Printed in The Netherlands

BIBLIOGRAPHICAL DATA

Bruce Velde, Directeur de Recherche in the Centre National de la Recherche Scientifique, now works in the Laboratoire de Géologie, Ecole Normale Supérieure in Paris. He began his undergraduate work in the University of Illinois in 1956 and obtained a PhD from the University of Montana in 1962. He was a fellow at the Carnegie Geophysical Laboratory, Wash. D.C. in 1962-1964 and 1976. His career in C.N.R.S. began in the Sorbonne, Laboratoire de Pétrographie in 1965.

PREFACE

This book follows another which must be considered as a first attempt to put some order in the house of clay petrology. Its limited success was encouraging enough to begin again the long process of reviewing the current literature, extracting the pertinent data, summarizing and finally analyzing the information at our disposal. A certain number of the questions posed then can now be answered, yet many others await investigation by clay mineralogists. Whatever the short-comings of this book are, they reflect those of the author and not those of his many helpful colleagues and friends. I would like to express my gratitude to John Hower for his guidance and patience over the years, to Alain Meunier for bravely attempting to make sense of my enthusiasm, to Jacqueline Beauquin for calmly accepting and correcting persistent inconsistency.

CONTENTS

I - INTRODUCTION

The study of clay minerals has made a series of advances which were due to new methods of investigation ; such as X-ray diffractometry, or new ideas concerning their origin and evolution, such as the concept of clay petrology proposed by C.E. Weaver (1959) and the concept of clay mineral association proposed by G. Millot (1964). In fact, as has been the case in many other disciplines, progress in understanding the fundamentals of clay mineralogy has come in uneven steps. The essential work in the 19th and early 20th century was that of discovery, isolation and identification of the minerals. Later work in the mid-twentieth century concerned a definition of the structure of clays and their chemistry which is related to this structure. The Geological Survey in the United States produced a number of fundamental papers which defined the chemistry of clay minerals and the mineralogy of phyllosilicates. The next endeavor was to determine the geology of clays-developed by Weaver in the United States and Millot in France among others. Meanwhile experiments were conducted, mainly in France and the United States which attempted to quantify the chemistry of clay mineral genesis by experiment or calculation. These two themes have continued sporadically until the present. In 1977, I attempted to summarize the available data, interpret and sort out the major evident "truths" and then propose a series of geochemical and petrographic systems which might explain why many clay assemblages are found commonly in nature. Since that time, the electron microprobe has come on the scene. This tool permits one to determine, in favorable circumstances, the spacial and chemical factors which result in the genesis of clay minerals. This new information allows one to make a further stride in the science of clay mineralogy. However, the era of electron microprobe studies is just beginning which means that we have much more to learn in the immediate future.

The new information, and that resulting from subsequent more "classical" studies, has changed the ideas which I had developed in certain cases but in a general way they have served to amplify and extend the domains of investigation which can now be analyzed. For example, we can now look at the problems of clay mineral genesis during weathering in a mineralogical and chemical way which was previously impossible. The same is true for hydrothermal alteration as well as sandstone diagenesis. A new field of endeavor has occurred recently, that of the deep-sea alteration of basalts, which allows one to consider the major chemical transfers which influence the composition of the upper oceanic crust as well as that of the sea. These new fields of investigation will be covered in this book using the "old methods" which were applied to the previously available data for clays in sedimentary and sedimentary rock environments.

What then are these old methods ? First, it is considered necessary to determine which clay phases are commonly present and which phases have been sufficiently studied to give an idea of their chemical composition limits. These limits are defined according to the results published in the literature. Most data used appeared between 1950 and 1982. These studies are based upon pure mineral samples which were analyzed by classical methods and which could be identified by X-ray diffraction methods. These are "well characterized" minerals. Microprobe data are compared to these data because, in most instances, X-ray diffraction information is not available for the exact mineral analyzed. Also, classical analysis methods allow one to distinguish Fe^{2+} from Fe^{3+}, a very important measurement as we will see.

One must stop here a moment to consider the processes that are involved in a mineral analysis. Most important, when one makes a classical determination either for X-ray or chemical analysis, a large amount of material is necessary, several hundreds of milligrams, which almost by definition involves material of several different compositions. The microprobe has shown us this. Thus classical analyses are frequently average values for mineral mixtures. However, averages are only useful as long as they are considered as such. The author feels, that adequate X-ray data are absolutely necessary to assure that one knows which mineral species is present. Thus microprobe data must be compared, in most cases, to data gathered by other means. Once the types of chemical substitutions are determined for a mineral species, it is possible to extend the limits of our knowledge with electron microprobe data.

The next step is to determine the mineral associations of the different clay minerals. This is the method of facies used in metamorphic petrology with such great success. Which minerals occur together and where ? Using these generalizations one can attempt to construct a chemiographic framework for clay petrology. The major problem with such an approach is the possible metastable persistence of a phase or its crystallization outside of its stability field. These problems occur in metamorphic petrology and even more frequently in igneous petrology but the practitioners of these arts have not yet been severly hampered by them. There is no reason why clay mineralogists should be. However, we will use possibly more caution in our pronouncements since we know that kinetic problems are great at lower temperatures (which are relative anyway) and that the domains of clay mineral stability are notably difficult to determine at low temperatures, at least as far as geological conditions are concerned.

The phase diagrams established in this way will be useful to interpret clay mineral assemblages found in nature with regard to their geological significance. Certain shortcomings will be pointed out (others will undoubtedly remain and will be pointed out by the interested reader). The object of this book then is to propose a method for considering the geology of clay minerals which will be modified and perfected as time goes on. Science means re-interpretation of the past. One can never expect to formulate eternal truths in all their detail - at least not in the natural sciences during the latter part of the twentieth century.

What then will be used here for the foundations of the analysis ?

1 - Choice of Information

The information which is used to construct this petrologic interpretation of clay mineral assemblages is essentially of three types : chemical analyses of natural minerals, assemblages of minerals reported in the literature and experimental determinations of clay mineral stabilities. In using data from the literature one is forced to select from the mass available, that which seems most accurate and that which is most directly applicable to a given problem. Inherent in such a process is the problem of personal bias and unintentional oversight. It is certain that pertinent studies have been omitted from the compilation presented here, but it is hoped that these omissions do not prevent an understanding of the petrology of clay minerals. Basically only studies posterior to 1950 have been considered, because information before this time could not be correctly characterized due to relatively poor X-ray diffraction techniques. The main criterion for using studies reporting natural mineral compositions is the quality of X-ray diffraction data permitting the verification of the presence of single phase or multiphase samples. Low angles of 2θ are especially critical where the detection of highly expandable phases is concerned. Thus certain chemical analyses have been arbitrarily eliminated for lack of assurance that a given sample is monomineralic. Nonetheless this problem cannot be discounted even in the analyses selected.

Each chemical analysis thus chosen has been calculated into a chemical structural formula using a computer program. The method of calculation is that used by Foster (1953 ; 1962) where a given number of oxygens and hydroxyls is assumed to be present ; $O_{10}(OH)_2$ for a 2:1 structure, $O_{10}(OH)_8$ for a 2:2 chlorite type structure and $O_5(OH)_4$ for a 1:1 structure. The following site occupancies disqualified an analysis from use : > 3.05 octahedral ions, > 4.05 silicon and > 1.10 interlayer ions for non-chlorite structures. Calcium contents above 0.20 ion in low temperature micas and in chlorites were considered to be excessive. Trioctahedral, low-alkali phases are considered in the vermiculite-corren-

site group. The possibility of significant secondary iron
oxidation in numerous samples is considered to be small and
in any event inconsequential to the general trend of mineral
compositions, thus water contents were not calculated into
the structural formulas.

The experimental studies have been chosen mainly
for the completeness of reported experimental conditions and
for their apparent approach to an equilibrium assemblage.
These criteria are difficult to adhere to in that experimental data are not abundant and frequently one must make do
with what is available in order to gain an understanding of
a given problem. However, where several studies overlap,
that with the longest experimental durations or reversal
equilibria is chosen by preference. Nevertheless a certain
amount of caution is necessary to interpret the available
experimental results.

TABLE 1

SOURCES OF MINERAL CHEMICAL ANALYSES

Dioctahedral montmorillonites

Allietti and Allietti (1962) ; Anderson and Reynolds (1966) ; Early et al. (1953) ; Foster (1956) ; Schultz (1969) ; Stringham and Taylor (1950) ; Walker et al. (1967).

Dioctahedral mixed layered

Ball (1968) ; Bonorino (1959) ; Brown and Weir (1963) ; Cole (1966) ; Hower and Mowatt (1966) ; Kodama (1966) ; Schultz (1969) ; Steiner (1968) ; Tomita et al. (1969) ; Weaver (1956) ; Hamilton (1967) ; Chen and Brindley (1976).

Trioctahedral montmorillonites

Cahoon (1954) ; Deer et al. (1962) ; Faust et al. (1959) ; Foster (1963) ; Whelan (1961) ; Trauth (1977).

Celadonites

Hendricks and Ross (1941) ; Pirani (1963) ; Wise and Eugster (1964).

Glauconites

Bailey and Atherton (1970) ; Bentor and Kastner (1965) ; Hendricks and Ross (1941) ; Pirani (1963) ; Wise and Eugster (1964).

Illites

Gabis (1963) ; Gaudette et al. (1966) ; Hower and Mowatt (1966) ; Mackenzie (1957).

Chlorites

Data compiled in Velde (1973) and new analyses.

Sepiolite-Palygorskite

Brown (1961) ; Ehlmann et al. (1962) ; Frank-Kamenckiji and Klockova (1969) ; Vanden Heuvel (1966) ; Kulbicki (1959) ; Nagy and Bradley (1955) ; Preisinger (1959) ; Tien (1973) ; Trauth (1977).

---

2 - Clay Mineral Names and Structure

In order to avoid confusion or misunderstanding, it is necessary to define the major terms which will be used in the following discussions. No new definitions will be proposed here but a simple outline of the basic vocabulary is given which will be used to permit a discussion of the problems of physical chemistry, of phyllosilicates and other silicate minerals found in clay mineral suites.

a - Basic Divisions

It is useful as a point of departure to briefly describe the basic crystal lattice common to phyllosilicates. The elementary character is the Si-O tetrahedral linkage of an essentially two-dimensional, hexagonally symmetric, network. One side of this "sheet" network is coordinated through a common oxygen atom with other cation-oxygen-hydroxyl complexes. These are linked by an important component of covalent bonding or van der Walls type bonds. The key to phyllosilicate structures is the silicon-oxygen network which determines the shape and extent of the structure.

A superficial classification of the common clay minerals can be based upon the number of ions present in the octahedrally coordinated sites. There are three sites available and their occuppancy is two ions in the case of dioctahedral minerals and between 2.5 and 3 ions for the "trioctahedral" minerals. There appear to be no intermediate occupancies except where lithium, or possibly a certain amount of sodium , is present. These alkali-minerals are rare and difficult to identify. As a result they will not be considered here. It appears, according to ion exchange experiments and synthesis experiments, that it is easier to displace octahedral ions than tetrahedral ions, especially divalent octahedral ions (unpublished observations by the author).

Thus the number and kinds of ions in the octahedral and tetrahedral site define the mineral groups (Table 2 ;

Figure 1). In cases where cations are bonded in ionic coordination to the oxygen nets (interlayer ions), the negative attractive charge arises from substitution in either the tetrahedral (SiO_4) or octahedrally coordinated positions. These substitutions increase the net negative charge for the whole 2:1 structure, and, since the oxygen network is fixed in kind and quantity, this large imbalance is satisfied by the addition of predominantly ionically bonded cations in the interlayer position. The basic 2:1 network contains $O_{10}(OH)_2$, the hydroxyls are in coordination uniquely with the octahedral ions. The negative charge is -22.

It is important to note that dioctahedral minerals with a high charge imbalance (0.7-1.0) are potassic and behave as micas (6 in table 2). These minerals have a fixed basal spacing (001) which is near 10 Å. No sodic or calcic micas are stable at low temperatures in what can be considered a clay mineral range. Some Na and Ca can be present but it is minor in amount. Paragonite $[NaAl_2Si_3Al\ O_{10}(OH)_2]$ which is the sodic analog of muscovite, occurs at the extreme limit of what one can call clay mineral facies. No high charge mica phases (fixed 10 Å basal spacing) are present in the trioctahedral types at low temperatures.

Expanding phases are those minerals with an interlayer charge between about 0.6 and 0.25 ; such minerals can easily accept various combinations of ions and polar molecules in the interlayer position thus changing the overall cell dimension in the c sin ß (basal direction). Normally, water, glycerol or ethylene glycol are used to change the interlayer spacing and thus identify a mineral. The term fully expandable is used here when a mineral attains a 17-18 Å repeat distance upon saturation in an ethylene glycol atmosphere. It is possible to have an interlayering of the different types of basic structures. Although each layer maintains its chemical and structural identity, X-ray diffraction by interlayered minerals gives average values for the whole crystal. As a result, a mixed-layered mineral will give diffraction characteristics intermediate between those of the two constituent layer types. "Fully expandable montmorillonite" distinguishes between 100 % montmorillonite layers and a structure that is built of a mixture of expanding and non-expanding layers.

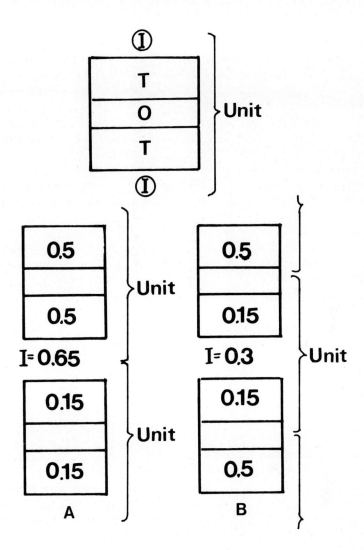

Figure 1 - Representation of possible unit cell structures for interlayered minerals.

T = Tetrahedral layer, O = octahedral layer, I = interlayer site. Possible charges in tetrahedral sites are 0.5 for a mica layer and 0.15 for a beidellite(smectite) layer. Total charge on a mica is 1.0 due to charge on two tetrahedral layers of the TOT structure and 0.30 on a beidellite TOT structure. If TOT charge = 1.0 and 0.3 in a mixed layered mineral, the charge on each interlayer site is 0.65 (case A). If the unit layer is considered to be $\frac{1}{2}$OT - T$\frac{1}{2}$O, as in case B, the interlayer charges are 0.3 and 1.0 successively.

NAME	TETRAHEDRAL LAYERS	OCTAHEDRAL OCCUPANCY	PREDOMINANT INTERLAYER ION	INTERLAYER CHARGE
1. Kaolinite	1	2	0	0
2. Serpentine–7 Å chlorite	1	3	0	0
3. Pyrophyllite	2	2	0	0
4. Talc	2	3	0	0
5. 14 Å chlorite	2	3	$(Mg, Fe^{2+}, Al)OH$	–
6. Micaceous minerals ; illite, celadonite, glauconite	2	2	K	0.7–1.0
7. Vermiculite–saponite	2	2.5–3.0	Na, K, Ca, Mg	0.2–0.8
8. Smectite ; montmorillonite, beidellite, nontronite	2	2	Na, K, Ca, Mg	0.2–0.6

TABLE 2

The expanding phases are called smectites, the classification of which must first be divided into dioctahedral and trioctahedral types. The latter will be called saponites. The dioctahedral smectites are known to occur with two types of charge-creating substitutions. One occurs in the octahedral site M $(R^3_{2-y} R^3_y) Si_4 O_{10} (OH_2).nH_2O$ where a divalent ion substitutes for a trivalent ion. This is montmorillonite, a name formerly used in a general way for dioctahedral smectites. Another substitution M $R^3_2 (Si_{4-x} R^3_x) O_{10} (OH)_2.nH_2O$ is that of beidellite and nontronite where a trivalent ion replaces the quadrivalent silicon. The term smectite will be used in this text as a non-specific term for dioctahedral expanding phases. Montmorillonite, beidellite and nontronite will be used when the substitution is specifically known or highly suspected.

Vermiculite is generally considered to be a highly charged saponite which has varying expanding properties depending upon the origin of the sample and the care with which the expandability determination is performed. It is possible that natural saponite and vermiculite form one continuous series. However not enough data is available at present to substantiate this position. The problems will be considered in a later chapter.

b - Mixed Layering

We have thus far dismissed mixed layering as the mixing of different mineral layers in a single structure. It is necessary to go further. If we consider the different layers which must be stacked into a coherent sequence we must look at the cell dimension of the layers in the sheet directions, a and b. Lattice dimension in the b direction has been determined by the present author for several synthetic dioctahedral smectites and Suquet et al. (1977) have looked at some trioctahedral minerals (saponites and vermiculites). The b cell dimension can change as a function of hydration state and as a function of the exchange cation present (Fig. 2). However, neither of these effects in either type of dioctahedral smectite, beidellite or montmorillonite, will produce b cell dimensions which are those of a dioctahedral mica-potassic muscovite or sodic paragonite. Since the smectite layers must "fit" with mica layers in a stacking sequence in order to be interlayered, it seems reasonable to expect that cell dimensions in the sheet direction should be as compatible as possible. Figure 2 does indicate that more hydrous montmorillonites will approach a mica dimension to a greater extent than will beidellites. It is also evident that in any event the greater hydration state favors an approach to a potassic mica value. This is important in that potassic mica is the only form found at low temperatures. Velde and Weir (1979) did show that increased

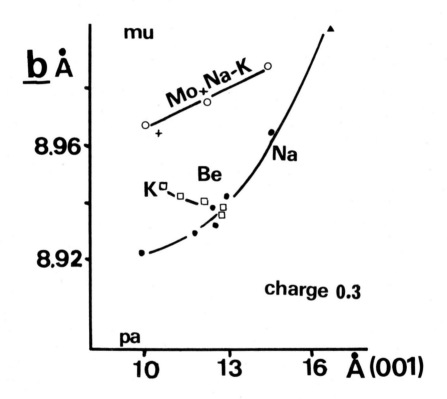

Figure 2 - Plot of b cell dimension as measured by the (060) reflection against the basal spacing (001) of synthetic alumino-magnesian smectites. Circles show sodium exchanged and crosses potassium exchanged montmorillonites : dots sodium exchanged beidellites and squares potassium-exchanged beidellites. Triangle shows sodium montmorillonite value of Ravina and Low (1972). mu = muscovite ; pa = paragonite cell dimensions, charge on all smectites is 0.3 per unit.

silica content in mica - which produced illite - decreased the **b** cell dimension of a mica-like non expandable layering. This occurs commonly because the **b** cell dimensions are the most compatible forms.

If this is the case, what can one expect of such a structure on a layer by layer scale ? It is assumed that the low surface charge (0.2-0.6) on a smectite layer allows its swelling ability to occur. A high charge in dioctahedral minerals, produces a mica (10 Å) when potassium is present. Hower and Mowatt (1966) and Huff and Turkmenoglu (1981) demonstrate that the potassium content of mixed layered dioctahedral minerals is a function of the mica (non-expanding) layers present and of the total charge of the structure. In fact the smectite layers present can be considered to have a charge between 0.3 and 0.4, a much more restrained charge than that for single phase fully expanding smectites in general. Cation exchange capacity is found to be an approximate measure of the number of expanded layers present. However, these authors did not wish to follow Weaver's (1956) suggestion that there are two consistent and different unit layers present - a mica and a smectite. What is then the problem ?

If we consider figure 1, where a beidellite$_{50}$ -mica$_{50}$ structure occurs, it is apparent that the interlayer site, where polar liquids enter, does not have a symmetric charge distribution on either side. One surface is high charge (mica), the other is low charge (smectite). Should a regular mixing of mica-smectite occur, what will its behavior be ? We know that mixed layered minerals show a systematic relation between charge and swelling capacity (Hower and Mowatt, 1966) and we know that it is possible to easily quantify the low charge expandable layers in mixed layered minerals as smectites through treatment with water of glycol (Reynolds **in** Brindley and Brown, 1980). A smectite layer somehow expands even in a regular mixed layered structure as shown in the figure 1, where all interlayer spacings have a high and low charge component.

We have assumed thus far as conventional wisdom (Brindley and Brown, 1980 is the latest) that the clay sheets are symmetrical on either side of the octahedral site, i.e. a mica or smectite tetrahedral layer is found above and below the octahedral layer. Thus the center of symmetry

in the **c** sin ß direction is the octahedral layer. This places a high charge surface opposite a low charge surface in
all interlayer sites. How then will there be some expanding
and some non-expanding interlayer sites ? If we assume that
the center of the structure is in the interlayer site and
thus on each side facing one another there are tetrahedral
layers with surface charges of the same nature (Fig. 1), it
should be possible to have expanding and non-expanding
interlayer sites. This representation means that the octahedral layer is common to a mica tetrahedral and a smectite
tetrahedral sheet. It must by consequence have a chemistry
and dimension common to both mineral types. This will be
discussed further in the chapter concerning smectites and
interlayered minerals.

c - Regular Mixed Layered Minerals

Allevardite is one specific mineral name and/or mineral group which should be more closely defined (Caillère
et al., 1950). Essentially this is an ordered, mixed layered
mineral, that is one with regularly alternating non-expanding and expandable layers. The major character of these
minerals is the presence of a "superstructure" reflection
due to the regular interstratification of expanding and
non-expanding layers. Sodic or sodi-potassic minerals tend
to contain less Mg + Fe than potassic forms and are thus
beidellitic (tetrahedrally charged) ; the more potassic types are predominantly montmorillonitic. The variety with
50 % mica-like (illite) layers is most often sodic or sodi-
potassic and called rectorite (Brown and Weir, 1963). There
are more potassic forms or regularly interstratied minerals
which have a strong tendency to contain fewer expandable
layers present ($\simeq$ 30-35 %). The ordering of the layers results is an apparent decreased number of expandable layers
which would be assessed as being about 20 % using conventional curves for X-ray diffraction diagrams (Reynolds and
Hower, 1970). A later section will deal more specifically
with the bulk compositions of these minerals, one type is
essentially the illite-beidellite series, the other the
illite-montmorillonite series. Solid solution between the
two is probably complete.

Although the type mineral allevardite is sodi-potassic the term is useful to include also the ordered struc-

ture with 30-50 % expandable layers, containing principally potassium as an interlayer ion and significant quantities of Mg^{2+} and Fe^{2+} in the octahedral position. It is certain that this designation or use of the term allevardite is not historically precise, nor in exact concordance with the original sample from Allevard, France (Caillère **et al.**, 1950) but its usefulness as a descriptive term is undeniable. In any event, the actual mineral name has been put in doubt by Brown and Weir (1963) since they assimilate it to the 50-50 expanding-mica structure which is both highly aluminous and sodic, and which is called rectorite. In the following discussions, the term rectorite will be reserved for the sodic paragonite-beidellite 1:1 interlayered mineral, allevardite for the essentially illite-montmorillonite ordered interlayered mineral commonly containing 30 % expandable layers. It is expected that a nearly complete series of bulk compositions can exist between the minerals. Both minerals are characterized by a superstructure which results in a definite X-ray diffraction maxima in the 24-29 Å region.

Another mixed layered structure which is quite important is the IMII-type which is described by Reynolds in Brindley and Brown (1980, chapter 4). Here the expanding layers normally make up less than 15 % of the structure. The ordering unit is no longer one mica and one smectite. High spacing ordering peaks are rare and one finds normally upon glycollation a < 10 Å peak of high intensity and another, low intensity peak whose spacing decreases from 12 Å to be lost in the 10 Å peak as the smectite content decreases (≃ 4 % smectite). Little compositional data is available for this structure and thus it has no mineral name as yet.

The trioctahedral minerals can also be interlayered. Most often the interlayering is between a smectite or vermiculite and a chlorite. One thus finds a 14 Å unit mixed with an expanding unit. Our present knowledge of the type of mixing, ordering, etc., is very limited. Basically one can divide the trioctahedral natural clay minerals into smectite (fully expandable), vermiculite (poorly expanding with no apparent segregation into expanding and chlorite layers) and corrensite (most often regularly ordered 1:1 (chlorite-smectite) groups. These are not mineralogic names or mineral types as such but they are useful to characterize the minerals found in clay mineral environments.

There are other known types of mixed layered minerals - some with more than two components - but their occurrence is apparently sporadic, or at least their identification has been sporadic up until now.

The composition and specific character of mixed
layering found for the di- and trioctahedral minerals will
be dealt with in detail in separate chapters.

d - Non-sheet Silicates

There are several other types of minerals commonly
found in clay particle size mineral assemblages (i.e., < 2
microns diameter ; Krumbein and Pettijohn, 1938). Apart from
quartz and amorphous materials, the two most important
groups are sepiolite-palygorskite and zeolites. These two
groups are similar in that they both contain free H_2O molecules in their structure. However the Si-O linkage is quite
different in each case.

Zeolites are tectosilicates whose structure is similar in certain respects to that of feldspars. The major
chemical and structural substitution is $M^+Al = Si$, i.e.,
silicon replaces aluminum plus one alkali (or in the case
of calcium) ion. Usually the exchange of one ion for two is
accompanied by an increase of free zeolite water in the
structure. As this substitution increases in importance, the
structure becomes more "open" and more variable
substitutions can take place, for example NH_4^+ for K^+, and so
forth.

Sepiolite and palygorskite are frequently associated in natural deposits. They are both fibrous in form, a
characteristic dictated by their chain-type (linear) structure. They contain hydroxyls, zeolitic and bound water. The
minerals are predominantly silico-magnesian containing va-
rying amounts of Al^{3+}, K^+, Ca^{2+}, Fe^{2+}, Fe^{3+} ions. Ideally :

Sepiolite   : $Si_{12}Mg_{8\ or\ 9}O_{30}(OH)_{4\ or\ 6}(OH)_4$.5 or 8 H_2O
Palygorskite : $Si_8Mg_5O_{20}(OH)_2(OH)_4$.4 H_2O

There can be significant Fe^{3+} substitution in sepiolite giving the species xylotile, but normally sepiolite contains
less R^3 than palygorskite. The mineral maintains a constant

structural dimension during normal clay mineral identification treatments. Most often cation exchange capacities are intermediate between non-expanding phyllosilicates and expandable forms. However these may be due to impurities.

3 - Chemical Systems

The essential problem in describing clay mineral assemblages is to establish the forces which were active in producing the aggregate of observed silicates. It is difficult to determine the extent to which all of the minerals present have reacted with their total environment - the measure of their approach to equilibrium for a given set of physical and chemical conditions. This difficulty essentially represents the difference between the most simplified treatment of phase equilibria and the reality of natural existence. Initially, all rocks which are found at the earth's surface must be judged to be grossly out of equilibrium with their environment. The means by which they have escaped the attainment of thermodynamic harmony with their environment are undoubtedly multiple, but nonetheless they present us with serious problems of kinetics, activity and crystallization. If all silicate materials were in equilibrium with their immediate environment, the entire surface of the earth would be made of clay minerals and oxides at the bottom on an aqueous solution which would contain large amounts of dissolved material. This not being the case, a large part of the raw material of geology is out of equilibrium with the forces which act upon it at the earth's surface.

This is not unexpected when one considers the definitions commonly imposed upon the thermodynamic systems used to describe the forces and reactions in geologic settings. A thermodynamic treatment of a problem imposes strict rules in order to allow a consistent and calculable description of physical-chemical phenomena. The usefulness of such conditions is demonstrated by the often heard statement that at present thermodynamic rules of behavior have not been observed to be violated. The differences noted between simplified thermodynamic prediction and actual examples are usually attributed to non-ideal behavior or metastable behavior of substances and thus dismissed by many authors as abberations in the general scheme of things due to the essentially capriceous behavior of the "real world". This "unpredictable" behavior is largely due to the fact that not enough

information is available to describe the observed phenomena
accurately. The difficulty does not lie with thermodynamic
theory but with the present state of our knowledge. Such
problems apart, thermodynamic principles prove to be extrem-
ly useful in the interpretation of natural phenomena and, in
fact, they are the best means at hand for dealing with these
problems. Utility is rarely synonymous with perfection.

Because the intent of this essay is not perfect
symmetry nor total rigor, the basis and derivation of the
thermodynamic principles involved in our discussions will
not be developed or discussed. There are numerous books
which do this in a more elegant way than could be expressed
here. We will use only the end products of such reasoning as
they apply most directly to the problem dealt with in the
pages to follow.

Chemical potential can be considered to contain
about three terms (Prigogine and Defray, 1954) :

$$\mu_i = \mu_i^\theta{}_{(P,T)} + RT\ln \gamma_i x_i + g_i^E$$

1 - where μ_i^θ refers to a pure substance. The variation in
   chemical potential is a function of the intensive variables of the system which are pressure and temperature ;

2 - where $RT\ln\gamma_i x_i$ refers to the effect of variable composition of a phase upon the chemical potential of component
   i ; $\gamma_i x_i$ = α or the activity of i. This is the function
   of mixing.

3 - where g_i^E refers to the importance of structural configuration of a phase upon the chemical potential of i which
   gives an excess function of mixing.

It is possible at present to assess the first factor for phyllosilicates fairly well, the second with somewhat less success and the third with great difficulty. The
first and second factors can be calculated for aqueous solutions with varying success. It is common current practice to
concentrate on thermodynamic properties of elements in
aqueous solution, equate the chemical potential of ions in
solution to that in solid phases and calculate mineral stability curves through the chemical potential of ions in solution. This is, of course, justifiable from a theoretical

standpoint when one assumes chemical equilibrium where $\mu_i^A = \mu_i^{B*}$, the chemical potential of i in phases A and B is identical at equilibrium.

Since the chemical potential is an intensive variable independent of the absolute number of ions present, it
can be determined at one point in a system and will be valid
for all phases present. This is very useful for geologists
in that one need not determine the size of the system for a
measurement. However, it is essential to know over what area
or distance the chemical potential of an element is constant. The scale of the system must be known in order to use
this measurement in an estimate of phase equilibrium.

Korzhinskii (1959, 1965) divides chemical components into two types - those whose mass is important in the
system and thus the quality of this element determines its
contribution to the Gibbs free energy of the system (inert
component) and those whose chemical potential is an intensive variable of the system (mobile component). This gives :

$$dG_0 = -SdT + VdP + \Sigma n_i d\mu_i + \Sigma \mu_e d_e$$

where the extensive function G is a factor of the intensive
variables temperature (T), pressure (P), the chemical potential of the perfectly mobile components (i) and the number
of ions of the inert components (e) which are extensive variables. It is very important to note that inert components
(extensive variables) can migrate into and out of a given
system. Their inert character is only relative to the mobile
(intensive variable) components.

The definition of perfectly mobile and inert components should also be valid for cases of ionic diffusion in
rocks and where no fluid is involved (Korzhinskii, 1965),
but this possibility does not concern us here since clay
mineral equilibria are dominated by the presence of liquid
or fluid aqueous solutions.

Although thermodynamic calculations are not made in
this text, the results of such exercises are displayed (as
phase equilibria diagrams) and discussed. Basically, solution chemistry-type systems are considered to have more components perfectly mobile than those commonly found at more
elevated physical conditions. Whether or not this is strict-

ly true remains to be seen, however, the approach of most investigators is in this direction.

One basic principle of Korzhinskii is that as chemical components become mobile, their role in the system changes from an extensive to intensive variable. If we use the phase rule $F = C + V_{int} - P$, where F = degrees of freedom, C = chemical components, V_{int} = intensive variables and P = number of phases present, the change of a component from inert to mobile decreases the value of C and increases the value of V_{int}. The result of this operation can be seen as follows : let us fix the degrees of freedom to be equal to the intensive variables so that general conditions of these variables can exist (one can vary to a reasonable extent the pressure, temperature or chemical potential of an element without changing the number or kind of phase present). Thus $F = V_{int}$ and the left hand side of the phase rule written as : $F - V_{int} = C-P$, becomes zero so that : $0 = C-P$ and $P = C$; since $F = V_{int}$ the left hand side and as a result the phases are equal in number to the inert chemical components. Thus for non-specific conditions of chemical potential, each element which becomes mobile reduces the number of phases which will be present by one. In clay systems with many mobile elements, the number of phases will be small in a given zone. This leads to mono-mineral rocks in the extreme. Thus clays which crystallize into multimineral assemblage zones will be influenced by several inert components while those which form few phases will indicate that most of the component elements were mobile.

What does this mean in concrete terms ? Simply this, if a solution permeates a rock, the response of the rock will be a function of the relative influence of the elements in the rock compared to those already in the solution. When the new phases reflect the character of the rock more than the incoming solution, the elements in the rock behave as inert components. If the phases formed in the rock reflect the composition (chemical potential) of the incoming solution, the majority of the chemical species are mobile components (i.e., their chemical potential is controlled from outside the immediate system). These are the parameters of clay mineralogy solids and solution. Clay mineralogy is most often concerned with the recrystallization of solids under the influence of aqueous solutions. Thus it is important to distinguish the origin of the chemical activity of a species - outside or inside the mass of the solids - in order to understand the reason for the assemblage observed. Again, one can witness loss or gain of a given inert component in a system. What is important is whether or not the new phases which are formed are controlled by the solids present or the chemical potential of the elements in solution which is imposed from outside the system.

Another factor which is very important to remember is that certain elements can be common to silicates, oxides and carbonates. Our attention regarding clays is normally focused on the silicate portion of the system or rock but one should not forget that iron for example can form an oxide which remains indifferent in many instances to the silicate reactions. If we put the silicate composition into a phase diagram we must be certain to take into account a loss of an element through the introduction of a new type of phase. They can be explained alternatively by saying that we add a variable, such as oxygen fugacity or carbonate activity which adds the possibility of creating a supplementary phase. Our natural tendency will be to ignore this further complication but it is often unwise. Thus attention should be paid to the presence of oxides and carbonates if they change their composition during a clay mineral sequence or if they suddenly appear and simultaneously the clay assemble changes. Iron can be extracted through oxidation and Mg, Fe^{2+} ions can be taken into carbonates. Other potential reactions are the destabilization of oxides and carbonates in the presence of silicates which can release iron, magnesium or calcium to the silicate system. In this way the activity of certain elements should be considered as a potential variable. These considerations are especially important when dealing with organic material in clay assemblages which can not only release CO_2 but which becomes chemically active as a reducing agent.

4 - Stability and Meta-Stability

The stable mineral or mineral assemblage for a given set of physical and chemical conditions is that with the lowest free energy under those conditions. The determination of this thermodynamic function for silicates is very difficult because :

- reaction rates in the laboratory and nature are very slow ;

- the atomic and hence energetic configuration of silicates is complex and subtle.

The experimentally determined values for certain minerals (Clark, 1966) and those calculated by different methods (Helgeson, 1968 ; Zen, 1969) indicate that gross differences in structure, or what are considered to be so from the standpoint of a mineralogist, result in relatively small (in percentage of the total) differences in free energy of formation for comparable numbers of atoms in the structure. This is even more striking when two alternative silicate assemblages are compared. It is frequently seen that ΔG for a possible reaction is only several percent of the total value (for example, Garrels, 1957). This obliges the initial determinations or calculations of the free energy for the individual minerals to be quite precise - frequently more so than can be done in the laboratory. This problem is increased as temperatures and pressures become significantly greater than those of 25°C and one atmosphere, where factors affecting the derivative of the free energy are poorly known.

Beyond the problem of an accurate determination of the thermodynamic value which can be used as a criterion to establish the stable assemblage or configuration of a system, there is the problem of metastability. This concept (and occasionally unfortunate reality) can be illustrated with the use of a free energy-temperature diagram (Figure 3). The relative free energies of three phases representing the same component are given as a function of temperature.

At point T_1 phase A is stable because its free energy is lowest ; B and C are metastable. Temperature T_2 maintains both A and B stable, only C is metastable. However, at T_3, this phase becomes stable. In moving from temperature T_1 to T_3, all phases have a metastable and stable range of tempe- rature. If the passage is rapid, it is likely that phases stable at T_3 will remain present and unreacted or only par- tially reacted at temperature T_1. This is a reaction between metastable phases, neither being the stable form. It is pos- sible to observe such a reaction in the laboratory, at times to the annoyance of experimentalists. Since the very defini- tion of metastability is contrary to the treatment of sys- tems at equilibrium, the problem of reaction between phases which are metastable , presents a great problem to the propo- sed thermodynamic treatment of phase studies, most frequent- ly called phase equilibria. Thermodynamic considerations are certainly capable of giving the correct answers to a problem involving metastable phases. However at present, the exact form of the functions concerning kinetics and configuratio- nal energy in silicate reactions are not known. This fact prohibits, along with incomplete basic data, the exact treatment of phenomena involving metastable phases.

Most changes in nature occur at finite rates and these rates are variable with different reactions. The rapi- dity of the portion of reacted material produced in a given time period, is a function of various effects, some due to structural state or physical state (grain size for example), others due to the influence of non-reacting substances which enhance or impede a reaction (catalysts and impedants). An- other important factor can be attributed to the inherent nature of the materials involved. It happens that some mate- rials have an organization which at new physical conditions is difficult to change. These materials might be called "stably metastable". They then become a truly inert portion of the chemical system and will not affect the mineral pha- ses which are responsive to the thermodynamic variables ope- rative. As might be expected, it is difficult to determine this "stably metastable" state of a mineral. Let us consider a simple example. Figure 4 shows the stability fields of phases A, B and C, all of the same composition, as they occur in pressure-temperature space. Let us assume that the transformation of A into C and B into C is very difficult, requiring a large amount of excess energy in order to re-ar- range the constituent atoms into a complex configuration.

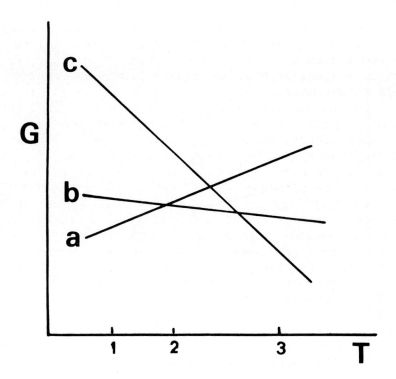

Figure 3 - Free energy-temperature diagram for phases a, b, c. Phase a is the form most stable at low temperature (1) and then b and c become stable as temperature rises

However the A-B transformation involves little difference in atomic configuration and one finds that the reaction occurs with ease. If we take phase A at point 1 it will transform partially into B because this is easier energetically than the A → C transformation. The A → C transformation will not occur at point 2 either, but the A → B transformation will. Above the dotted line A is metastably present and below it B is metastably present. A is **more** metastable than B at point 2. All that interests us from a practical point of view is that A becomes B at point 2 in a short time span while the stable phase C will not appear until a great period of time has elpased. Therefore, all of the phases present which accompany A or B in nature will be in equilibrium with and their appearance will be controlled by the particular thermodynamic properties of A or B instead of those of phase C.

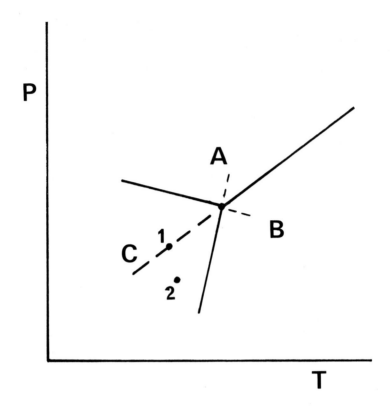

Figure 4 - Phase diagram for a one component system in P-T space. Three phases are present, A, B and C. Point 1 lies on the metastable extension of the reaction A = B. Point 2 lies in the field of stability of C.

Taking a concrete example, as mentioned previously, amorphous silica appears more readily than does quartz as a newly formed phase at or near the earth's surface. The solubility of amorphous silica is much greater than quartz. Then most aqueous solutions at the earth's surface can contain more dissolved silica than would be permitted by a quartz-water equilibrium and they will not precipitate the stable silica phase which is quartz. Further, other phases such as zeolites, whose composition is silica-rich will form at low temperatures where the assemblage feldspar-quartz is thermodynamically the most stable assemblage. These zeolite phases will persist until the system becomes energetically capable of producing quartz plus sodium feldspar (near 100°C). Zeolites are then metastable phases relative to quartz plus feldspar but their persistance in nature is such that we must deal with them as a reality over geologic time spans. Their apparent stability field must therefore be limited to conditions where quartz does not crystallize in P-T-time space. However, when quartz does not crystallize the rigors of the phase rule will apply to the phases present just as they would to a more stable set of phases (see Kujawa and Eugster, 1966, for a more learned discussion of these concepts). Thus metastable phases can be dealt with using the phase rule and thermochemical constraints just as well as stable phases can. The trick is to recognize which phase will occur for a given set of conditions.

In the end, the most practical method of dealing with stability determinations is to use the best available experimental information and then to observe what phases are actually present and being formed in natural geological situations where time is less of a factor. In this way, it is possible in certain cases to establish the effective stability of a phase even though it may not represent a true thermodynamically stable equilibrium. This empirical method is not particularly rigorous, nor will it be useful in all of the cases in which it will be applied, mainly due to the lack of pertinent information concerning the physical and chemical conditions operative in nature. However, it is a useful approach in many instances and ultimately more useful than strict thermodynamic calculations whose basis in reality is known at best only approximately.

In dealing with clay minerals and related silicate species, the following criteria will be used, admittedly in an arbitrary manner. The crystallization **in situ** of new phases will be considered on the average to represent an approach to effective equilibrium conditions. This statement is based upon the belief that metastability will be more likely to be expressed by the persistence of a previously crystalline phase than the crystallization of an entirely new mineral. In considering the existing knowledge of metamorphic and plutonic rocks, it has been rarely demonstrated that a mineral has crystallized outside of its domain of stability (out of equilibrium with other co-crystallizing silicates) while it is well known that silicates persist intact outside of their range of stability in the presence of other phases crystallizing under new physical conditions.

The problem is certainly more complex at conditions of low temperature and pressure where thermal energy is low and slight fluctuations in configurational energy can probably provide metastable crystallization, as often experienced in the laboratory. However, we will retain the general principle that authigenic minerals will more closely represent equilibrium phases than will detrital minerals inherited from other geological cycles.

5 - Stability and Reaction Rate

A critical problem is encountered in observing and interpreting natural mineral assemblages and experimental results. The object of most experimentation is to establish which is the stable assemblage at given P-T-x conditions, i.e., that which will remain at infinite periods of time when maintained under the same physical and chemical conditions. This criterion is especially important for geologists in that time can be an important factor in their interpretations. Observations such as those made by Weaver (1959) or Bartholomé (1966.a) concerning the clay mineralogy of sedimentary rocks as a function of their age, i.e., certain parageneses are typical of rocks of a certain age or older, indicate the potential importance of reaction kinetics in clay mineralogy. However, the time scale involved in these studies, $1.3 - 2.3 \times 10^7$ years, probably excludes consideration for most diagenetic problems.

Experiments by Eberl and Hower (1976) suggest that a time span of 10^6 years is necessary at 60°C to transform smectite to a mixed layered mineral with low expandibility. However, if this reaction will occur at low temperature, 20°C, it requires 10^8 years to be completed. These values begin to interest the geologist. In this sequence, it is certain that when a sediment has reached 80°C, it will be reacting "instantaneously" in a geologic sense (10^5 years) and one can consider that the phases present represent a near approach to equilibrium. However, if the sediments never were brought to temperatures above 50°C, the problem of the significance of the mineral assemblages found, must be considered. In the Gulf Coast (U.S.A.) sections, it is not uncommon to find sediments at 1.5 km depths at temperatures less than 50°C. These materials must then be considered as likely to contain much argillaceous material which has not recrystallized.

There is an unfortunate gap in the experimental growth rate data as far as temperature is concerned. We are obliged to jump from data at 300°C at 1-2 Kbars (Eberl and Hower, 1976) to temperatures of 150-25°C. Nevertheless, it has been demonstrated by Decarreau (1982) that one can form a dioctahedral smectite (nontronite) from gels which is identifiable using classical X-ray diffraction methods in periods of weeks at 150-100°C and by extrapolation of his growth rate data, one would expect the same after 10 years at 25°C. The same synthesis would take 100 years at 5°C, sea bottom conditions. Synthesis of magnesian saponite (stevensite) takes only one half this time and transition metal forms (excluding Fe^{2+}) are more easily synthesized. It is evident that, in geological terms, these processes are almost instantaneous. Decarreau indicates that the synthesis of aluminous phases is more difficult but not impossible. Harder (1974) has also succeeded in the synthesis of illitic minerals at surface conditions. We can then assume that most clay minerals will crystallize at rapid rates under surface conditions when the configuration of the silicate material is amenable. It appears that a coprecipitated gel of silica and appropriate cations is quite favorable for the crystallization of clay minerals under surface conditions.

One can deduce from the above that the rate of dissolution of the geologic material available at the surface : glassy basalt, phyllosilicates, metamorphic or igneous minerals, will determine the rate at which clay minerals will be formed. Of course, these highly unstable materials will recrystallize very rapidly upon burial where temperatures reach 50-70°C. The laboratory experiments show crystal growth to identifiable sizes (a hundred ångstroms) after 20-60 days under these conditions. One can expect to see new clay mineralogies forming quasi-instantaneously when the starting material is greatly out of equilibrium with the new phases.

Comparing the two types of experimental data, hydrothermal and surface (pressure) conditions, it appears evident that crystal growth from unstable (gel) material to phyllosilicates (smectites) is rapid but the conversion of one phyllosilicate to another is a slower process. We can expect then that weathering will be a relatively rapid process while that of clay mineral diagenesis (burial) will proceed at a slower pace, leaving at times relicts of former mineralogies amongst new mineral assemblages.

Another interesting aspect of the work by Decarreau (1982) is the demonstration of near chemical equilibrium between elements in aqueous solution and crystallizing smectites. Distribution coefficients between magnesium and transition metal ions were obtained which shows that a close approach to a chemical equilibrium was attained over periods of 20-60 days. This suggests that the saponites give a rapid response to their environment and that they can be used to indicate the chemistry of the solutions with which they were in contact during their formation.

6 - Geological Environments

The geological environments which form clay mine-rals can be basically divided into five types : weathering, sedimentation, burial, diagenetic and hydrothermal altera-tion. The weathering environment frequently presents a che-mical system where T,P are constant and many chemical ele-ments are mobile. Usually they enter solution from the rocks present at the earth's surface through the process of hydro-lysis. The major problems are :

a - Determination of rates of reaction among the mine-rals present, i.e., determination of those which participate in equilibria and those which remain unchanged although metastable.

b - Determination of the elements which remain inert in the system and those which are perfectly mobile in a thermodynamic sense.

Some weathering systems will be described by acti-vity diagrams with one or more elements considered immobile. Other portions of weathering profiles will establish, at any given point, an equilibrium between the fluid or aqueous solution and the silicate-oxide solids in the soil. Each portion of the profile will represent a different series of chemical conditions, i.e., the total relative masses of the various components will change with, for example, K_2O in-creasing downwards in the profile. However, the phase equi-libria are such that the different portions of the profile can be analyzed on a P constant, T, constant, chemical po-tential constant, X variable diagram for any small segment of the profile.

The term sedimentation environments, both marine and fresh water, should be strictly applied to those reac-tions which take place at or very near (several centimeters) the sediment-water interface. The reaction between detrital silicate material and the relatively constant composition of the lake or ocean water dominates these equilibria. Reac-tions are effected through dissolution and precipitation of material in aqueous solution. The reactions which take place are controlled by the supply and quality of the detrital material being deposited. For the most part the composition of the aqueous solution remains constant in a given geographic zone. It is certainly more constant than that of sediments being introduced into the basin. This fact is due to the greater mobility of material in solution which tends to even out local fluctuations in concentration through the action of waves and currents. The sediment is much less subjected to such a homogenization process and tends, therefore, to attain equilibrium by localized mineral reaction. The type of thermodynamic system operative is most likely to be "open" where each point of sediment has some chemical variables fixed by their concentration in the sediment (inert components due to their low solubility in the solution). Other chemical components, which are soluble, will have their concentration in the sediment fixed as a function of their activity in the aqueous solution. The bulk composition of the resulting sediment will be largely determined by the composition of the water in which it is sedimented and the length of time it has reacted with this environment. The composition of the aqueous solution is, of course, determined to a minor extent by these reactions. This schema will be generally true for the ocean but will certainly be less true for smaller basins where there is a greater dependence on local factors of supply and their fluctuation as a function of time. Since P-T conditions are relatively constant in most sedimentary environments, these sediment aqueous solution systems will be represented by potential-potential or potential-composition or simply composition diagrams when equilibrium is attained between a solution of constant composition and silicates.

Despite a few striking examples to the contrary, there is little evidence available at the moment to indicate that equilibrium of detrital clay mineral assemblages in sediments is achieved in most depositional environments. Mineralogical studies of provenance and deposition (Biscaye, 1965 ; Weaver, 1959 ; or Griffin, 1962, for example) appear to demonstrate that sediments most often reflect the mineralogy of the source area from which the sedimentary material has been derived. Even deep sea sediments which remain in contact with sea water for relatively long periods of time remain faithful indicators of their terrestrial origins. The exceptions to this generalization are the minerals formed

from the devitrification of glassy volcanic materials, submarine "weathering" of eruptive or metamorphic rocks in the
deep sea, the precipitation of sedimentary glauconites or
7 Å chlorites. Most other apparent mineralogical changes
during sedimentation are probably the result of differential
sedimentation rates such as those observed by Porrenga
(1966) for montmorillonite-kaolinite-illite sedimentary materials.

After initial sedimentation, the burial of sediments is usually accomplished rapidly in nearshore or lacustrine basin environments. Hamilton (1959) has shown that a
150-700 meter-thick layer of unconsolidated sediments exists
even on most deep sea floors. Let us consider a little more
closely then the difference between the "open" sea situation, where sedimentary clays are in contact with sea water
of roughly constant composition and an unconsolidated sediment which contains a pore fluid. Meade (1966) shows that
claystones have a porosity decreasing to 0 % at 1 km depths
and sandstones < 20 % at the same depth. Manhein (1970) shows
that ionic diffusion rates in sediments are 1/2 to 1/20 that
of free solutions when the sediments have porosities between
100-20 %. It is evident that the burial of sediments creates
a very different physical environment than that of sedimentation. As a result of reduced ionic mobility in the solutions, a different set of silicate-solution equilibria will
most certainly come into effect with the onset of burial.
The activity of ions in solution will become more dependent
upon the chemistry of the silicates in the system as porosity decreases. The system will change from one of perfectly
mobile components in the open sea to one approaching a
"closed" type where ionic activity in solution is entirely
dictated by the mass of the material present in the
sediment-fluid system. Although this description is probably
not entirely valid even in rocks with measured zero porosity, for practical purposes, the pelitic or clayey sediments
must certainly rapidly approach the situation of a closed
system upon burial. The abrupt change in the composition of
pore fluids in deep sea cores found to occur at depths of
several tens of centimeters (Bischoff and Ku, 1970, 1971 ;
Bischoff **et al.**, 1970 ; Mangelsdorf **et al.**, 1969) tends to
corroborate this deduction.

The porosity of sedimentary rocks and the migration
of water between pore spaces (permeability) influence sili-

cate mineral equilibria in another way. Fluid mobility in a rock leads to the realization of a mechanical equilibrium where fluid pressure (hydrostatic pressure) is not equal to the total overburden pressure. Since water and rocks have very different densities, a column of rock will exert more static pressure with depth than a column of water. If the rock is mechanically competent enough, or the recrystallization process slow enough, to permit a difference in hydraulic (pore) and solid pressure, the P_{H2O} exerted in a mineral assemblage in a rock will be less than lithostatic pressure (P_{lith}). The difference between P_{lith} and P_{H2O} will be a function of the permeability of the rock units containing the fluid and those which it must traverse in order to be in effective equilibrium with a fluid in hydraulic communication with the surface (Bredehoeft and Hanshaw, 1968). If $P_{H2O} < P_{total}$, the stability of hydrous phases will be significantly influenced (Thompson, 1955, 1970) and it is possible to calculate this effect if the pertinent mineral stability data are available (Greenwood, 1961). Essentially three types of situations are possible : one where P_{H_2O} = hydraulic pressure (P_{hyd}.) and thus at a given depth P_{H_2O} is a certain percent of P_{total}. Pressure will be a function of the average density of the rocks in the column. Another situation can exist where $P_{H2O} > P_{hyd} < P_{lith}$ due to slow migration rates in a rock of low permeability. Finally the situation can exist where $P_{H2O} = P_{lith}$ due to an impermeable structure of the rock which blocks hydraulic communication. The first instance is probably typical of sandstone and fractured carbonate rocks as far as one can tell from oil well and aquifer tests. One can assume that shales with 0 % measurable porosity at depths of 1 km or more would approach the latter example where $P_{H_2O} = P_{lith}$.

The overall effect of decreasing the partial pressure of water is to decrease the thermal stability of hydrous phases. One might expect for example that a sandstone and shale at the same levels would contain micaceous minerals in the porous rock and montmorillonites in the more impermeable shale ; the sandstone would be likely to have $P_{H_2O} < P_{lith}$ whereas the shale would have $P_{H_2O} = P_{lith}$.

Now we might consider what is in fact the common clay mineralogy of sandstones. Shelton (1964), Bucke and Mankin (1971) find it to be most often dominated by kaolinite. This mineral although hydrous, is conspicuous by its

lack of alkalis. Thus one could suspect that alkali activity
in pore solutions of sandstones is, or was, frequently low,
lower at any rate than adjacent mica-bearing shales. Laboratory studies by Hanshaw and Coplen (1973) and Kharaka and
Berry (1973) would give a plausible explanation for such a
phenomenon. If solutions are forced hydrostatically across
the argillaceous membrane, ionic species in solution selectively left behind by a process called ultrafiltration. In
fact hydrocarbons are the first material to pass and thus
one could expect a petroleum-bearing, kaolinite-producing
fluid to emerge into a porous sandstone layer upon compaction of the shale.

If we now consider tuffaceous and claystone sediments such as those in the Salton sea thermal area, Wairakei
thermal area and the tuffs of Japan, we will be looking at
the intermediate situation where $P_{lith} > P_{H_2O} < P_{hyd}$. Clayton
et al. (1968) consider the mineral assemblages to be in isotopic (oxygen) equilibrium near 100-150°C in the Salton Sea
area, as do Eslinger and Savin (1973.a) for rocks from the
New Zealand hydrothermal area. This is the temperature range
where many of the important phase changes take place among
the phyllosilicates. In the pyroclastic rocks, zones near
fractures are noted to contain mineral assemblages of higher
"grade" or temperature than the surrounding rocks or the
general pattern of mineralogy for that point in the stratigraphic column. This indicates that a general geothermal
pattern has been established in the total column and that
rapidly circulating warmer water has only local effects on
the clay mineralogy. The mineralogy of these different types
of semi-permeable rocks corresponds, on a depth-temperature
basis, rather closely to that found in pelitic shale rocks
of other studies. It is likely therefore that high permeability gives a noticeably different set of chemical parameters
(intensive variables) to a rock whereas medium to low permeability can be assimilated to a "closed" system where rock
and fluid are effectively part of the same physicochemical
unit.

Deep burial then introduces the variables of pressure and temperature to an essentially closed system in argillaceous rocks. Although it has seldom been demonstrated that sedimentary rocks represent series where major chemical transfer has taken place over great distances, the
possibility must always be entertained. Generally, in rocks

which are predominantly argillaceous permeability is low and local silicate equilibrium is likely to pertain. However, in sandstones large-scale aqueous migration is a well established fact at least as far as the H_2O component is concerned. In sandstone layers it has frequently been noted that the clay mineralogy is dominated by kaolinite. It is possible that to have two types of thermodynamic systems in rocks which are side by side in a sedimentary sequence - one "open" to certain mobile components and the other essentially closed to externally controlled chemical potentials of elements in the fluid phase. Both types will be subject to variations in pressure and temperature as the position in the earth's crust varies. Thus sedimentary rocks will be represented by P-T-x or P-T-x-µ diagrams, the latter needing simplification of some sort for graphical representation.

The fifth major geological environment in which clays are formed is that of hydrothermal alteration, often accompanied in nature by ore deposition. This is the most complicated and variable of the environments due to its local nature. Essentially, the mineral assemblages are formed through the action of a fluid, usually warmer than the rocks it invades, which is initially highly charged with dissolved material. As this fluid penetrates the rock, certain elements are removed and others deposited as a function of :

- the temperature of the fluid

- the composition of the fluid relative to the rocks it invades

- and the duration of the phenomenon.

Obviously any such system will be highly complicated and any mineral assemblage produced will be a factor of P-T-x-µ and time. There are enough variables possible to make each manifestation a special case in itself. Various theoretical aspects of this type of mineralization are treated by Korzhinskii (1970). Due to the complexity of the phenomenon and the general lack of information regarding all of the pertinent physical and chemical parameters, the cases of hydrothermal alteration will be only discussed briefly in the pages to follow.

7 – Chemical Coordinates for Phyllosilicates Assemblages

The basic representation of the clay mineral compositions has been chosen in the coordinates $M^+R^3 - 2R^3 - 3R^2$. SiO_2 and H_2O are considered components in excess, i.e., these oxides are always present in nearly pure monophase form so that no reaction is prohibited or promoted through a variation in their relative abundance in the chemical system. In this general system, the following identities are assumed : $R^2 = Mg^{2+}$, Mn^{2+}, Fe^{2+} ; $R^3 = Fe^{3+}$, Al^{3+}, Ti^{4+} ; $M = Na^+$, K^+ and $2 \times Ca^{2+}$. An M^+R^3 pole represents the bulk composition of feldspars, commonly found associated with clay minerals. They are the most alkali-rich minerals present (excluding zeolites). Calcium is considered to fulfill a chemical role similar to the alkali ions in most clay minerals. It is notably not present in micas stable at low temperatures (Velde, 1971 ; Hemley et al., 1971) and hence does not compare directly to potassic systems. It is also possible that the calcium concentration in a given aggregate of phyllosilicates could be largely controlled independently of them through its activity in aqueous solution in equilibrium with carbonates. Therefore its presence is difficult to interpret in a purely silicate framework. As a result, calcium is largely ignored in the analysis of clay minerals here. It is assumed that high calcium concentration will not provoke the crystallization of a specific clay mineral.

The poles $2R^3$ and $3R^2$ were chosen because such ions are present in these proportions in the clay minerals found to be composed of R^{2+} or R^{3+} ions plus SiO_2 and H_2O. Kaolinite and pyrophyllite are found at the $2R^3$ pole and serpentine or talc at the $3R^2$ pole. Further the choice of two R^3 ions is useful in that clay minerals either combine two ions in octahedral coordination, they are called dioctahedral, or three ions (ideally R^2), they are called trioctahedral minerals. The major advantage of combining the constituent elements in this way is the resulting convenient distortion of a more simple $M^+ - R^2 - R^3$ geometry. By spreading the components out, one can see more precisely the region of interest which contains the majority of clay minerals. They are found in-between the compositions of feldspar–kaolinite–serpentine.

The chemiographic relations of these phases are related to the chemical coordinates in Figure 5. In order to place the chemical analysis of a mineral in these coordinates one must perform the following operations :

1 - Convert the analysis to relative atomic proportions of the elements ;

2 - Set Na + K + 2 times Ca as the M^+R^3 component ;

3 - The R^3 component is calculated by adding Al + Fe^{3+}. Since R^{3+} is present in M^+R^3, one must subtract the value of the M^+R^3 component from Al + Fe^{3+}. The remainder is then divided by two to give $2R^3$;

4 - Mg + Fe^{2+} is summed and divided by three to give $3R^2$;

5 - Now the values for the three components are summed and each component is divided by the total to give an atomic percentage for each component.

We can take muscovite as an example. The formula is K Al$_3$Si$_3$O$_{10}$(OH)$_2$. Here only K and Al are considered in the coordinates. Then $MR^3 = 1$ since we have one potassium atom present. The $2R^3$ component is 3-1 = 2/2 which is equal to one. Thus $MR^3 = 2R^3$ component and muscovite is $(MR^3)_{50}$ $(2R^3)_{50}$ as in figure 5.

There are two obvious problems that come to mind when such a method of analysis is proposed - does $Fe^{3+} = Al^{3+}$ in all of the possible phases and does $Mg^{2+} = Fe^{2+}$ as well ? As we will see later on, probably the $Mg^{2+} - Fe^{2+}$ identity is effectively correct for most clay minerals and related phases. However, Fe^{3+} certainly does not always substitute with equal facility for aluminum. First we know that iron feldspars are quite rare in nature for the potassium forms and unknown for sodium species. The same is true for the micas. However aluminous and ferric clay minerals do exist. It is apparent then that some point of divergency will be reached where aluminous systems will contain one set of phases, and ferric systems, under the same physical conditions, will form another. Here usage is the best proof - we will see that only one major instance is evident where Fe^{3+} concentration provides the crystallization of a phase which would not be present in an aluminous system.

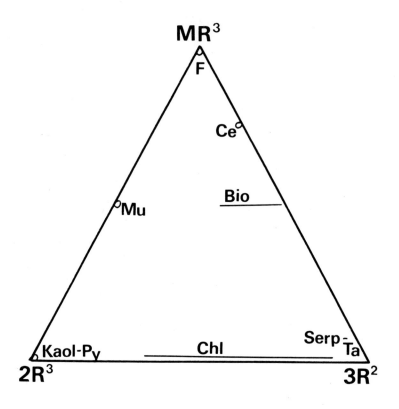

<u>Figure 5</u> - Chemiographic relations of some important phases
as they plot in MR^3-$2R^3$-$3R^2$ coordinates.
Mu = muscovite : F = alkali feldspar ; Ce = celadonite ;
Bio = biotite ; Chl = chlorites ; Ta = talc ;
Kaol = kaolinite ; Py = pyrophyllite ; Serp = serpentine

Further it is not enough to assign Fe^{3+} content a
fixed value in a given rock and then to forget about it in
the evolution of the sediment during burial and metamorphism. One should remember that Fe^{3+} is different from Al^{3+}
in its ability to change oxidation state and therefore to
change its identity as a coordinate in a simplified system
such as is proposed here. Let us consider the situation in
which the loss of Fe^{3+} by chemical reduction to Fe^{2+} sup-
presses a phase - the so called kaolinite-pyrophyllite
"anomaly". This problem is an illustration of the uses and
problems involved with representing rocks and clay minerals
in the MR^3-$2R^3$-$3R^2$ coordinates.

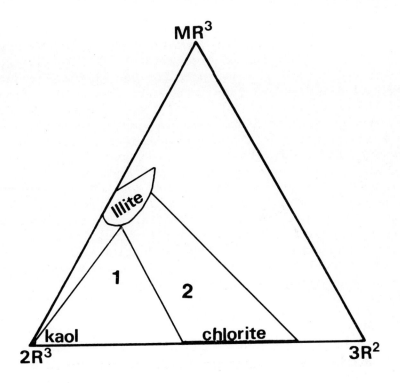

Figure 6 - Illustration of possible displacement of a sedimentary rock bulk composition due to reduction of Fe^{3+} to Fe^{2+} during burial metamorphism.
1 : Intral Fe^{3+}-rich assemblage kaolinite (kaol) + illite + chlorite ;
2 : Fe^{2+}-rich assemblage of illite + chlorite

The detailed arguments and geologic setting of the example are given by Velde (1968). Essentially, the geologic observation which has been made is that pyrophyllite is rare in sedimentary and epi-metamorphic pelitic rock assemblages. The question is posed : why does an aluminum silicate appear at low pressure-temperature conditions and disappear at higher ones (frequently to reappear as kyanite or andalusite upon strong metamorphism) ? The answer can lie in the inter-play between changing bulk compositions of sedimentary mineral assemblages and the constituent minerals stable at various physical conditions. The following chemiographic analysis is possible.

As a general fact, minerals and rocks contain less ferric iron as metamorphism becomes more apparent. Subsequently, the composition of a rock in the $MR^3-2R^3-3R^2$ system is displaced toward the $3R^2$ pole through chemical reduction of iron as pressure and temperature are increased. Figure 6 shows the relation of different clay mineral assemblages before and after this displacement. Simply stated, one moves from a three phase - kaolinite (aluminum-silicate)-bearing assemblage to a two phase (non aluminum silicate-bearing) assemblage of illite + chlorite. The chemical reduction in the rocks is assumed to take place through the agency of hydrogen-rich gasses, produced by the diagenesis of organic matter. If we now consider a kaolinite-bearing rock which contains initially relatively little ferric iron and which is rich in organic matter, the reduction effect will not take place during metamorphism. Concerning the aluminum silicate mineralogy in such a rock, pyrophyllite should appear at higher metamorphic grades through the reaction kaolinite + quartz = pyrophyllite. Thus we see that mineralogic evolution of a given rock in P-T space is not necessarily represented by fixed values of chemical variables. Even though little or no material is taken from or added to the rock, it can change its bulk composition in the chemical coordinates which have been chosen through oxidation or reduction of iron. As a result of this change a new mineral assemblage can be produced. One must conclude that the problem of iron oxidation state will be omnipresent.

As mentioned before, another important consideration is that of the elements which are active in the silicate systems and those which are found in other phases. One example is carbonates, another is oxides. If we consider dolomite, it contains an element important to silicates and another which is less so, Mg and Ca. Were dolomite to be destabilized, it could well react with kaolinite to produce magnesian chlorite for example. In such an instance, the presence or absence of dolomite would affect the bulk composition of the clay system in much the same way as did the change in oxidation state of iron. One adds to the $3R^2$ component and displaces the bulk composition of the system.

Iron oxide can behave in the same way. In sediments, iron is frequently present as hematite or hydrated Fe_2O_3. If this material is reduced during burial diagenesis, it will react with the silicates to form a chlorite. Again, we add to the $3R^{2+}$ component of the system and displace its bulk composition. In both cases, we add elements to the silicate system which were initially outside it. The reverse could as well be envisioned-changing Fe^{2+} into a ferric oxide which is not present in the clays. Thus the bulk composition would be displaced toward the $M^+R^3-2R^3$ side of the system. If we simply oxidized the iron in the silicates, the bulk composition goes toward the $2R^3$ pole.

It is of course useful to use more simple plots, such as R^2-Al-Si for example to define chlorites or use Fe-Mg-Al as variables to show better compositional differences between mineral types. One must be certain, though, that the essential variable is portrayed and that variations in one element are not due to variations in another which does not figure in the diagram. It is necessary to understand the type of substitution which occurs in the structure and its importance on the abundance of other elements present in the structure.

8 - Summary

This section has attempted to outline the principles which can be used to analyze the equilibria which determine clay mineral assemblages in the various geological environments. Due to the limitations of laboratory techniques, little use can at present be made of theoretical (calculable) thermodynamic variables controlling mineral equilibria. Heaviest reliance is placed upon natural occurrence and laboratory equilibrium studies. This is a method currently practiced with great success in the study of metamorphic and igneous rocks which finds a logical application in the field of clay mineralogy. Many of the results of such reasoning will be only approximate, mainly due to imperfect knowledge of natural occurrences and/or as yet unattempted studies of appropriate synthetic systems which approximate natural clay mineral assemblages. However, it is hoped that the initiation of such a procedure will lead to completed knowledge and eventually to the solution of the major enigmas of clay mineralogical studies.

II - MINERALS AND MINERAL GROUPS

The following pages give a review of the chemistry
of natural minerals, their typical occurrence in nature and
their common mineral associations. This review is used to
establish the major groupings of the common clay mineral
species as a function of the chemical system to which they
can be related. Because various forms of silica as well as
zeolites are commonly associated with clays, these materials
have been considered in the same manner as the phyllosilicates. It is evident that they have an influence on the clay
mineralogy and that they form an integral part of clays in
the broad sense of the term. However, they are not normally
considered to be clay minerals.

Neither carbonates nor sulfates are considered here
nor are the various more rarely occurring salts. In general
the elements in these minerals either do not enter into clay
structures in appreciable quantities (Ca, CO_2, SO_2), or the
occurrence of the minerals is sufficiently rare to represent
a special case - the various halide salts, for example.
However, dolomite and siderite present a special problem in
that the existence of R^2 is important to silicate equilibria
under consideration. The main trouble here is that the conditions of crystallization and stability of these carbonates
in sediments and sedimentary rocks is imperfectly known,
thus leaving a question as to its influence on silicates or
the influence of silicates on its presence. One is forced
more or less to ignore the importance of carbonates at present. This does not mean that it can be ultimately excluded
from a complete discussion of clay mineral stability.

1 - Silica

The forms of SiO_2 found in sediments and sedimentary rocks are quite varied, but those which could be suspected of near surface origin are generally as follows : quartz, chalcedony, opal, amorphous gels and ionic forms in solution. Natural occurrences indicate that the solid forms of silica precipitate have crystallized after the time of initial deposition (Siever, 1962).

The problem critical to an analysis of the phase relations of silicates is the determination of the stable or the most currently found form of SiO_2 in the various clay mineral environments. Since the different forms of silica are all relatively pure or mono-component phases, it is often considered convenient to ignore the actual silica phase present assuming that it is ubiquitous and equivalent to quartz. Further, systems containing quartz are frequently considered to be saturated with respect to silica or SiO_2. This presupposes that all phases in the system can be considered saturated with this phase. If these generalizations are valid they allow the number of components in a system to be reduced by one because the addition of silica or the subtraction of silica will not affect the number or kind of phases present ; "quartz" will always remain. Such a step is useful in that it reduces the necessary number of chemical variables by one, and the graphical representation of a chemical system is thus facilitated. At is happens, there are different observable solubilities in aqueous solution, giving different apparent stabilities for the different forms of silica at atmospheric conditions.

Low temperature solution chemistry studies have indicated that solutions might be saturated with respect to quartz when they contain 5-15 ppm SiO_2 in solution at 25°C (Morey et al., 1962 ; Dapples, 1967.a and b ; Kittrick, 1969 ; Siever, 1962). Experimentally, opal and chalcedony appear to have the same solubilities (Krauskopf, 1959). Solutions are saturated with amorphous silica at 100-160 ppm at pH < 9 (Krauskopf, 1959). Experimentalists have not been able to precipitate quartz or another phase from solution below 80°C. Harder and Flemig (1970) formed quartz from an amorphous silica-iron precipitate in solutions containing silica concentrations below those of amorphous silica solubility at temperatures less than 80°C. Mackenzie and Gees (1971) were able to crystallize quartz on abraded grains. These two experiments illustrate that it is difficult to precipitate quartz directly from solution except when using methods which eliminate the apparent kinetic barriers to quartz equilibria at low temperatures. As a result, the only pertinent data obtained are relative to amorphous silica. In order to establish equilibrium experimentally, reversibility of a reaction should be demonstrated. This involves observing both the dissolution and free precipitation of the phase in question. However, in the absence of this information, the next best approach is to calculate the relative free energies from solubility data at higher temperature or to observe the polymorphic transactions of the different forms of silica at elevated temperatures. Using these two methods one can establish that quartz is the stable phase at normal atmospheric conditions (Siever, 1957 ; Mizutani, 1970).

If quartz is the stable phase at low temperatures, other forms of silica are found nevertheless in nature. It is apparently difficult to form quartz in the laboratory as well as in nature at low pressure and temperature conditions. The question can be asked, "at what concentration will a solution be saturated with silica ?". It would appear that laboratory and theory do not give a simple answer. Let us then look at forms of silica found in different geologic environments.

a - Weathering

Under conditions of intense weathering, silica is unstable in the crystalline form. Bauxites, soils representing the most intense weathering conditions, contain no quartz and little combined silica. High rates of water influx remove SiO_2 at low solution concentrations. Normal ground water and streams carry about 17 ppm SiO and less in high rainfall areas (Davis, 1964). In some weathering profiles silicification or deposition of silica has been observed. Most often the form of the phase deposited is cryptocrystalline, either opal or chalcedony. In these cases quartz grains do not show overgrowths (Elouard and Millot, 1959 ; Millot, 1964). However, some quartzites are reported to contain grains with quartz overgrowths due to deposition during weathering (Millot, 1964). These cases must be considered as a possible stable desposition of quartz, although it could simply be due to crystallization upon a pre-existing structure.

b - Sedimentary Environment

Corroded quartz grains have been reported in association with chert in modern carbonates (Bartholomé, 1966.a), and they are known to occur in sand and salt deposits (Dapples, 1959, 1962 ; Braitsch, 1971). Chalcedony is found associated with quartz in marine sediments formed from devitrified glass (Müller, 1961). Amorphous silica is common in recent ocean sediments (Biscaye, 1965 ; High and Picard, 1965 ; Calvert, 1971) and has also been identified in deltaic terriginous sediments (Millot, 1964). Recent non-oceanic sediments where zeolites are known to form most often contain cryptocrystalline silica (Brown et al., 1969 ; Heath, 1969 ; Moiola, 1970 ; Hay, 1964).

c - Sedimentary Rocks

Examples have been reported where quartz overgrows quartz grains and the interstitial spaces are filled with chalcedony (Kautz, 1964), but more classically the only phase present is quartz which grows on older detrital grains (Siever, 1959, 1962). Iijima (1970) reports opal present in a series of buried pyroclastics to a depth of 1.5 Km at a temperature of 50°C where it is replaced by quartz in more deeply buried rocks. Steiner (1953) reports the formation of quartz at depths greater than 500 m and temperatures above 200°C. Samples above this level (at lower temperatures and pressure) contained chalcedony or cristobalite.

d - Hydrothermal Alterations

Gaseous emanations near the surface are known to produce opal or cristobalite (microcrystalline) (Kesler, 1970 ; Steiner, 1953 ; Schoen and White, 1965) and quartz or amorphous silica at greater depth (Keller and Hanson, 1968 ; Fournier, 1967).

SUMMARY

It would appear from the above summary of natural occurrences that quartz is the most stable form of silica at near-surface conditions but that other metastable phases, representing initially poorly organized material, predominate in the natural occurrences or newly formed silica. Experiments demonstrate the persistence of metastable amorphous or cryptocrystalline hydrated SiO_2 at low temperature (Kittrick, 1969 ; Krauskopf, 1956, 1959) and slow conversion at higher temperatures (above 100 bars) (Frondel, 1962 ; Heydemann, 1964 ; Carr and Fyfe, 1958 ; Mizutani, 1970). The difficulty in attaining equilibrium both in the laboratory and in nature is apparent.

What then can be said about equilibria involving silica in chemical systems at low temperatures and pressures ? First of all it is apparent that natural aqueous fluids are easily super-saturated with respect to quartz. Since sediments and sedimentary rock pore waters and especially hydrothermal solutions have been frequently observed to contain more than 15 ppm SiO_2 (Dapples, 1959 ; Ellis and Mahon, 1964 ; Hay, 1966 ; Hess, 1966 ; Krauskopf, 1959 ; Harriss and Pilkey, 1966 ; Ellis, 1968), it is apparent that a phase other than quartz controls silica concentration. In fact it is most likely necessary to have silica concentrations higher than those of quartz saturation in order to form silicates such as the zeolites (Hay, 1966). Alternatively, quartz grains in soils and sediments show very little reactivity with their environment. Isotope studies for oxygen indicate almost no exchange, therefore, no deposition on grains of micron size (Savin and Epstein, 1970 ; Rex et al., 1969). This indicates that the chemical reactions at low temperatures involving silica in solution have bypassed crystalline quartz. It is evident then that quartz is largely inert in many weathering and sedimentary environments. A study by Mizutani (1970) indicates that the transformation amorphous silica $\rightarrow$ cristobalite (opal, chalcedony) $\rightarrow$ quartz takes 10^9 years at 0°C, 10^6 years at 100°C at 100 bars. This ensures that amorphous silica will be present for significant periods of time in sedimentary rocks after its deposition from solution. Calvert (1971) confirms this in his study of deep-sea ocean sediments and Murata and Larson (1975) in Miocene sediments.

In this context it is interesting to note the persistently low levels of silica concentration in river and sea water. This suggests that the concentration of silica is controlled by other silicate equilibria or biologic processes (Garrels, 1965 ; Wollast and de Broeu, 1971).

It is most likely then that the effective (although metastable) SiO_2 equilibria in most geological environments of low temperature and pressure, weathering, sedimentation and the early stages of compaction as well as surface hydrothermal alterations, are governed by the solubility and precipitation of amorphous silica in aqueous solution. As a result, the existence of quartz in an assemblage of clay minerals in these environments does not necessarily represent a compositional limit or saturation with respect to SiO_2 and, therefore, such an assemblage cannot be considered, **a priori**, as a system with silica as an effective component in excess.

The polymorphic transformations from amorphous silica to cristobalite to quartz, determined by X-ray diffraction, have thus been found to occur in sequences of buried sediments and in laboratory experiments. These reactions have also been observed at the surface of deep ocean sediments which have experienced approximately constant temperatures. This data allows us to establish time-temperature relations for the production of quartz. However observations on buried sediments (Kano, 1979 ; Mitsui and Taguchi, 1977 ; Iijima and Tada, 1981) and various laboratory experiments (Kastner et al., 1977 ; Rimstidt and Barnes, 1980 ; Lahann and Roberson, 1980) indicate that other factors are involved. Solution composition, as well as impurities in the cristobalite or opal, affect the reaction rate and hence the observed temperature of conversion for a given time span. It is also possible that the reaction-mechanism can influence the rate. Iijima and Tada (1981) argue that solid-solid reactions occur much slower than do dissolution-precipitation reactions.

The observed transition temperatures of opal-cristobalite to quartz in tertiary sediments ranges from 22-33°C to about 70°C (Iijima and Tada, 1981 ; Mitsui and Taguchi, 1977 ; Iijima, 1970 ; Aoyagi and Kazama, 1980). It should be noted for further reference that the alkali zeolite mineralogy changes rapidly in this temperature range in the rocks observed. At ocean bottom conditions one finds that the transformation occurs in late Cretaceous age material (Calvert, 1971). It should be possible then, to tell whether or not a sedimentary rock of recent age has been deeply buried by observing the silica polymorph. Also, one can, to a certain extent, estimate the geothermal gradient in the sedimentary column.

Summarizing the natural occurrences of the silica polymorphs, it is possible to make several statements about the silicate-silica equilibria. In weathering situations, saturation of fluids with SiO_2 relative to any species of pure silica is probably only rarely achieved. In continental and shallow sea deposits, silica is precipitated in some initially amorphous form, opaline or chert when lithified or extracted by living organisms. Authigenically formed silicates are probably not in equilibrium with quartz when they are formed. As compaction increases in sediments, silica concentrations in solution are again above those of quartz saturation (15 ppm) and again it must be assumed that the diagenetic minerals formed are not in equilibrium with a silica polymorph, except where amorphous silica is present. It is possible that burial depths of one or two kilometers are necessary to stabilize effectively that quartz form. It must be anticipated that the minerals formed under conditions of silica saturation near the earth's surface, will be a minority of the examples found in natural rock systems.

2 - Kaolinite, Pyrophyllite, Gibbsite and Talc

Gibbsite and the "neutral lattice" minerals, 1:1 or 2:1 represent the extremes of chemical variation in the clay minerals. Gibbsite is a hydrated form of alumina. Kaolinite and pyrophyllite can be considered to be almost strictly aluminum-silicates, i.e., no ions other than Al, Si, O, H are present in appreciable quantities in these minerals. This is not strictly true in cases of minerals formed under conditions of intense weathering. One finds that a small percentage of Fe_2O_3 can enter into these minerals under strongly oxidizing conditions (Hogg et al., 1975 ; Rozenson et al., 1979 ; 1982). However, the extent of compositional solid solution is small and as the aluminates occur with iron oxide at the surface only, it can be considered that their stability will not be affected by this solid solution compared with kaolinites which are exempt of iron oxide.

For various reasons, gibbsite and kaolinite are really the only minerals of the "neutral lattice" type which occur with any frequency in non-metamorphic rocks which contain clay minerals. These minerals are formed in soils, most noticeably from argillic pelitic and granitic rocks but they are also commonly found forming from basic rocks during the weathering processes (Millot, 1964 ; Tardy, 1969 ; Hay and Jones, 1972). The transition granite (feldspar) → kaolinite has been studied in nature by many authors, in the laboratory (Hemley, 1959 ; Hemley et al., 1961 ; Garrels and Howard, 1959 ; Hemley et al., 1980) and by methods of thermodynamic calculations (Helgeson et al., 1969 ; Garrels, 1957). This information indicates that both gibbsite and kaolinite or possibly its hydrated form halloysite (Kirkman, 1975 ; Busenburg, 1978) are stable at 25°C, 1 atmosphere. The common existence of kaolinite in sedimentary rocks (Weaver, 1959 ; Millot, 1964) and its authigenic formation during early diagenesis (Kautz, 1964 ; Gluskoter, 1967 ; Füchtbauer and Goldschmidt, 1963 ; Wilson and Pittman, 1977 ; Shelton, 1964 ; Karlson et al., 1979) indicates that it frequently can form, and remain stable, at depth.

By contrast, gibbsite is very rarely reported in sedimentary rocks although reported in recent marine sediments (according to Deep Sea Drilling Project reports). Gibbsite seems to be a common product of weathering in the earliest stages of the alteration of coarse grained plutonic rocks in temperate and humid climates (Macias-Vasquez, 1981). The plagioclases are the source of this mineral (Young and Stephen, 1965) as proposed by Helgerson (1968) in a thermodynamic study of the crystallization process. However, this gibbsite is not found in the upper parts of the weathering profile. Gibbsite or other forms of hydrated alumina and some iron are of course common in highly weathered soil profiles. The transformation of gibbsite to diaspor has been reported by Gout **et al.** (1980) and estimated to occur at 100°C and 800 bars pressure. They observed that the reaction occurred in the presence of abundant iron oxide, whereas gibbsite was transformed into boehmite in more iron-free sedimentary rocks. This suggests that minor element concentrations in the phases can influence the crystallization rate of normally simple dehydration-reaction. The composition of the hydrated alumina phase remains nevertheless close to the pure aluminum pole. One report of gibbsite transformation in sedimentary rocks indicates that it is replaced by kaolinite at 50°C at about one kilometer depth (Iijima, 1972).

During the burial of a sedimentary series and its subsequent diagenesis or metamorphism, kaolinite disappears from the clay mineral parageneses for different reasons ; combination with Mg from destabilized dolomite (Muffler and White, 1969), combination with other phases to produce illite + chlorite (Velde, 1968 ; Boles and Franks, 1979) or mixed layered minerals (Hower **et al.,** 1976) or by combination with quartz to produce pyrophyllite (Winkler, 1964) near 275°C at 1-2 Kbars total pressure. The temperature and depth at which kaolinite is eliminated vary from one sequence of rocks to another. Figure 7 shows some recorded temperatures where kaolinite content is greatly reduced in sequence of buried sediments. The great variability of T-depth conditions supports the idea of a non unique cause of kaolinite instability, an observation made by Dunoyer de Segonzac (1969).

Kaolinite is a frequent product of hydrothermal alteration, commonly associated with mica or expanding pha-

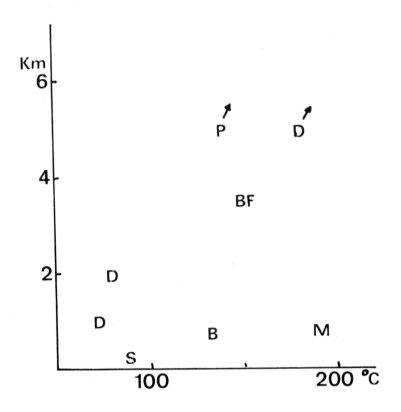

Figure 7 - Depth-temperature coordinates of apparent
kaolinite upper stability in various pelitic rock sequences
of Tertiary or younger age in deeply buried sediments.
D = Dunoyer de Segonzac (1969) ; B = Browne and Ellis (1970)
M = Muffler and White (1969) ; P = Perry and Hower (1970)
BF = Boles and Franks (1979) ; S = Steiner (1968)
Arrow indicates that kaolinite is stable to the greatest
depth in the sequence.

ses in the "argillic" type alterations (Burnhamm, 1962 ;
Keller and Hanson, 1968 ; Rose, 1970 ; Lowell and Guilbert,
1970 ; Keller, 1963). These studies indicate that kaolinite
can be formed by hydrothermal alteration at the surface as
well as to depths of several kilometers. Although precise
information is lacking for low temperatures, intermediate
conditions at pressure and temperature are known to permit
the stability of the potassic mica-beidellite mixed layered
composition series which excludes the stable coexistence of
K-feldspar and kaolinite (Meunier and Velde, 1982). If one

accepts the argument that both beidellites - sodic and potassic - are stable and that there is complete solid solution between the two, the mineral pair kaolinite-potassium feldspar should not exist under these conditions. As a result kaolinite would be restricted to purely phyllosilicate assemblages and will not coexist stably with feldspar or zeolites, as we shall see in the following sections.

Kaolinite is also a typical mineral in the alteration of acidic rocks by fumarolic action. Lombardi and Sheppard (1977) estimate that it can form at 80°C in the presence of alunite.

The above use of "stable coexisting minerals" is of course based upon the fundamental consideration that the chemical system is "closed" - that is, the chemical components K, Si and OH are "inert" and that their relative proportions, mass, in the system determines the phases formed. This can assumed to be valid for many argillaceous sediments and rocks. However, in some geological environments, aqueous solutions containing alkalis and hydrogen ions in various concentrations (whose chemical potentials, therefore, are variable but constant throughout a given system) react with kaolinite or other minerals to influence stability under otherwise constant physical and chemical parameters.

The most commonly observed transformation of kaolinite under intense weathering conditions is to hydrated alumina (gibbsite) and soluble silica (Jackson, 1959). This reaction has been observed to be reversible in soil profiles (Dapples, 1962 ; Millot, 1964). High alkali concentrations produce mica at the expense of kaolinite in certain alkaline lakes (Hay and Moiola, 1963) ; however, the reverse process, the kaolinization of muscovite has only been observed in sedimentary rocks (Dunoyer de Segonzac, 1969). Relations between gibbsite, kaolinite and smectite in weathering profiles, sediments and sedimentary rocks are not, as yet, well enough defined to be certain whether a reaction relationship can be inferred to exist between two minerals or, whether multiphase assemblages are stable.

a - Chemiographic Character of Kaolinite, Gibbsite and Talc

Because of its simple chemical composition, the

role of kaolinite in clay mineral assemblages is peripheral
to, or a limiting case for, chemiographic representation of
clay mineral systems which contain free silica forms as a
compositional pole. Most often during epi-metamorphism, kaolinite is incorporated into other phases due to a displacement of the bulk composition of the silicate system in which
it is found, either through the increase in total R^{2+} ion
content due to chemical reduction of ferric ion (Velde,
1968) or by the increase in availability of R^{2+} ions through
the destabilization of dolomite (Muffler and White, 1969).
Its existence in a mineral assemblage will then not generally indicate the important factors of silicate equilibria ;
that is the ultimate stability of the clays present.

Gibbsite, a mineral more and more frequently identified in the early stages of rock weathering (especially
magmatic rocks) is not usually important in river sediments,
but has been noted in small quantities over large areas in
deep sea sediments (Griffin **et al.**, 1968 ; Biscaye, 1965).
It seems to be quickly lost during burial because it is rarely reported in sedimentary rocks. Undoubtedly the activity
of silica is too high in most sedimentary environments to
permit the persistence of free alumina. The existence of
gibbsite in different weathering zones under widely varied
climatic conditions, and its formation from a wide range of
rock compositions, leaves its genesis slightly enigmatic. It
can only persist under conditions where aqueous fluids have
very low dissolved mineral contents - either at the very
beginning of the weathering process or in its final stages
in lateritic soils.

Although gibbsite and kaolinite are important in
quantity in some soils and hydrothermal deposits, they have
diminishing importance in argillaceous sediments and sedimentary rocks because of their peripheral chemical position.
They form the limits of any chemical framework of a clay
mineral assemblage and thus rarely become functionally involved in critical clay mineral reactions. This is especially true of systems where most chemical components are inert
or extensive variables of the system. More important or characteristic relations will be observed in minerals with more
chemical variability which respond readily to minor changes
in the thermodynamic parameters of the system in which they
are found. However, as the number of chemical components
which are intensive variables (perfectly mobile components)

increase, the aluminous phase becomes more important because alumina is poorly soluble in aqueous solution, and becomes the inert component and the only extensive variable.

Kaolinite and gibbsite will be found either at coordinate poles (R) or on triangular boundaries (R^2-R^3-Si, for example). Again solid solution is negligible in these phases, as is the case of talc. One can therefore represent all three by points on phase diagrams with composition being an intensive variable.

b - 2:1 Structures

Pyrophyllite is probably unstable below some 273°C at 1 Kbar pressure. This temperature will be reduced at lower total water pressure but will probably remain at a substantial value (Hemley **et al.**, 1980). Its existence in sedimentary rocks should be indicative at relatively high temperatures if it is stable. It is typically found with illite-chlorite or occasionally with allevardite (Dunoyer de Segonzac, 1969 ; Ehlmann and Sand, 1959). The reaction kaolinite + quartz = pyrophyllite is an important marker in phyllosilicates parageneses when it can be observed.

Experiments at pressures of one Kbar and above indicate that talc is produced between 100-300°C (Hohling, 1958). However, its occurrence in salt deposits (Braitsch, 1971 ; Füchtbauer and Goldschmidt, 1959) and carbonates (Millot, 1964) indicate that it continues to be stable at lower temperatures. The experimental work of Siffert (1962) indicates that talc could be precipitated from concentrated basic solutions (pH > 9) at temperatures below 80°C where other magnesian silicates such as sepiolite and trioctahedral montmorillonite are not stable.

Talc when found in terrigeneous sediments is then most probably always of detrital origin as is that found in recent Gulf Coast sediments (Isphording, 1971). The Mg-Fe^{2+} substitution can apparently cover the range of possibilities : in weathering of basic rocks (Fontanaud, 1982) 88-95 % Mg, at 280°C in deep sea deposits (Lonsdale **et al.**, 1980) 75-90 % Mg and low grade metamorphism (Klein, 1974) 57-8 % Mg. Talc found in sediments and sedimentary rocks is apparently magnesian (Millot, 1964). Talc, then is found in the full range of clay mineral environments, from weathering to hydrothermal alteration, and a complete Mg-Fe solid solution is possible. However we know only magnesian forms at low temperatures (< 280°C) and apparently a greater solid solution occurs at metamorphic conditions. Talc compositions are almost uniquely those of Mg,Fe and Si cations. The lack of significant solid solution towards an aluminous component at low temperatures (Fawcett and Yoder, 1966) allows one to fix the talc compositions as R^2-Si variables. They form a limiting composition in a ternary diagram such as R^2-Si-R^3 or MR^3-$2R^3$-$3R^2$ where talc will be placed either on the triangle's edge or at an apex respectively. Total solid solution in Fe-Mg variables is possible.

Talc can occur over the full range of P-T conditions of clay mineral parageneses. Pyrophyllite, on the other hand, will not be present below 270°C and it will thus represent the extreme limits of the clay mineral parageneses.

Conclusions

Among the neutral-lattice phyllosilicates only kaolinite is an important constituent of sediments, sedimentary rocks and hydrothermal alterations. Gibbsite is a product of weathering in a reasonable number of soils but it is usually lost upon transport. This is due to its low tolerance for silica in solution (< 5 ppm). Talc is infrequently found in sediments ; usually it is of detrital origin. Its presence in sedimentary rocks most likely indicates quite alkaline conditions. Pyrophyllite is a mineral of metamorphic origin (270°C or greater). This leaves kaolinite as the only important neutral-lattice mineral in clay assemblages. Because of its extreme composition, i.e., the most aluminous phase possible in the presence of free silica and a strictly alkali-free mineral, it is a limiting case of clay mineral composition. This coupled with the fact of its chemical invariability, restricts its usefulness as a diagnostic in tracing the history of a rock or soil. It is stable throughout the range of most clay mineral environments at its bulk composition. Thus the appearance of kaolinite would be governed by chemical activities or bulk composition of a chemical system. As we will see later this will be useful in conjunction with the identification of accompanying clays.

3 - Potassic Micas and Mica-like Minerals

It is important to establish an initial basis of
terminology for these minerals because the terms used have
undergone a considerable evolution since their inception.
The first distinction to be made is between true micas and
mica-like phases. Mica is defined here as a mineral (in virtually all instances it is dioctahedric, i.e., two ions are
present in the octahedrally coordinated layer) which has an
interlayer cationic charge of 1.00 ± 0.10 per $O_{10}(OH)_2$ anio-
nic charges.   Such a structure has a basic crystallographic
repeat distance (c sin ß) of 10 Å ± 0.2 when potassium is
the interlayer ion.   Treatment with polar ions such as ethylene glycol does not change this distance nor does it change
the shape of the X-ray diffraction peak present at 10 Å.   In
the low temperature environments, < 200°C, the dominant interlayer ion in micas is potassium, neither sodium nor calcic micas are stable (Chatterjee, 1968 ;   Velde, 1971 ;
Hemley et al., 1971).

Mica-like phases have a c sin ß spacing near 10 Å,
between 10.1-10.3 Å, which is asymmetrically formed with a
slope toward high d-spacings (Figure 8).   This asymmetry has
been the object of quantitative studies (Kübler, 1968 ;
Dunoyer de Segonzac, 1969) aimed at determining the amount
of non-mica material present relative to the mica component.
Basically, the wider and more asymmetric peaks indicate a
chemical component that has less interlayer charge (0.8-0.7)
and a higher silica content ($Si_{3.0}$ for mica and up to $Si_{3.4}$
for mica-like minerals such as illites).   Experiments in the
system muscovite-pyrophyllite (Velde, 1969 ; Velde and Weir,
1979) indicate that the solid solution or amount of non-mica
component decreases as temperature increases for a constant
total pressure. In these experimental studies, the mica-like
phase contained up to 25 % non-mica (pyrophyllite) component.

If the above description of illite has served for
several decades as a mineral group name, certain precautions
should nevertheless be taken in mineralogical determinations. Sròden (1980.b) has shown that small amounts of smec-

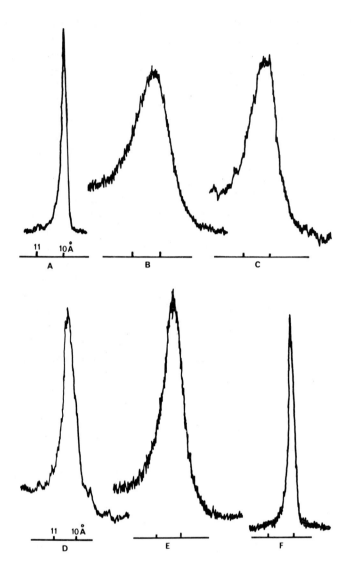

Figure 8 - Typical X-ray diffraction traces of the (001)
reflection for mica and mica-illite minerals.
Asymmetry is shown towards large $\underline{d}$ values.
A = natural $2M_1$ muscovite ; B = natural illite (1Md) ;
C = synthetic illite (1Md), 75% mica, 25% pyrophyllite
composition ; D = synthetic 1M muscovite ; E = natural 1M
glauconite ; F = synthetic 1M celadonite mica.

tite layers (up to 10 %) will be difficult to identify unless great care is taken in X-ray measurements. Velde and
Weir (1979) have shown that even in simple chemical systems
using synthetic materials, it is still difficult to determine the exact crystalline state of what could be generally
called illite. We do not really know if a wide, asymmetric
(001) reflection can be produced by a non-expanding mica. As
a consequence of this uncertainty, we do not really know if
an interlayer occupancy of 0.7 ions instead of 1.0 can
really be attributed to a mica-like (**i.e.** non-smectite
containing) phase. Since this book is based upon an
empirical approach, we will use what has been assumed to be
generally valid as a basis for discussion. However, we must
always consider that the illite composition (mica-like, low
charge, silica-rich phase) is potentially an interlayered
mineral with 0-10 % smectite present. It appears that as the
temperatures of formation increase the amount of smectite
can be more precisely determined in the ordered mixed layered mineral of the IMII type (Reynolds **in** Brindley and Brown,
1980). The basic character of low charge mica-like mineral
compositions is the low alkali content which is compensated
by a high silica content in the case of aluminous phases or
high silica and a R^2 component in the case of celadonite-
type substitutions. These substitutions can be considered to
be :

Muscovite		**Celadonite**
$K\ Al_2Si_3Al\ O_{10}(OH)_2$		$K\ R^2R^3Si_4O_{10}(OH)_2$
$\downarrow$	and	$\downarrow$
$K_{0.6}Al_{2.0}Si_{3.4}Al_{0.6}O_{10}(OH)_2$		$K_{0.6}R^2_{0.6}R^3_{1.4}Si_4O_{10}(OH)_2$
aluminous illite		**glauconite**

a - Illite-Phengite

Probably the most passionately debated mineral (if
one might use this adverb in a discussion of clays) found in
argillaceous sediments, rivalling perhaps the enigmatic dolomite and dolomitization in the realm of sedimentary rocks,
is the mineral or group name illite. Defined and re-defined
by its originator, R.E. Grim ; debated and further re-defin-

ed, denied a proper existence and reprieved, this species has attracted the attention of clay mineralogists for many decades. It represents, in fact, the dominantly potassic, dioctahedral, aluminous, mica-like fraction of clay-size materials. Known as sericite or hydro-mica in studies of hydrothermal alterations, soil mica or illite in soils and illite in sedimentary rocks, the material represents a wide range of compositionally solid solutions. It is possible to determine its origin by age determinations, thus establishing its detrital or sedimentary origin in a given setting (Hower et al., 1963 ; Hurley et al., 1962 and 1963) ; however, this proves rather unwieldy and costly. Extraction for chemical analysis presents much the same problem and still does not give a good definition of the origin of a particular specimen. The difficulty of identification thus remains, but why is this so problematical ?

Initially, there are several types of micas which have similar properties but which have different physical and chemical origins. Illite, the low potassium aluminous mica-like mineral ($\simeq$ 10 Å, non-expandable structure upon glycollation) can form during burial metamorphism (Velde and Hower, 1963). The crystal structure is apparently disordered (1Md using the criteria of Yoder and Eugster, 1955) and the relative content of K, Mg, Si, Fe^{2+} and Fe^{3+} is variable. Illite also appears to be the early product of weathering in cycles of intense alteration or one of the stable products under intermediate conditions (Jackson, 1959 ; Meunier, 1980). It is apparently stable, or unaffected by transport in rivers for relatively short periods of time (Hurley et al., 1961) but does change somewhat in the laboratory when in contact with sea water (Carroll and Starkey, 1960). It has been reported to be converted to chlorite or expandable minerals upon marine sedimentation (Powers, 1959). However, Weaver (1959) claims that much sedimentary illite is "reconstituted" mica which was degraded to montmorillonite by weathering processes. It is evident that a certain and usually minor portion of illite found in sedimentary rocks is of detrital origin (Velde and Hower, 1963) whether reconstituted or not. Laboratory studies at atmospheric conditions (Harder, 1974 ; Mattigod and Kittrick, 1979 ; Lin and Clemency, 1981) demonstrate that illite can be crystallized from an aqueous gel, and that muscovite tends to lose potassium and aluminum while gaining silica (relatively) thus forming an illite phase.

Thus detrital sediments can contain illite of at least four origins ; material crystallized during weathering, reconstituted degraded mica, detrital mica formed at high temperatures and of course unaffected detrital illite from sedimentary rocks. Illite can also be formed in sedimentary environments (Gabis, 1963).

During the process of lithification and deep burial, illite appears to remain stable or at least is slow to react with other minerals. It is by far the most dominant species of clay mineral in argillaceous sedimentary rocks (Grim, 1968 ; Millot, 1964). In early burial, the overall illite content of a specimen may decrease during adjustment to bulk chemical and physical restraints (Perry and Hower, 1970) ; however most studies of deeply buried sediments show a definite increase in illite as pressures and temperature increase (Millot **et al.**, 1965 ; Dunoyer de Segonzac, 1969 ; Perry and Hower, 1970 ; Iijima, 1970 ; van Moort, 1971 ; Weaver and Beck, 1971). Typically illite-rich sediments develop the assemblage chlorite-illite-quartz or chlorite-illite-biotite-quartz upon epi-metamorphism (Maxwell and Hower, 1967 ; Dunoyer de Segonzac, 1969 ; Nicot, 1981).

Studies of hydrothermal alteration products associated with ore mineralization in acidic rocks, have established the general propensity for the original minerals to be replaced by illite, sericite or hydromica in the innermost zone near the source of hydrothermal fluids, and by kaolinite or expandable minerals further from the vein or center of fluid emanation. The newly-formed "mica" can be 2M, 1M, or 1Md in polymorph and range compositionally from muscovite to a low potassium, silicic species which can be assimilated in the term illite (Schaller, 1950, Lowell and Guilbert, 1970 ; Schoen and White, 1965, 1966 ; Kelly and Kerr, 1957 ; Bonorino, 1959 ; Tomita **et al.,** 1969 ; Yoder and Eugster, 1955 ; Meyer and Hemley, 1959, among many authors).

If then illite, or a potassic mica-like mineral, is present in most of the geologic environments, the variation of its structure and chemistry must be examined with care in order to establish its chemical stability relative to the system in which it is found.

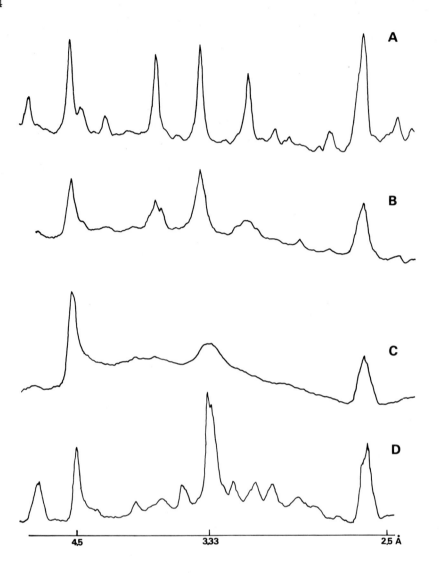

4,5   3,33   2,5 Å

Figure 9.a - X-ray diffractograms of non-oriented illite and celadonites.

A - Synthetic 1M muscovite
B - Synthetic 1M plus 1Md muscovite
C - Synthetic 1Md muscovite. Crystallite size is very small indicated by the low intensity (003) reflection at 3.3. Å.
D - Typical natural sedimentary illite with a large 1Md component and also 1M and 2M polymorph component.

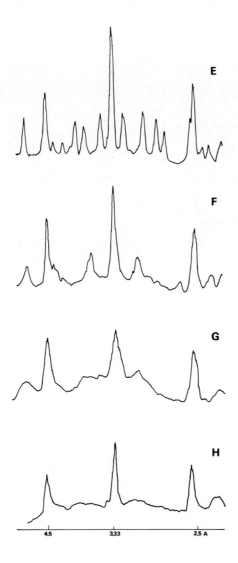

4,5   3,33   2,5 A

Figure 9.b - X-ray diffractograms of non oriented illite and celadonites.

E - 2M polymorph natural muscovite from a pegmatite.
F - 1M plus 1Md polymorph sample from a hydrothermally altered tuff.
G - 1Md plus 1M polymorph natural sedimentary illite.
H - 1Md synthetic celadonite $[KMgFe^3Si_4O_{10}(OH)_2]$

1 - Polymorphs

The main method used to distinguish the relative quantities of neoformed illite is by the polymorph or structure of the material. Using the criteria that 2M and 3T polymorphs of dioctahedral potassic mica are high temperature forms (Velde, 1965a), the determination of the relative quantities of 1Md, and 1M vs. 2M, 3T polymorphs permits a semi-quantitative estimation of the proportion of neo-formed or low temperature illite present in a specimen. A method commonly used is a determination of relative intensities of (hkl) X-ray diffraction peaks of non-oriented mica (Velde and Hower, 1963 ; Maxwell and Hower, 1967). Usually only 2M and 1Md polymorphs are present in illite specimens which simplifies the problem. The 1M polymorph is typical of ferric illites and celadonite-glauconites, the more tetrasilicic types (Figure 9).

In sediments and sedimentary rocks 1Md is the predominant polymorph of illite which is used as an indicator of a diagenetic origin of the material. In deeply buried sequences of rocks this polymorph can become predominantly 2M (Dunoyer de Segonzac, 1969) ; glauconite is not known to change polymorph under these conditions.

It should be remembered though that a purely aluminous phase can have the three common polymorphs - 1Md, IM and 2M (Yoder and Eugster, 1955 ; Velde, 1965.a ; Baronnet et al., 1976) and that these polymorphs can be the result of crystallization kinetics alone, and thus will not be related to the composition of the mineral nor necessarily to the temperature at which the phase crystallized, since time enters in as a factor.

It is interesting to note that the 1M polymorph represents an ordered form while 1Md structures are disordered (Guven and Burnham, 1967) and that the typical sequence in the process of glauconitization is 1Md to 1M (Burst, 1958). Illite remains disordered, for the most part, even in Paleozoic sedimentary rocks (Velde and Hower, 1963). This would suggest that the glauconite structure, being more symmetric, might be more stable than illite, a point which will be discussed when experimental studies are considered.

2 - Synthesis of phengites and "illites"

a - Phengite

There is, among the potassic micas one main series of chemical variation which lies between muscovite $KAl_2Si_3AlO_{10}(OH)_2$ and celadonite $KR^{2+}R^{3+}Si_4O_{10}(OH)_2$. Such micas are called phengites (Ernst, 1963). They are similar in composition to illites in divalent ion and silica content but differ by having a higher potassium content. Synthesis and stability experiments at high pressure (1-8Kbars) indicate that the greatest solid solution from muscovite toward celadonite is found in substituting Mg^{2+} in the octahedral site and compensation by adding Si^{4+} in the tetrahedral si-

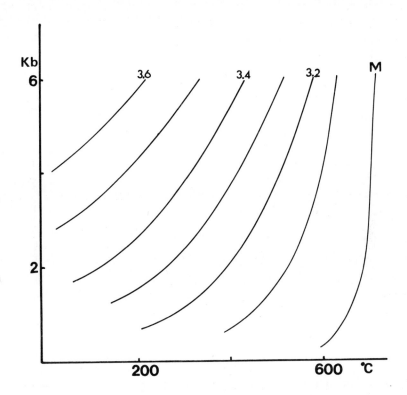

Figure 10 - Stability of mica phases produced from compositions in the series muscovite-MgAl celadonite (Velde, 1965b). Silica content of the mica produced where $Si_{3.0}$ = muscovite (M), $Si_{4.0}$ = celadonite. Curves indicate Si content of micas.

68

te. Eighty per cent of this substitution is effected at 8-10
Kbars pressure and 200°C. This solid solution diminishes
with pressure. Thus the phengite substitution should be
minor in micas from clay mineral environments (Figure 10).
Massone (1981) demonstrated the existence of a di- trioctahedral substitution in limited amounts (up to 12 %) which
occurs at high pressures and temperatures (above 400°C and 6
Kbars). This is not of great importance for clay mineralogy
but, as we will see, both phengite and di- trioctahedral
substitutions are found in low potassium micas, illites.

If we consider the solid solution in the mica compositions between muscovite-MgFe^{3+} celadonite (Figure 11),
we see that significant amounts of celadonite are present in
solid solution at 250°C, 2 Kbars pressure. It appears that
at the lowest temperatures and pressures more MgFe celadoni-

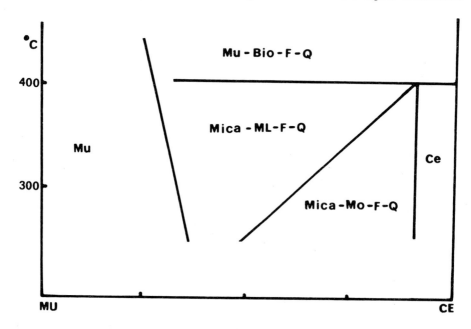

Figure 11 - Phases present along the compositional join
muscovite (Mu) - MgFe^{3+} celadonite (Ce) at 2 Kbars
pressure.
Mu = muscovite-phengite ; Mica = dioctahedral mica of
unidentified composition ; Ce = celadonite mica ;
ML = mixed layered mica-montmorillonite ;
F = feldspar ; Q = quartz ; Bio = biotite ;
Mo = montmorillonite.

te is soluble in muscovite than MgAl celadonite. This is the reverse relation to that found at high pressure conditions (> 3 Kbars). At low pressures and temperatures, the mica fields are separated by smectite-containing assemblages.

Natural mica compositions of the dioctahedral, potassic types have been discussed by Velde (1965b) in connection with the solid solution between muscovite and the different celadonite mica molecules. It was shown that both natural and synthetic micas formed two distinct compositional and genetic groups. The important point made in the discussion is the definition of the term mica. The most restrictive criterion as previously mentioned is the necessity for the mineral in question to have a net charge (the sum of octahedral and tetrahedral electrostatic imbalance) of -1.00 ± 0.10 per $O_{10}(OH)_2$ cations. This is the "true mica"

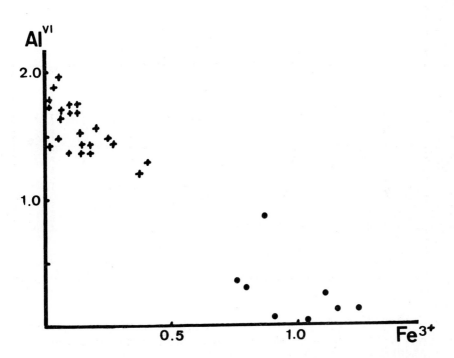

Figure 12 - Compositions of natural potassic micas as a function of their Al^{VI} __ Fe^{3+} contents (octahedrally coordinated ions). Crosses represent phengite micas and dots celadonite-glauconite micas.
(K + Na + Ca/2 = 1.00 ± 0.10). Data from Velde (1965.b)

structure where K + Na + 2Ca = 1.00 $\pm$ 0.10. The natural minerals complying with such a definition can be divided into
two genetic groups ; glauconite-celadonite and muscovite-
phengites. The distribution of ionic species in these two
groups is also distinct and can easily be seen when Al and
Fe^{3+} content in octahedral sites of natural micas are compared (Figure 12). The phengites, micas produced by high
pressure and moderate temperature conditions, are typically
low in ferric iron while the celadonite-glauconite micas
contain Fe^{3+} in large quantities and are typical of sedimentary or low pressure-temperature conditions of formation.
Natural mica composition reinforces the conclusion based
upon synthesis studies, confirming the bimodal distribution
of mica solid solutions (Velde, 1965b, 1972). This is shown
in synthesis studies (Figure 11) and plots of natural mica
compositions (Figure 12). It can be concluded that
there is probably no complete series of mica compositions
between muscovite and celadonite mica $[KAl_2 Si_3 AlO_{10} (OH)_2$ -
$KR^{2+}R^{3+}Si_4O_{10}(OH)_2]$, formed under conditions normally attributed to clay mineral environments.

b - Illite

The experimental system muscovite-pyrophyllite
(Velde, 1969 ; Velde and Weir, 1979) gives an insight into
the nature of illite. Although the components of the system
do not include iron or magnesium, the solid solution in muscovite obviously forms what can be considered as the aluminous end of the illite series. Figure 13 shows the solid
solution estimated for the mica-like phase at 2 Kbars pressure. The non-expanding mineral near the muscovite composition is a siliceous, low-charge species containing about
20 % pyrophyllite and excess water which resembles illite in
both chemistry and X-ray diffraction properties. It forms a
solid solution with montmorillonite by interlayering of the
two types of mineral structures. This series is apparently
continuous at low temperatures ($\simeq$ 150°C) but it is discontinuous above 200°C. This problem is more fully discussed in
the smectite section.

The general character of low charge and high Si-
content of illites can be attributed to solid solution with
a chemical component such as pyrophyllite in the aluminous
system or chlorite in an Fe-Mg system. This solid solution

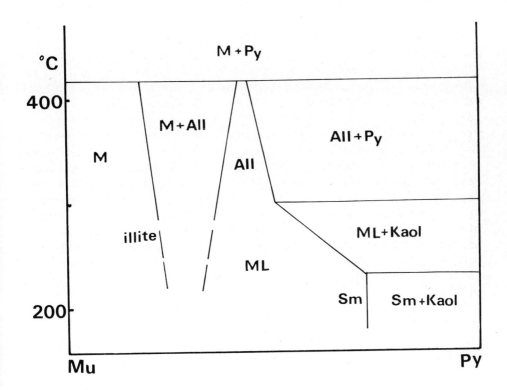

Figure 13 - Phases found between the compositions muscovite
(Mu)-pyrophyllite (Py) at 2Kbars pressure
(after Velde, 1969).
M = mica (tending to an illite-like phase) ; ML = random
mixed layered phase ; All = allevardite-like phase ;
Sm = fully expandable phase ; Kaol = kaolinite ;
Q = quartz ; Py = pyrophyllite

is, most likely, of an ion-for-ion type, that is to say the
so-called pyrophyllite component is equally distributed in
the different 2:1 mica layers forming a siliceous, low potassium structure which has nevertheless enough interlayer
charge, near 0.80 per $O_{10}(OH)_2$, to "collapse" the layers so
that they do not expand when saturated with polar molecules
such as water or ethylene glycol. This solid solution is
very distinct in any event from the interlayering of this
non-expanding structure with smectite (zone designed as ML
in figure 10) which occurs at 70 % pyrophyllite content at
300°C. It is, of course, possible that there is a segrega-

tion of mica and non-mica component in the mica-like phase which has not been detected. However, this being the case, the average c sin ß or basal spacing should be less than 10 Å since a pyrophyllite component would have a 9.6 Å (001) dimension. X-ray diffractograms of the synthetic material indicate a 10.0 to 10.2 Å spacing.

It is also important to note that the extent of this ion-for-ion solid solution is diminished at higher temperatures. There is a gradual exsolution, in the compositional join studied, to form the mixed layered phase. One can, therefore, only speak of the non-expanding component present in the mica-like phase and not of pyrophyllite as such. This has no significance as far as the phase relations are concerned since solid solutions are not necessarily molecule for molecule, i.e., the identity of a component does not persist in the solid solution.

It should be noted that illite type minerals have been synthesized from precipitated gels at or near atmospheric conditions as well as elevated P-T conditions (Harder, 1974).

3 - Natural illite compositions

Nineteen well-characterized illite compositions are plotted in the $MR^3-2R^3-3R^2$ coordinates (Figure 14). The main features of their formulae are traditionally compared with muscovite, the mineral closest to illite compositions. Where muscovite has the ideal formula $KAl_2 Si_3 AlO_{10} (OH)_2$, illite can be represented by $M^+_{.7-.9} (R^{2+} R^{3+})_{2.00} (Si,Al)_4 O_{10} (OH)_2$. Illite does not have a total lattice charge equal to 1.00, and the total silica ion in the tetrahedral sites exceeds 3.00. The charge, distributed between octahedral and tetrahedral sites, is usually compensated by potassium and sodium ions, more questionably by Ca^{2+} or H_3O^+ (Hower and Mowatt, 1966). Two main compositional trends are evident in looking at this information. The first is the tendency to have a low lattice charge relative to mica, therefore a smectite type compositional solid solution. The second is the substitution typical of phengite micas $R^2 Si = Al$. These two trends are shown in Figure 14. The scatter of points simultaneously indicates a combination of these two substitutions and thus, although illite has essentially a mica structure (i.e., 10 Å non-expandable) it most often has a bulk composition not found in high temperature micas. This extension of the illite chemical domaine is very important in determining the relation of illite or sedimentary "mica" to that of other phyllosilicate phases. It should be noted here that the solid solution at low P-T conditions is complete between muscovite and extremes of illite compositions ; all phases are stable at these P-T conditions. As a result the readjustment of detrital muscovite to chemical conditions of sedimentation will be made slowly, if at all, and as a result sedimentary illite will contain newly crystallized material as well as older, inherited detrital micas which have not come to equilibrium with the new chemical conditions, i.e., the average composition of the illite does not represent the phase in equilibrium with other neoformed silicates.

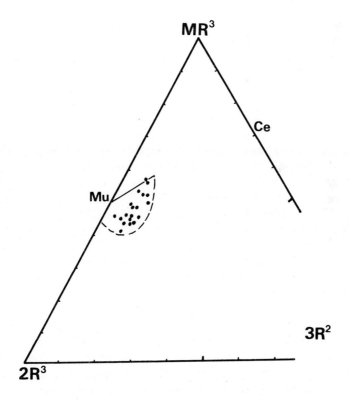

Figure 14.a - Natural illite compositions plotted in MR^3-$2R^3$-$3R^2$ coordinates.

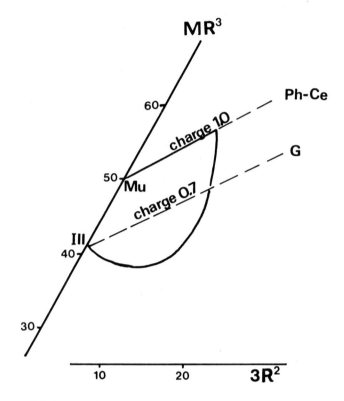

Figure 14.b - Relations of low charge and high charge
micaceous phase compositions in $MR^3-2R^3-3R^2$ coordinates.
Mu = muscovite ; Ph-Ce = phengite-celadonite compositions ;
G = glauconite-type composition ; Ill = illite.

      Figure 15 indicates the necessary change in compo-
sition which a muscovite would need to become stable under
conditions in a sedimentary rock where chlorite is present
(x to y). The solid solution for mica-illites is de-limited
by the shaded area which represents a much larger variation
than is possible under metamorphic or igneous conditions.
The detrital muscovite (composition x) is in itself stable
if the bulk composition of the sediment is projected into
the coordinates found at x. The ΔG between the assemblage of
muscovite + chlorite at composition y and illite of this
composition is likely to be relatively small and the
tendency to recrystallize the muscovite from x to y
compositions will be small at sedimentary conditions.
However, as more thermal energy is added to the rock system,
under conditions of deeper burial, the re-crystallization
will proceed more rapidly as the temperature is increased.

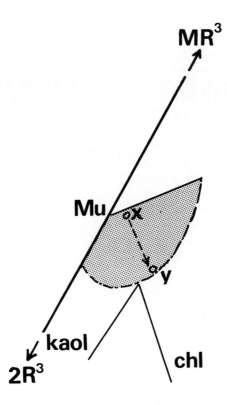

Figure 15 - Representation of the phase relations near the
   illite compositions in the $MR^3-2R^3-3R^2$ coordinates.
Mu = muscovite ; y = illite solid solution in equilibrium
with chlorite ; x = possible composition of a detrital mica
with some phengite component present.

      Several microprobe studies can be used to illustra-
te the compositional variation of illite as a function of
P-T and x. Initially, one must be forewarned that electron
microprobe analyses will not distinguish between the different oxidation states of iron. If the chemical analysis produced were perfect, one could calculate the Fe^2-Fe^3 ratio by
assuming all tetrahedral sites to be occupied and watching
the charge balance on the octahedral and tetrahedral sites
compared with the alkali ion content of the mica. This requires
very high precision on the part of the microprobe, less than
one percent error on the silica content for example. At present, we do not have such analyses available (they would be
more precise than the limits proposed at the beginning of

this chapter). Therefore, the probe data which will be used in the following discussion are considered as follows - in the $MR^3-3R^2-2R^3$ coordinates, all iron is grouped as the $3R^2$ component. We know that this is not going to be the case, yet there are no reasonable criteria to use a priori. The Fe^{3+}/Fe^{2+} relations in the 19 bulk analyses of illite ranges from 0 to 62 % ferrous iron. We will see that the arbitrary assignment of iron to the $3R^2$ component does not seem to distort the chemiographic relations of the phases to a great extent in high grade diagenesis or hydrothermal alterations. However, it does seem that kaolinitic sandstones, for example, contain clay with only Fe^{3+} present.

Meunier (1980) shows that illitic micas can form in the early stages of granite weathering. These are grain-contact phases found between muscovite and orthoclase. Figure 16A shows the micaceous mineral compositions for several samples cited in his study (the analyses are those given by Meunier and several unpublished newer ones). The minerals are magnesian, tend to have low $3R^2$ components and show a decided tendency toward low alkali contents (0.7-0.9 atoms K). If there is a mixture of phases it will be between illite and kaolinite. The R^2 components are lost through weathering.

New mica and old minerals (unpublished mica analysis by the author) in sedimentary rocks of the allevardite-type mixed layered mineral zone from the southern pre-alpine mountains (Lantaume and Haccard, 1961) are shown in figure 16B. The mixed layered minerals are accompanied by chlorite. These samples show occasional overgrowth zones on detrital micas in sandy shales. The new micas plot on the edges of the illite zone while the internal, "detrital" micas plot toward the muscovite composition but they have compositions normally attributed to illites. Some other detrital phases with no apparent new growth zones, plot much closer to the muscovite composition. One sees that the old micas which are related to the new phases seem themselves to have been changed in composition somewhat, becoming alkali-poor and $3R^2$-rich. If would seem that they have participated chemically in forming the new phases.

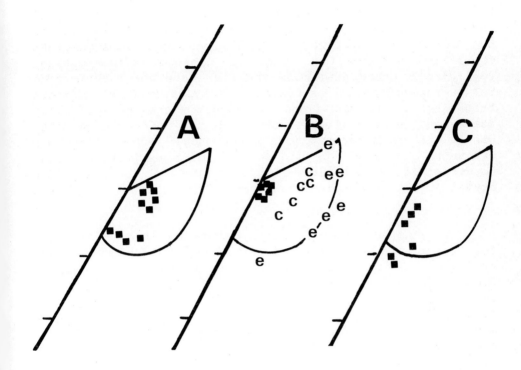

Figure 16 - MR^3-$2R^3$-$3R^2$ plot of natural illitic micas.
A - From mica-feldspar contacts in weathering
B - Old micas (squares) and transformed micas (c) with
overgrowth zones (e) from epi-metamorphic rocks
(allevardite-type mixed layered mineral facies)
C - New mica patches in diagenetic sandstones

      In some kaolinitic sandstones from the North Sea Triassic (3.000-4.000 meters depth) the detrital and new mica which is formed has a tendency to be R^{2+}-poor. When iron is present in significant amounts, it is necessarily in the Fe^{3+} state if one wishes to balance the charges of the mineral formula. Hence, the plot in figure 16C shows iron as R^3. These micaceous minerals occur with large amounts of vermicular form kaolinite which is present in most pores. The illites can occur in the center of the kaolin and thus should be assumed to coexist with this latter phase. The rocks contain illite, kaolinite and a mixed layered mineral with about 25 % smectite component.

These analyses show the possible re-adjustements of old grains to new conditions which gives the detrital grains a new composition as indicated in figure 15. In some cases the energy necessary to change the composition was available, while other grains in the rock were not transformed. The overgrowth zones, as those noted by Nicot (1981) demonstrate that although old grains are not necessarily entirely converted, a new phase which reflects the new diagenetic conditions will be crystallized at their edges. Thus in sedimentary rocks one can expect to find new illites which correspond to diagenetic P-T-x conditions.

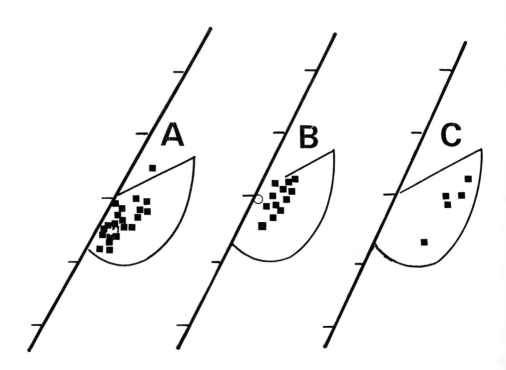

Figure 17 - Micaceous phases present in a hydrothermally altered granite.
A = Sericites in feldspars (plagioclase and orthoclase)
B = Old magmatic micas (circle) and recrystallized muscovite
C = Overgrowth edge on magmatic micas.
Outlined area shows illite field in $MR^3 - 3R^3 - 2R^2$ coordinates.
All iron is considered to be divalent in calculation of microprobe results.

Meunier and Velde (1982) report analyses of sericite-illites formed during the hydrothermal alteration of a granite. The highest temperature (earliest) alteration mica is formed as an overgrowth on magmatic micas. Their compositions are shown in figure 17C. They tend to contain iron in quantities equal to that of magnesium and form a series at the limits of the illite zone as defined earlier. A second type of mica, that of recrystallized magmatic muscovites is plotted in figure 17B. These minerals contain less $3R^2$ component with iron representing about one third of these ions. A third mineral type is found in altered plagioclases and orthoclase. Iron forms usually less than a quarter of the $3R^2$ component. These mica-like phases are decidedly illitic in many cases, i.e., low charge and high silica content minerals (Figure 17A). The sequence of mineral compositions observed is to a certain extent interpreted as reflecting changes in temperature, but above all changes in solution composition which shift the micas from high potassium-high R^{2+} to low potassium and low alkali content. The illites which are formed in these hydrothermally altered rocks appear to be quite sensitive to their physico-chemical environment.

MacDowell and Elders (1980) and Nicot (1981) have shown the variation in mica composition in high temperature-low pressure diagenetic environments. These authors show that there is a strong tendency towards R^2-rich illites at low temperature. The divalent ion content decreases as does silica and at the same time alkali content (potassium) increases. A muscovite composition is approached and then a distinct shift toward phengite is observed. In the mica-biotite zone one can still see that alkali content is low - 0.9 atoms instead of 1.0. As phengite content increases, sodium becomes a more constant component in the 0.1-0.2 atoms concentration range. Illites are not sodic (Nicot, 1981). Beaufort (1981), Ramboz (1980) and Cathelineau (1981) present microprobe data on hydrothermal sericites which indicates that a di- trioctahedral substitution at 0.85-0.90 atoms of potassium is probable. This is the upper range of temperatures for illite stability. The compositions are found in MR^3-$2R^3$-$3R^2$ plots towards the extreme of the illite range where it joins the phengite compositional line (Figure 14). The illite compositions might be useful in determining temperature conditions of the biotite facies at low pressures.

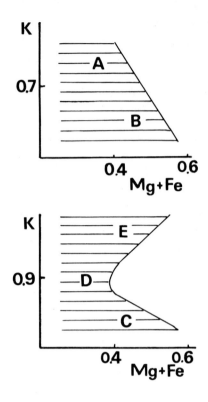

Figure 18 - Solid solution of illitic minerals as a function
   of potassium and magnesium plus iron content (atoms).
 A - Weathering and hydrothermal alteration illites of low
   temperature ; B = Mixed layered phases in contact with
   ferro-magnesian phases ; C = Low grade metamorphism or
   diagenesis ; D = Highest grade diagenesis, end of clay
   mineral facies (mica-chlorite ± biotite assemblages) ;
         E = Metamorphism in the phengite facies.

        Even though studies are not extensive, one can
possibly summarize the major variations in illite composition in relation to their geological environment.
Considering systems with abundant Mg and Fe (i.e., excluding
hydrothermal and kaolinite-bearing rocks), one can project
the above compositional groups into a facies versus Mg + Fe
plot (Figure 18). We can see that the Mg-Fe solid solution
is low during weathering and it increases as one
moves into the mixed layered mineral facies. There seems to
be a slight tendency to "overfill" the octahedral sites in
these minerals (2.05-2.12 ions) which might well indicate

the di- trioctahedral solid solution found by Massonne (1981) for high temperature phengites. However, in the clay mineral facies, the illites have a low alkali content and cannot then be compared directly to micas. One can see a parallel between illite and dioctahedral phengite substitution and illite-di- trioctahedral substitutions. Figure 18 shows the zones where one can tentatively assign the illite compositions as they relate to facies of mineral genesis. The very R^2-poor zone E indicates the presence of kaolinite and illite ; it might also be designated as one where illite and aluminous smectite co-exist. Zone D is the area where illites in most shales will fall similar to the mixed layered mineral zone. Area D is the zone in lower biotite facies where some di- trioctahedral substitution is found. Higher temperatures at low pressures will give micas nearing muscovite in composition, zone C.

In the illite-chlorite facies the Mg-Fe content decreases and continues to do so into the biotite facies. Higher pressures will create the normal, dioctahedral phengite substitution series where the alkali content is between 0.95 and 1.00. In these minerals, the sodium content will increase. Typically, sodium is low in illites from diagenesis and low-grade metamorphic facies. Also a characteristic difference between metamorphic or magmatic minerals and diagenetic illites is the titanium content which is generally less than 0.02 atoms per $O_{10}(OH)_2$ in diagenetic minerals. One can then use Na-Ti variations to distinguish high temperature from low temperature minerals.

In summary one can place the compositional range of illites in a general clay mineral context with reference to $MR^3-2R^3-3R^2$ coordinates. Figure 19 shows the general areas where one would expect to find illites from different geologic environments. The R^{2+}-poor zone is that of weathering, hydrothermal alteration at low temperature, and sandstone diagenesis. The R^{2+}-rich zone is where one finds abundant chlorite associated with the illites and mixed layered phases. High grade diagenesis, approaching metamorphism where mixed layering between illite and smectite is almost non-existant and where biotite can begin to appear in low pressure sequences, gives intermediate compositions between muscovite and other illitic types. The muscovite composition, frequently sodic, is that of magmatic rocks, while metamorphism gives the muscovite-phengite series.

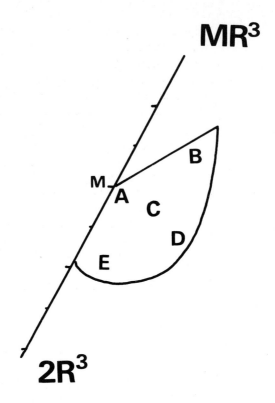

Figure 19 - Representation of illite compositions in MR^3–$3R^2$–$2R^3$ coordinates near the muscovite composition (M).

A = Magmatic micas ; B = Metamorphic micas (phengites) ;
C = High grade diagenetic origin slightly illitic micas ;
D = Illite associated with chlorites ;
E = Illites in sandstones, illites forming in early stages
of weathering and illites during hydrothermal events in
granitic rocks.

It might be noted here that the so-called hairy or filamentous illites found in diagenetically recrystallized sandstones are in fact mixed layered phases of the allevardite-type (see smectite section). This has been verified by Mc Hardy et al. (1982) and Guven et al. (1980). This occurrence should then be related to the origin of mixed layered minerals and not illite.

b - Celadonites and Glauconites

The occurrence of celadonite micas and minerals approaching this composition is less common than that of pelletal glauconite. In sedimentary rocks rich in sedimentary glauconite, obvious secondary or diagenetic formation of a green mica-like material has been observed either as vein fillings or replacement of other minerals (Millot, 1964). Glauconite or ferric illite has been found in other rocks formed from detrital acid and intermediate volcanic materials (Ojakangas and Keller, 1964 ; Keller, 1958 ; Peyrone et al., 1965 ; Pirani, 1963) where the stage of its development-sedimentary or diagenetic cannot be verified. Still other sedimentary rocks are known to contain layers rich in ferric illite where the exact nature of original sediment is not certain (Gabis, 1963 ; Porrenga, 1968). These minerals are related to illite, both in type of occurrence and chemistry as we will see later.

Celadonite, on the other hand, has a more restricted occurrence in nature largely because the term is used to describe green micaceous minerals of low temperature origin found in altered basic eruptive rocks and tuffs. The chapter on deep sea basalt alteration details this occurrence. There is no great difference between the terms glauconite and celadonite when they describe mineral species formed under diagenetic or low temperature metamorphic conditions. The major distinction to be made in using the terms glauconite and celadonite is geologic. The method of formation from solution equilibria by transfer of material to a localized center of crystallization at low temperatures, $\approx 20°C$, characterizes glauconite. Celadonite seems to be the result of recrystallization of a given appropriate bulk composition and thus their origin is governed more or less by the global chemistry of a given rock.

1 - Synthesis

The studies of Wise and Eugster (1964), Velde (1965b, 1972) and Harder (1978) on the synthesis and stability of celadonite micas define in a fairly complete manner the physical and chemical conditions under which this mica solid solution can exist and the extent of the solid solutions which can be present. There is considerable flexibility in the structure to accept octahedral ions of the MgAl, MgFe^{3+} and Fe^{2+} Fe^{3+} pairs. The central type is MgFe^{3+} - celadonite which forms solid solution to about a 30 % maximum with MgAl and 80 % Fe^{3+} Fe^{2+}. However, there is little apparent substitution between MgFe^{2+}, MgAl, Fe^{2+} Fe^{3+} and the FeAl type which was not crystallized as a single phase mica.

One aspect of the experimental studies which is noteworthy with respect to the application to sediments and sedimentary rocks is that the celadonite with the highest thermal stability (Velde, 1972) can exist over a temperature range of at least 200°C and most likely over 400°C since the formation of near-mica glauconites is known to take place at 25°C or less in nature (Porrenga, 1966, 1967b ; Caillère and Lamboy, 1970) and the laboratory (Harder, 1980). As a result this mica is not at all useful to distinguish between rocks of different origin in a sedimentary series since it can exist over the full range of sediment to epimetamorphic conditions. Thus, even though much time and energy has been spent on determining the genesis of this mineral, its usefulness as an indicator of physical conditions is almost nil.

Another important result of the experiments is the evident association of mica and smectite. Experiments in the muscovite-MgAl or MgFe system show that there is no solid solution between the two mica types : tri- and tetrasilicic : KAl$_2$Si$_3$AlO$_{10}$(OH)$_2$ and KMgFe^{3+}Si$_4$O$_{10}$(OH)$_2$. The phase relations are rather complicated in that they include minerals which do not fall on the compositional join studied nor do they form a simply designated planar series among the five components K, Al, Fe^{3+}, Mg and Si. However, the summary relations are shown in the diagram representing the phases stable at medium temperatures (200-400°C and 2 kilobars pressure ; Figure 20).

The mineral types familiar in sediments and sedimentary rocks are present in this system : micas, mica-like phases, fully expandable phases and mixed layered series. In a sense, celadonite mica is isolated from dioctahedral mica by a multiphase zone where smectite is stable with a feldspar and mica. It is evident that the only way to produce celadonite mica under high potassium concentrations is by having a proper bulk composition toward that of celadonite.

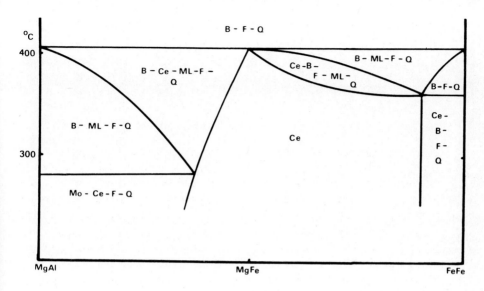

Figure 20 - Phases produced from compositions between MgAl, $\overline{MgFe^{3+}}$ and $Fe^{2+}Fe^{3+}$ celadonite bulk compositions at 2 Kbars total pressure and under nickel-nickel oxide oxygen fugacity (Velde, 1972). ML = mixed layered expandable-mica ; Mo = fully expandable montmorillonite, probably trioctahedral ; Ce = celadonite mica ; B = biotite ; F = feldspar ; Q = quartz.

The possibility of producing celadonite in a potassium deficient system, i.e., where smectite coexists with a non-alkali bearing phase, has not yet been studied experimentally.

2 - Sedimentary glauconites (pelletal)

One of the few clay minerals to be identified as definitely having an origin at the sediment-water interface is glauconite, i.e., the green micaceous material which forms pellet-like agglomerates. This has been conclusively demonstrated in recent sediments (Porrenga, 1967b ; Lamboy, 1967 ; Ehlmann et al., 1963 ; Caillère and Lamboy, 1970 ; Caillère and Giresse, 1966 ; Bell and Goodell, 1967 ; Giresse and Odin, 1973 ; Birch et al., 1976 ; Pryor, 1975). One interesting factor in these glauconite occurrences is the depth of formation. In temperate latitudes, glauconite pellets are found as shallow as 10 m. In tropical climates, the minimum depth increases to 100 m or deeper. They are found as deep as 2000 m in both situations. In each of their occurrences in present day sediments, they become evident at a constant bathymetric level indicating the necessity of either specific temperatures or possibly pressures which, in combination with the chemistry of the sea water, organic material and the silicate sediments available, permit the development of this mineral.

The formation of sedimentary glauconite is rather similar in mode to that of chamosite or berthierine except in the greater range of depth, Eh and pH at which the process takes place. In both cases the role of organic material is evident and similar, acting as a motor in changing the aspect of the silicate in the pellet both in chemistry and mineralogy from that of the enclosing sediment. The reasons for the development of one or other mineral species are at the moment somewhat obscure but, considering the similarity of the occurrence, the mechanism is probably the same. With this in mind the analysis which follows for sedimentary glauconites can be considered applicable for sedimentary 7 $\overset{0}{A}$ chlorite pellets.

3 – Thermodynamic description of the formation of sedimentary glauconite pellets

Mineralogical studies of incipient formation of glauconite pellets (Ehlmann et al., 1963 ; Porrenga, 1967b ; Pryor, 1975) indicate that they are formed initially from the same material as the matrix of the sediment in which they are found. However, the mineralogy is somewhat transformed by some animals (Pryor, 1975). The original material is frequently multi-mineralic (Burst, 1958), but during glauconitization the proportion of the mica-like phase increases in the pellet, the potassium and iron content increases and eventually the mineralogy becomes uniquely that of a 10 $\overset{0}{A}$ mica phase (Hower, 1961). This tendency for the total number of phases in a pellet to be reduced to a single phase appears, by virtue of its regularity, to be independent of the initial material upon which it operates, i.e., weathered biotite, chlorite, illite, kaolinite, smectites or other minerals (Burst, 1958). The end-product of the process, i.e., the mica, has a reasonably constant composition but represents a mineral with several possibilities of solid solution (Hendricks and Ross, 1941). Individual pellets in different sedimentary environments generally present sharp boundaries with the enclosing matrix material, whatever its nature, leading to the conclusion that the original volume of the pellet might have been respected during the process. The global sedimentary environment of glauconite formation (Grim, 1953 ; Hower, 1961 ; Millot, 1964 ; Weaver, 1959) is one of low, if not negative, sedimentation rate and one which is slightly oxidizing. By contrast the incipient glauconite pellets are considered to represent a local reducing environment and concentration of these pellets is often associated with pyrite. The minerals are however predominantly ferric. An important factor in the formation of glauconite is the necessity to have free access to sea water (Hower, 1961) or in cases of lacustrine origin (Parry and Reeves, 1966 ; Millot, 1964) simply the water of deposition.

The organic remains in the initial pellets are generally accorded great importance in the process of glauconitization. Indeed it appears that the incipient pellet is mineralogically and chemically similar to the surrounding sediments but notably different in organic matter. The material within the pellet would then be more reducing than the sediment in which it lies, and would have a higher local Eh potential. Thus, the initial impetus to the process is a Δ Eh between sediment and pellet. The concentrations of the elements which must be present in the sea water solution to promote glauconite formation are largely governed by the type of sediment in contact with the water. Equilibrium is thus established punctually between pellet and sea water effecting a transfer of material between the two media. On a larger but still somewhat local scale the dissolution of detrital silicates in sea water provides the basic "reservoir" of material in solution and hence determines the activities of various elements in the solution.

Basically the characteristics of the glauconitization process described above are similar to those of infiltration metasomatic replacements. In thermodynamic terms (Korzhinskii, 1959, p. 18) the system is one in which a number of chemical components is present in variable quantities and their chemical potential is considered to be controlled by equilibria exterior to the system under consideration, the glauconite pellet. These are perfectly "mobile" components which affect the mineral equilibria in the same way as do physical parameters such as pressure and tempera-ture. They are thus intensive variables of the system. The basic characteristic of such a thermodynamic system is that the greater the number of chemical constituents whose chemi-cal potential is controlled from the exterior (intensive variables) in this case in solution, the smaller the number of phases which will be at equilibrium under general or uns-pecified values of the intensive variables. The important point to remember about the glauconitization process is that the end-product is always a single phase ; $p = 1$. Regarding the phase rule for infiltration metasomatic processes (Korzhinskii, 1959) :

$$f = c_i + c_m + v_e - p$$

where f = degrees of freedom (the number of variables which can be changed slightly without change in the number or kind or phases present) ;

c_i = inert components whose relative mass determines their role in phase equilibria ;

c_m = perfectly mobile components whose chemical poten-tial determines their role ;

v_e = intensive physical variables (in this case fluid pressure, temperature, Eh) ;

p = phase present = 1 in the case of glauconitization gone to completion. For non-unique conditions of pressure, temperature, Eh and activity of the mobile components, the degrees of freedom due to these variables are :

$$f = 3 + c_m$$

the remaining degrees of freedom are thus :

$$f = c_i - 1$$

When the maximum number of possible phases are present, $f = 0$ and therefore $c_i = 1$. When the number of inert components is one, a multicomponent phase such as glauconite must be precipitated from the perfectly mobile components and one which is immobile or inert. In the instance of sediment-sea water reactions alumina seems a good candidate for the immobile component, due to its low solubility at normal sea water conditions.

If a system is established with mobile components in an infiltration diffusion process, one can expect that the mineralogy and bulk composition will vary in steps and gradually within these steps (Korzhinskii, 1970 ; Fisher, 1977). Odom (1976) and Velde and Odin (1976) found that glauconite pellets vary only slightly in composition in their centers ($<$ 10 % of the iron) but show outer rims which are aluminous (2-3 % of Al_2O_3) and contain less iron (5-8 % of the iron). This outer rim seems to be an intermediate step in the compositional change of smectite-rich materials to iron glauconites. The microprobe determinations confirm the supposition that glauconite pellets represent diffusion-controlled systems isolated physically from their environment but nourished from it chemically.

c - Compositional relations of low temperature micas

The bulk compositions of natural illite, celadonite and glauconite (*) appear to form a continuous series of solid solutions between their various compositional poles. Plotted as a function of $MR^3-R^3-R^2$ coordinates, the illite "field" discussed previously appears contiguous with that which encompasses celadonite-glauconites (Figure 21). A word of caution must be added initially with regard to the compositions and the mineralogy which they represent. If the illites have been well characterized structurally and physically for apparent chemical and monophase purity, the glauconites and celadonites selected from the literature here have not. Only the more recent analyses have been used as the norm in this study, but little X-ray diffraction information is available for each of the published analyses. The

(*) The M^+ component was calculated as being equal to the residual charge on the lattice. This eliminates problems of exchangable cations which have not been analyzed, such as $H_3O^{\pm}$. This procedure also proved necessary for smectites.

notorious multiphase character of the minerals (Burst, 1958 ; Hower, 1961) would suggest that caution should be used in interpreting smaller variations in bulk compositions. We see that some points in Figure 21 are found in areas where theoretical one phase micas cannot exist, i.e., above the muscovite-celadonite compositional line (Mi - Ce). Also, the scatter to low M^+R^3 values, i.e., below the muscovite-celadonite, indicates non-mica compositions which could be the result of smectite interlayering or the presence of other phases such as chlorite, kaolinite or iron oxide.

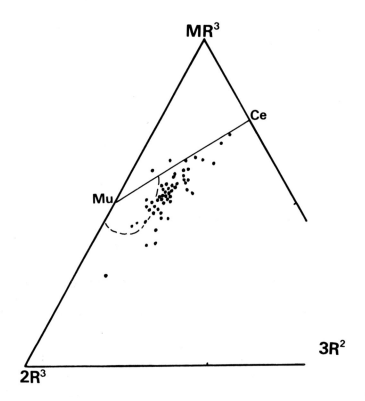

Figure 21 - Celadonite-glauconites as a function of their composition in the MR^3-$2R^3$-$3R^2$ coordinates. It is important to remember that glauconites contain large quantities of Fe^{3+}. Crosses are celadonites and circles glauconites.
Ce = celadonite mica ; Mu = muscovite.
Dashed line shows illite field.

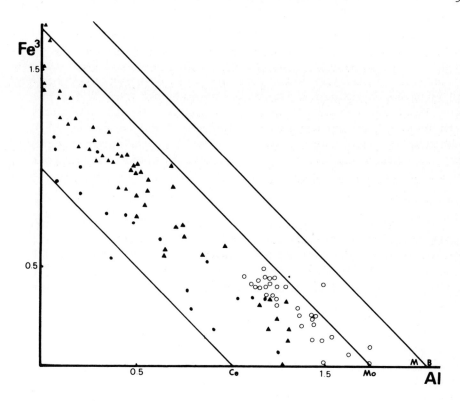

Figure 22 – Fe^{3+} and Al in octahedrally coordinated sites
of illite, celadonite and glauconites.
M-B = muscovite beidellite theoretical compositions ;
Mo = montmorillonite (octahedral charge) ;
Ce = celadonite ; open circles = illite ;
triangles = glauconites ; dots = celadonites.

However, it is evident that the celadonite-glauconites form a continuum between the tetrasilicic mica composition, illite and dioctahedral smectite or the $MR^3 - 2R^3 - 3R^2$
plot. If we look at the trivalent ions present in the octahedral sites in the calculated formulae (Figure 22), the
three mica-like mineral groups can be fairly well distinguished. Illite is alumina-rich, forming a series from mica-
beidellite-montmorillonite towards a ferric ion pole. Glauconite compositions extend from the ferric side towards the
celadonite mica montmorillonite compositions. Celadonites
form a series much closer to the theoretical celadonite mica
compositions. The important point here is the apparent continuous compositional series of the three mineral groups as

a function of Fe^{3+} and Al^{3+} in the octahedral sites. This continuity is an illusion due to an incomplete projection of the mineral compositions on the figure axes which give the positions of montmorillonites as well as micas which are quite closely spaced. The diagram does not distinguish between mica or expanding phase and thus is not an incisive method of distinguishing or comparing the mineral groups. However, it does point out the continuous substitution of the two types of trivalent ions which shows an increasing predominance of ferric iron in the mineral structure going from illite to glauconite.

There is no reason to distinguish between glauconites and celadonites in the sense that a continuous series of compositions appears in Fe^{3+}-Al variables. Buckley et al. (1978) and the recent mineral terminology commission would give a name to each mineral based on the contents of these two ions. There is, one must admit, little overlap in composition but there seems to be no reason why there could not be a continuous series, at least on chemical solid solution grounds. Most likely the chemical separation of the minerals is due to the chemical environments in which the two groups form - glauconites come from ferri-aluminous sediments while celadonites come from magnesian-ferrous basalt and andesitic rocks. The mineral names are thus of geological use but not of mineralogical significance.

There is, therefore, a difference between the true mica minerals which can be separated into two mineral groups based on Al^{VI}-Fe^{3+} occupancy of octahedral sites (Figure 21) and the wider compositional variations present in illite, glauconite and celadonite minerals with lower alkali contents. This being the case we must look at other chemical variables in order to distinguish these various similar mineral groups. Velde and Odin (1976) investigated the chemical and physical properties as well as phase relations of some natural pelletal glauconites. The approach used is to compare the composition of mixed layered mineral series - the illite-montmorillonite and the glauconite-montmorillonites. The relationship between expandability (or its inverse, mica content) and alkali content (K_2O + Na_2O) in illite mixed layered mineral and glauconite series is quite similar according to Thompson and Hower (1975) and Velde and Odin (1976) (Figure 23). Thus the alkali content of either type of mixed layered minerals can be considered a reliable

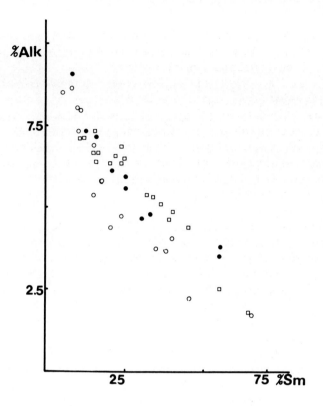

Figure 23 - Relations between alkali content of potassic illite-smectite and glauconites compared to expandability. Squares are aluminous smectite-illites (Hower and Mowatt, 1966) ; Dots are points from Velde and Odin (1976) for iron-rich glauconites ; Circles are for aluminous glauconites (Thompson and Hower, 1975). Aluminous glauconites show lowest expandability for a given potassium content. The similarity of the trends is evident.

indication of the amount of mica-like material present. The next comparison to be made is between alkali content and the amount of iron present (Fe_2O_3 + FeO). It is widely known that glauconites are very iron-rich, while illites contain lower quantities of this element. Figure 24 shows the rela- tion between glauconite, illite and ferric illites (those found in terrestrial closed-basin deposits). It is evident that as alkali content increases and, therefore, the propor- tion of mica-like layers increases, there is a division into two groupings, glauconites and illites. The latter type has iron content of 1-10 %, the glauconites 10-25 %. Due to this comparison of the two mineral groups, one can suppose that glauconites are formed by potassium and in some cases iron-enrichment of initial detrital sedimentary mixed layered material, since at low alkali content they join the illite series. A striking example of iron-enrichment of a detrital silicate material is presented by Giresse and Odin (1973). Here, recent kaolinite-rich sediments containing about 8 % total iron on the West African Continental Shelf are transformed into pellets rich in nontronite which contain 16-21 % total iron. This material is then progressively enriched in potassium to form glauconite.

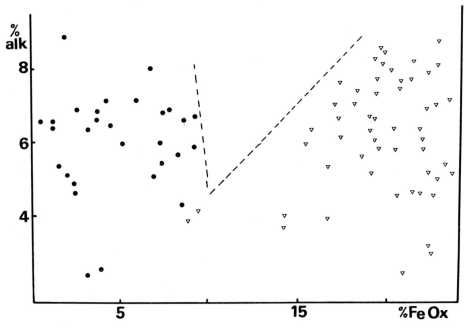

Figure 24 - Alkali weight percent versus total iron content (FeO + Fe_2O_3) of illites (ferric illites included) shown by circles and of glauconites shown by triangles (Velde and Odin , 1976).

d - Phase Diagram for the Illite-Glauconite Mixed Layered Minerals

It is possible to reconcile the apparent contradiction of overlaping bulk composition in the two mineral series illite-mixed layered and glauconite mixed layered mineral if one assumes mechanical mixtures of two chemically distinct groups of minerals which are indistinguishable by common methods of identification (i.e., X-ray diffraction, infra-red absorption, bulk chemical analyses). We know that the general tendency during glauconitization is one of potassium enrichment which increases the proportion of mica layers in the mixed layered mineral. It is also known that other phases can be present when these mixed layered minerals are formed in the glauconite pellet. Figure 24 shows that when potassium content is low, glauconite pellets can have a wide range of iron content. In assuming that illite and glauconite mixed layered mineral series do not overlap in composition at any point, a μ - x phase diagram such as that of Figure 25 will result. The arrows on dashed lines show the evolution of the bulk composition of a glauconite pellet which tends towards celadonite mica compositions. In the early stages of the process, multi-phase assemblages such as iron oxide, nontronite and kaolinite, or kaolinite, two smectites will be present. As the potassium enrichment continues in the solids, iron-rich and alumina-rich phases are eliminated (iron oxide + kaolinite) and glauconite mixed layered minerals are formed in their stead. When starting compositions contain little iron (dashed line 1), a region is crossed where the two mixed layered minerals coexist. This will appear as a single-phase mineral using X-ray diffraction due to the great similarity of illite and glauconite mixed layered minerals. As the potassium content of the solids increases, the mica portion increases simultaneously in both of the mixed layered phases. However, the proportion of glauconite mixed layered mineral increases over that of the illite-aluminous smectite mixed layered mineral. Eventually only glauconite remains in the last stages of glauconitization.

In this demonstration we see that potassium (a mobile element) increases in the solids. Also, there is a tendency to uniformize iron content to that of the single-phase glauconite composition. This means that iron can enter or leave the system even though it is an extensive (inert) component. Potassium is the key element whose chemical potential drives the silicate-solution microsystem.

There is, therefore, a difference between the true mica minerals which can be separated into two mineral groups based on Al^{VI} -Fe^{3+} occupancy of octahedral sites (Figure 24) and the wider compositional variations present in illite-glauconite and celadonite minerals with lower alkali content. This being the case we must look at other chemical phases. However, the proportion of glauconite mixed layered mineral increases over that of the illite mixed layered mineral. Eventually, only glauconite remains in the last stages of glauconitization.

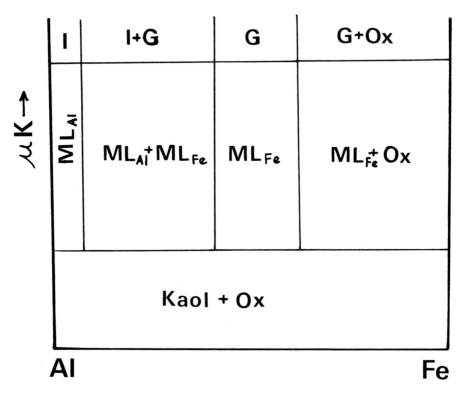

Figure 25 - Proposed phase relations where K⁺ is mobile component and Al, Fe are immobile components at about 20°C and several atmosphere water pressure for aluminous and ferric-ferrous mica-smectite minerals. This is a μ-x diagram representing both fluid and solid phases.
Symbols are as follows : I = illite ; G = non expanding glauconite ; Ox = iron oxide ; Kaol = kaolinite ; Mo = montmorillonite smectite ; N = nontronitic smectite ; ML_{Al} = aluminous illite-smectite interlayered minerals ; ML_{Fe} = iron-rich glauconite mica-smectite interlayered mineral. Dashed lines 1, 2 and 3 indicate the path three different starting materials might take during the process of glauconitization. The process involves increase of potassium content and the attainment of an iron-rich octahedral layer in a mica structure.

Different possible paths of glauconitization are indicated in Figure 25. These paths indicate the variation in bulk composition of the pellet as a function of μK-Fe-Al variables. Depending upon the mineral (and chemical) composition of the starting material, different assemblages will be found in the pellets at different stages of development which is what has been found in natural minerals.

One should notice the possibility of producing single-phase illite materials by the same type of process. If, for reasons unknown at the moment, the path of chemical change leads to aluminous illite instead of iron glauconite, **i.e.**, parallel to the μK axis with low initial iron content, one could produce single phase illite or mixed layered mineral assemblage. These are apparently rare, but such a theory could be used to explain the illite and mixed layered mono-mineral layers of "metabentonite" deposits which cannot be explained as recrystallization of an eruptive rock but by metasomatic replacement (Velde and Bruzewitz, 1982). Mono-mineral layers in carbonate rock, the so called shale partings, might also be due to such a mechanism. If we accept this demonstration as a general case, it is obvious that the MR^3-$2R^3$-$3R^2$ representation for bulk composition of minerals will superpose the two mineral series due to a confusion of Al and Fe^3 at the $2R^3$ pole. Thus figure 22 will give us no information useful in distinguishing between the potassic mica-like minerals illite and glauconite.

If the process of glauconitization is an equilibrium system, one should be able to reverse the chemical trend given the proper chemically varying system. This means that the reactions will be reversible and instead of forming glauconite gradually from smectite-kaolinite-iron oxides, one should be able to destabilize glauconite gradually to form less potassium-rich assemblages. Loveland (1981) and Courbe **et al.** (1981) present microprobe data which demonstrates precisely the reverse of the glauconitization process. Weathering profiles of glauconitic sandstones were investigated using microprobe techniques. Data from Courbe **et al.** (1981) in figure 26 show the gradual transformation of a rather potassic series of glauconites, 0.70-0.85 atoms per 1.0 sites, into various mineral assemblages. It was found that new, less potassic mixed layered minerals (green in thin section) were formed outside of the old glauconite pellets which themselves became brown. This new interstitial glauconitic material has a large range of potassium content, 0.5-1.0 atoms, indicating that it can be a mixed phase assemblage such as glauconite plus kaolinite. The general compositional trend during weathering is one of simultaneous potassium and iron loss from the silicates which is the same, in reverse, as the major trend of glauconitization described by Hower (1961). It crosses the two-phase field of Al and Fe^{3+} mixed layered series. Few bulk compositions indicate the coexistence of kaolinite and iron oxides which are of relatively low abundance in the profile. In a few secondary "argillan" zones near pores, new phases are potassic and

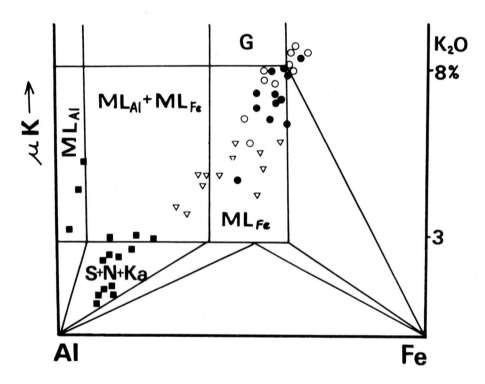

Figure 26 - Composition diagram showing glauconite weathering. Dots show green glauconite grains ; circles show brown glauconite grains ; triangles show green secondary plasmic material ; squares show brown plasmic and argillan zones. Note that the sequence is shown roughly as the inverse of the glauconitization path 1, in figure 24, that described by Hower (1961). Note also that some secondary argillan material has a composition of an aluminous mixed layered mineral. Data from Courbe et al. (1981).

aluminous. This indicates the crystallization of the illite-smectite mineral series within the glauconite profile. Thus the two series, Al and Fe^{3+} are present in the same rock, produced under different local chemical conditions.

Most notable in this weathering profile is the loss of iron from the system. It seems evident that the key to glauconitization reversal is that iron must be easily eva-cuated. Loss of potassium is, of course, to be expected during weathering. If iron remains in the local environment, oxides will form and one will immediately form the oxide-kaolinite assemblages described by Nahon et al. (1980). These authors show the rapid reaction of glauconite → iron hydroxide + kaolinite + isolated concentrations of silica which occurs during lateritic weathering or glauconitic sands. The accumulation of iron forms oolites in the weathe-red rock.

The role of iron mobility in the glauconite system is then the key to its origin and stability. Iron must enter or leave the silicate phase without blocking the system by forming hydroxides. We do not know how the iron is transfer-red from oxide to silicate in the process of glauconitiza-tion, but it is certain that iron oxide must be less stable than the potassic iron-rich silicate which is present. The whole system-silicate, oxide and solution-must be considered when treating the stability of glauconite.

The situation is not as simple for those mineral samples designated as celadonite. These micaceous minerals, formed for the most part in situ, in volcanic materials, are found to plot both on the illite and glauconite "site" of the alkali-iron plot as well as in between the two series. This is due to a more variable magnesium content which masks the Al-Fe relations. Magnesium enters into the illite-glau-conite series only as a minor component. Thus the chemical coordinates used to distinguish illite and pelletal glauco-nite cannot be used for celadonites. The question must then be posed as to the origin of these relations. How do illites and glauconites develop into different chemical series where celadonites cover the full range of Fe^{3+}-Al compositions ? More important, can the potassium micas be separated, for practical purposes, on the basis of iron content ? As far as illite-glauconites are concerned, that is in sediments and sedimentary rocks, it appears that glauconite represents an iron-rich series which is the result of special local chemical conditions. Thus it is possible to discount glauconites when considering illite genesis which is generally a bulk rock phenomenon. The two series will not overlap at high alkali contents where the mica-like phases appear. However, the phase relations in recrystallized volcanic rocks are apparently different. One finds $MgFe^{3+}$ micaceous phases but neither illites (aluminous) nor glauconites (ferric). At the moment there is insufficient data available to treat the subject correctly for all chemical environments. It should be possible though to distinguish between illite and glauconite in pelitic rocks and sediments.

It is obvious then that Al^{3+} is not synonymous with Fe^{3+} in sedimentary mica-like minerals. The increasing influence of trivalent iron in a sedimentary system will obviously provoke the crystallization of a specific mineral series which is not contiguous with illite and which would not otherwise be present. The development of glauconite in sediments should be due to specific local conditions which permit the chemical evolution of an initial montmorillonite material to celadonite mica-like phase. In fact previous observations have consistently led to this conclusion concerning the origin of glauconite in sediments and sedimentary rocks.

It would appear that the different types of potassic mica-like phases can be distinguished on the basis of alkali and iron content and geologic occurrence :

1 - Normal aluminous illite common in pelitic sediments, altered acidic volcanic ash beds, hydrothermal alterations of acidic rocks and weathering products of these rocks.

2 - Ferric illites found in small terrestrial basins, frequently in mono-mineralic layers (Porrenga, 1968 ; Jung, 1954 ; Keller, 1958 ; Ojakangas and Keller, 1964 ; Gabis, 1963 ; Kossovskaya and Drits, 1970 ; Parry and Reeves, 1966). The origin of the sediments is not known.

3 - Sedimentary pelletal minerals, glauconites.

4 - Alterations of basic or intermediate composition

eruptive rocks giving celadonite and related minerals (Peyrone et al., 1965 ; Pirani, 1963 ; Wise and
Eugster, 1964).

Type 1 and 2 are distinct chemically from type 3.
Type 4 seems to overlap the others.

If we look again at the octahedral ions present in
illites, glauconites and celadonites, it is clear that illites (or those whose chemical analysis is available) have a
rather tightly grouped range of compositions, whereas the
other types range widely. This encourages one to characterize illite as a well defined, little variable mineral type.
This is likely to be true in the largest number of cases
where a multimineral assemblage is present in a rock which
includes illite.

SUMMARY

If would seem necessary then to separate glauconite from illites in our analysis of the phase relations between clays. As we have seen, glauconite usually forms in rather special and isolated conditions in nature. The ultimate thermal stability of these micas reaches beyond the normal limits of clay minerals. They break down to a biotite-bearing mineral assemblage. It can be argued that celadonite-glauconite micas will not be sensitive to P-T conditions within the range of conditions common to clay minerals and thus their usefulness as indicators of these conditions is limited. There is limited solid solution between muscovite and celadonite mica at low pressures. Be this as it may, there remains the problem of distinguishing chemically between glauco-celadonites and illites. From certain standpoints (bulk chemistry mainly) there is a complete series. However, the existing information based upon phase equilibria studies in the laboratory suggests that this is only apparent and in fact overlap is due to a mixing of minerals.

The most important observation which can be made after the analysis of the chemical and phase equilibria information is that illite and glauconite mineral series, do not overlap. Solid solution is not continuous, neither in the mica-like phase alone nor in mixed layering between mica and expanding layers. Glauconite is not a subspecies of illite. This allows us to concentrate on the phase relations of illite and montmorillonite in the general context of pelitic or aluminous mineral assemblages. This is important because illite is one of the most common clay minerals while glauconite, although wide spread in occurrence, is not found nearly as often. The tendency of illite to interact with the general clay mineral assemblage of a rock - at least as far as can be detected by most current methods of analysis - is an important fact. It should be possible to separate illite and glauconite parageneses in a rock where glauconite pellets are surrounded by an illite-bearing matrix. Glauconite will be isolated in its pelletal form from the matrix. Two mineralogical evolutions will occur side by side in the same rock.

We will then concentrate upon the relation of illite with other clay mineral in the M^+R^3 - $2R^3$ - $3R^2$ system. Glauconite will be a special case, where the R^3 pole must be separated into Fe^{3+} and Al^{3+} components.

4 - Smectites

In the simplified model of the smectite structure, certain fundamental assumptions are arbitrarily made. For instance, the choice of the 2:1 unit itself as a basis for the crystallographic unit cell is not a unique possibility. One could choose the octahedrally coordinated layer of cations as the edge of the unit cell, and have the interlayer ions in its center. Such choices are equally valid on crystallographic grounds but they do not help us to understand the phenomenology of the clay minerals concerned. The choice of a 2:1 basic unit with interchangeable and changing interlayer ion populations is much closer to physical reality and thus a more valid conceptual choice of reference. However, when expressing the concepts of layer charge, expanding and collapsing layers, and interlayering of different types of structures the chosen terminology becomes necessarily vague due to our lack of precise information concerning the charge distribution, homogeneity of phases, etc... It has not yet been demonstrated, for instance, that each symmetrically equivalent layer of tetrahedrally coordinated ions has the same ionic composition for a given 2:1 unit. On the contrary, it seems that there is a certain inhomogeneity in the individual smectite layers of natural samples at least as far as their surface exchange properties are concerned (Lagaly, 1979 ; Mc Bride, 1980 ; Tailburdeen and Goulding, 1983). It appears that there might well be a range of compositions in a given sample which result in an "average" exchange capacity and chemical composition but which then must be considered as a continuum in a solid solution series. Sample inhomogeneity is of course well known in metamorphic minerals and minerals coming from eruptive rocks so that there is no reason, **a priori**, to get upset when this phenomena is encountered in clays. But since we can rarely assess the extent of homogeneity in a given sample, we will use its average composition and we will deduce an average, homogeneous layer structure with symmetrical tetrahedral layers in the 2:1 structure.

a - Smectite Solid Solutions

I would now like to propose, as a working hypothesis, two concepts of solid solution in smectites which are somewhat unusual. In continuing through the discussions, the major supporting evidence for these concepts will be pointed out and used to develop the idea of phase relations between clay minerals. It is then the reader who will judge the validity of the ideas both as the evidence is presented and as the concept is used in each instance.

The first proposition is very simple : at low temperatures and pressures there are two kinds of expanding phases, dioctahedral and trioctahedral. Within each group, there is complete solid solution, concerning all the various possible exchangeable interlayer ions. This means, when identifying phases, that the interlayer ion population is not important in kind, only in quantity. Whatever the chemistry of the 2:1 lattice, whatever immiscibilities might exist between different 2:1 lattice types, the exchangeable interlayer ion population is interchangeable. The main supporting argument for this statement are the results of cation exchange studies which have been performed on almost all of the forms of expandable minerals (Grim, 1968 ; Brown, 1961). From this work it is evident that at 25°C and 1 atmosphere Na, K, Ca and Mg are easily interchangeable. Further it is known that if different ionic species are simultaneously present in the solution, partitioning is effected between a smectite and solution (Garrels and Christ, 1965 ; Bladel et al., 1972 ; Glaeser and Mering, 1967 ; Hutcheon, 1966 ; Inoue and Minato, 1979 ; Levy and Shainberg, 1972 ; Levy et al., 1972 ; Maes et al., 1975 ; Mc Bride, 1979 ; Marshal, 1964). This partitioning can be affected by ionic concentration in solution and by temperature. However, most important is the concept that there are no solubility gaps in composition between K, Na, Ca, Mg end-members and that a given 2:1 expanding structure can have K, Na, Ca, Mg end-members. Experiments by Mackenzie (1963) indicate that at temperatures above 300°C, 1 atmosphere, some expandable structures selectively retain certain ionic species which become non-exchangeable. Further it is known that aluminum hydroxides can fill interlayer sites as non-exchangeable ions (Coulter, 1969). Fixing of non-exchangeable ions is not part of the normal smectite "behavior" and we will exclude such material from this mineral category.

A second departure from the conventional viewpoint is the treatment of solid solution in the 2:1 portions of clay mineral structures. In clay minerals there are straight forward homologous ion substitutions in a given lattice such as iron for magnesium. The previous example of interlayer ion substitution demonstrates this principle. Solid solution of this type is the rule rather than the exception for silicates in general. There is another type of mineral association which can, at times, be considered as a form of solid solution or continuous compositional variation within a single-phase structural form. This is the phenomenon of mixed layering. It is evident that there are strong chemical segregations within mixed layered minerals - in general two types of two dimensional structures are interlayered in the same grain. This is typically effected between a non-expanding and an expanding phase in a mixed layered mineral. There is little good evidence available for a clear decision as to what constitutes solid solution in clays from a theoretical standpoint (Zen, 1962). However, there is one known instance where the use of experimental data necessitates a choice between two possibilities. In the compositional series muscovite-pyrophyllite (Velde, 1969), mica-beidellite interlayering occurs in varying proportions. At temperatures above about 250°C, 2 Kbars pressure, a fully expandable non-interlayered beidellite is no longer stable but an expandable mixed-layered phase remains stable. It is apparent that one end-member of the series (beidellite) is no longer stable as a unique phase while an intermediate, mixed layered form remains. This sort of behavior is well known in other solid solution series such as olivines and plagioclase. It was therefore proposed that the mixed layered clay mineral sequence be considered as a continuous series of compositions, a solid solution. Other phase relations in the study tended to reinforce this decision from a chemiographic standpoint when geometrical relations between the phases were considered. As a result there are, or in any event we will consider it to be the case here, two main types of solid solution possible - intra-lattice and inter-lattice, i.e., within a structure and between structures. This viewpoint is acceptable on a macroscopic scale when dealing with gross phase relations between silicates. Closer analysis will undoubtedly necessitate a different viewpoint if chemical distribution in a single lattice is considered to be important (Truesdell and Christ, 1968).

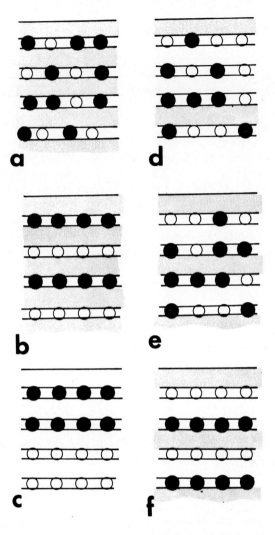

Figure 27 - Schematic representation of several possible
types of solid solution. Shaded and blank layers represent
expanding and mica-like units (2:1 structures). Solid and
unfilled circles represent two species of interlayer ions.
a = totally random in all aspects ; b = interlayer ion
ordering, single phase smectite ; c = ordered interlayer
ions which result in a two-phase mica structure, two phases
present ; d = randomly interstratified mineral, one phase ;
e = regular interstratification of the 2:1 layers giving an
ordered mixed layered mineral, one phase present ;
f = ordered mixed layered mineral in both the interlayer ion
sites and the 2:1 interlayering. This would probably be
called a single phase mineral.

   Let us now consider in detail some of the theoretical possibilities of solid solution. We will look at the
microscopic and sub-microscopic effect of each type and how
this determines the observed X-ray properties and treatment
of phase equilibrium relations of the minerals.

   Figure 27 indicates some possibilities of interlayer ion arrangement and interlayering between two 2:1 lattice types. In example (a) complete homogeneity is attained
in the distribution of two types of ions in interlayer positions. The silicate 2:1 units are uniquely of the smectite
type. This represents a single phase on both macro- and
microscopic scales. Type (b) shows ordering of the interlayer ions between smectite lattices. Such a situation suggests segregation of two phases on a microscopic scale but
the macroscopic properties will probably be identical to
those in type (a), a single phase structure. Type (c) shows
the complete segregation of interlayer ions by groups between the 2:1 unit layers. This represents macro- and microscopic ordering into two distinct phases. Intergrowths of
Na-K micas on a 5 to 10 micron scale (50 to 100 layers) has
been described by Frey (1970) using electron microprobe
techniques. These intergrowths are considered to be two phases. X-ray diffraction can be used in these examples to distinguish the presence of two species. Thus far it is assumed
that only type (a) and possibly (b) exist at low temperatures for smectite structures. This is largely done for lack
of contrary evidence. Inhomogeneity within a layer has been
proposed by Lagaly (1979), Lagaly et al. (1976) and McBride
(1980).

   The second type of mixing involving expanding phases is that of interlayering with a non-expanding lattice.
Type (d) shows random placing of the interlayer ions between
randomly interlayered smectite and non-expanding layers. On
both small and large scales the arrangement gives a single
phase. Type (e) presents a regular repetition in the sequence of mica-smectite layers (ordered interlayering or an
ordered mixed layered phase). The mica-smectite oganization
does not involve ordering of the interlayer cations which
are randomly distributed in all sites. This configuration is
considered to be a single phase solid solution. Type (f)
shows segregations of mica and smectite 2:1 units as well as
interlayer cations. However, structural continuity is maintained. Interlayering of this type could be considered as

producing two phases. However, there are no criteria to decide how such a structure would behave in a situation involving phase equilibria. We will consider this structure as mono-phase at present. In the above configurations for interlayering and interlayer ion distribution, only type (c) represents an assemblage of two phases. The other forms are solid solutions.

We have thus far discussed only the most simple and best known types of interlayering, those between expandable and mica structures. It is possible however, that several types of 2:1 lattice can coexist in the same structure (Lim and Jackson, 1980). For example, di- and trioctahedral forms of various types of each species. Because of their similarity under X-ray investigation, it is almost impossible to detect their presence in a mixed layered structure.

b - Dioctahedral Smectite

The natural occurrences of smectites are varied and complex, as is the mineralogy of this mineral group. Smectites are particularly variable chemically, due in part to the completely undefined interlayer ion position which can be occupied in part or entirely by almost any cation except silicon. Definitions and descriptions of these expandable minerals are necessarily vague since the response of these interlayer ions to different chemical and thermal treatments is the most current method of identification for minerals in the group. This leaves the basic 2:1 structure identified in many cases. A broad differentiation of the basic 2:1 unit types can be made using the occupancy of the octahedrally coordinated ionic position ; basically either two or three ions are present. Identification can be made by means of X-ray diffraction which is probably the most useful method to distinguish the expanding mineral groups. However this division is only gross and does not give much information about the mineral which might be present. In the discussion which follows, we will adopt out of necessity the di- trioctahedral terminology (i.e., two or three ions in the octahedrally coordinated site) thus grouping the expanding minerals beidellite, montmorillonite, nontronite, etc. together as dioctahedral smectites on the one hand, and vermiculite, expanding chlorite and trioctahedral smectites (saponite) on the

other. There is much more information available in the literature on the former group of natural minerals, both chemical and mineralogical, than the latter and thus our discussion of the natural minerals will more or less be concerned
with the dioctahedral expanding minerals. Nevertheless, one
should not ignore the importance of trioctahedral expanding
phases. It is probable that the complexities of identification of expanding minerals has frequently led to a grouping
of both types under the same heading in most geological studies. As we will see later, expanding phases are the precursors of most phyllosilicates stable at higher temperatures
and pressures. Thus classification of all these clay minerals under only two headings leads to gross imprecision with
respect to their chemical significance in a given environment.

1 - Dioctahedral smectite occurrences in nature

a - Weathering

This environment produces the widest variety and
the most poorly defined species of expandable phyllosilicate
material. A broad summary by Jackson (1959) indicates that
smectites and expandable minerals in general are the major
product of weathering for varied rock types under medium
intensity conditions - those found in the temperate climates where the drainage is moderately good. The attainment of
fully expandable species by weathering is frequently observed to be preceded by a mixed layered structure. Both di- and
trioctahedral mixed layered minerals are known to occur in
soils. At times regularly ordered interlayering between micas or chlorites and expanding layers is found (Kodama and
Brydon, 1966 ; Thorez and Van Leckwijck, 1967 ; Sudo, 1963 ;
Veniale and van der Marel, 1963 ; Johnson, 1964 ; Rich,
1958 ; Jackson et al., 1952 ; Bassett, 1963 ; Churchman,
1980).

In general, a weathering profile which produces
abundant smectites indicates that the weathering process is
moderately advanced. It would appear that expanding minerals
are the major product of weathering under the prevailing

conditions. The di- or trioctahedral character of the mineral produced is in a large part due to the composition of
the parent material or minerals. Ultrabasic or very basic
rocks produce magnesian minerals which tend to be trioctahedral and magnesian or ferric, dioctahedral smectites.
Acidic rocks and those containing larger quantities of iron
such as basalts tend to produce minerals containing trivalent ions which results in the production of dioctahedral
expanding minerals, such as nontronite, beidellite or montmorillonite. Smectites are also the most common clay
minerals found in soils which produce zeolites through the
weathering process (Hay, 1963 ; Hay and Iijima, 1970). There
are instances where, due to weathering, smectites are
transformed to the zeolite analcime (Frankart and Herbillon,
1970). This occurs in a context of high Na$^+$ concentrations
in solution. The relationship between smectite and zeolites
in alkaline environments, which is very important, is dealt
with in the chapter on zeolites.

A weathering sequence for phyllosilicates has been
established which indicates that their relative stability in
soils is as follows : mica, chlorite → mixed layered expandable, non expandable → fully expandable smectite → kaolinite + Al, Fe oxides (Jackson, 1959). This sequence is illustrated in Figure 28. It can be related to the intensity of
weathering prevalent in an area or it can be indicative of
the weathering intensity in a given point in a profile (B, C
horizon). As the intensity of weathering increases, i.e.,
tundra soils compared with laterites or C compared with B
horizon, the end-product mineralogy becomes impoverished in
alkali-bearing minerals. The soil horizons in a moderately
intense weathering profile show roughly the sequence in Figure 28 going from rock to mature soil at the surface. Thus
the "stability sequence" is equivalent to increasing the
intensity of weathering or to completing the process of
equilibration under conditions of high water content, low
concentration of alkali and silica ions and oxidation of
iron in a soil profile. In fact the weathering process in a
soil horizon sequence is much the same for pelitic rocks in
all environments ; the dominant sequence is repeated with
minor variations due to local conditions of pH or efficiency
of the oxidation process. As it turns out, expanding phases
are found in most soil sequences and they are frequently
dominant portions of the soil clay mineralogy.

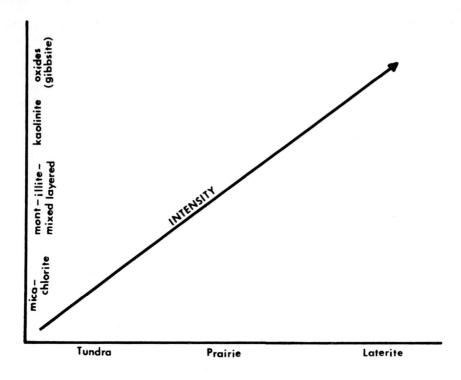

Figure 28 - Sequence of relative phyllosilicate stabilities shown as a function of weathering intensity. (Modified from Jackson, 1959).

Although many authors insist upon the sequential degradation of phyllosilicates, i.e., taking the same initial material and transforming it into the various types of expandable minerals in the weathering process (Weaver and Jackson, notably), this is undoubtedly not the only mechanism by which these clay minerals are formed in soils and possibly not the dominant one. Studies on the weathering of granites and more basic rocks show that feldspars and other minerals such as amphiboles are transformed to various phyllosilicates, often smectites, during the weathering process (Nichols, 1970 ; Bayliss and Loughnan, 1963 ; Wolff, 1967 ; Tardy, 1969 ; Tomita et al., 1970 ; Meilhac and Tardy, 1970 ; Meunier and collaborators, see chapter on weathering). The prevalence of smectites in river sediments and those studied as deep-sea cores in the numerous JOIDES reports leads one to believe that smectite is a very common weathering product. Certainly a portion of it is derived from degraded micas but if one considers that the next most common sedimentary mineral is illite, one is forced to conclude that either continental rocks are for the major part made of micas or that many other minerals are transformed into smectite during the weathering process. Arguments have been made by Velde and Hower (1963) against the idea that detrital smectites are simply potassium-stripped micas, this on the basis of mica polymorphs in sedimentary rocks which should reflect the origin of the layer-silicate material.

One might conclude by saying that the role of smectites in low temperature clay mineral facies is very important. There are, however, several points to clear up, mainly those dealing with the origin of the expanding material, before a complete geochemical cycle can be devised to include the expanding minerals in any detailed analysis of silicate phase relations. The problem resides in the fact that smectite compositions are much more limited than those of their precursors. Therefore much material is either lost to solution or is present in the form of other phases.

b - Sediments

Situations of marine sedimentation are primarily environments of dynamism and they are, therefore, likely to result in metastable phase assemblages. In sediments, all sorts of detrital minerals and amorphous material from various environments are deposited and frequently mixed together in a brief period of time. It is, therefore, often difficult to establish which phases could be authigenic in this environment. However, certain phases are known to form under sea water-sediment conditions. Smectites have been found, along with glauconite, 7 Å chlorite and palygorskite, to be authigenic (Rex and Martin, 1966 ; Heath, 1969 ; Chamley et al., 1962 ; Berry and Johns, 1966 ; Copeland et al., 1971 ; Lerman and Mackenzie, 1975) ; they have a composition different from that which is supplied to the ocean environment in general or the specific source material upon which the smectite in question was formed.

There is other evidence that smectites are not always stable at shallower levels of ocean deposition environments. The following conversions have been observed or deduced :

    smectite → glauconite (Ehlmann et al., 1963) ;
    smectite → chlorite (Rex, 1967 ; Porrenga, 1967b) ;
    mixed layered expandable → chlorite (Powers, 1959) ;
    smectite → palygorskite (Bonatti and Joenesu, 1968).

It remains a fact, however, that most ocean sediments contain a significant quantity of smectites which apparently persist through the consolidation process. This is particularly true in deep sea Pacific Ocean sediments where land-derived detritus is less important and smectites common (Griffin et al., 1968 ; Hoffert, 1980). Expandable phyllosilicates are also frequently found in lagunal environments where they are typically associated with zeolites forming from volcanic glasses. It does appear that when salinity increases great-ly, smectite decreases, being apparently replaced by more alkali-rich minerals such as potassic illite and feldspar, zeolites or palygorskite and magnesian sepiolite (Jones, 1965 ; Hay and Moiola, 1963 ; Parry and Reeves, 1966 ; Trauth, 1977).

    The ferric smectite nontronite is a common phase found as a product of chemical precipitation in ocean-floors (Bischoff, 1972 ; Hoffert et al., 1978.b). It is apparently the intermixing of hydrothermal waters and sea water which produces calcic, ferric smectite precipitates. These mine-rals are not aluminous. By contrast, the nontronites formed in the deep-sea "weathering" of basalts are potassic (see section on deep sea basalts) and ferric.

    In general, we can conclude that smectites are most often stable in the sedimentation environment and on the deep sea ocean floor. In certain specific instances which can often be ascribed to special chemical conditions, the expandable phase is not stable.

    c - Sedimentary rocks

    Smectites (dioctahedral) are very common in sequen-ces of sedimentary rocks, especially in younger sediments found near the surface. It would appear that their frequence decreases in older rocks, especially in the Paleozoic (Weaver, 1959). The assembled studies of Perry and Hower (1970), Dunoyer de Segonzac (1969), Muffler and White (1969), Browne and Ellis (1970), Weaver (1959), Weaver and Beck (1971), Burst (1959), van Moort (1971) and Iijima (1970) among others, demonstrate that the conversion of dioctahedral smectite to other minerals in sequences of deeply buried sedimentary rocks is to a large extent independent of time or geologic age and appears to be a function of the geothermal gradient which the rocks have experienced. These studies indicate that fully expandable dioctahedral smectite is not stable above 100°C at depths of two kilometers or more in argillaceous sediments. The occurrence of these minerals in sedimentary rocks can be considered to be controlled by their orogenic history.

The studies cited above deal with deeply buried sediments which occur in areas of low geothermal gradients. Further the rocks are basically sodi-potassic, at least in the silicate aggregates, and most often contain a potassic phase such as illite, feldspar or zeolites. In instances where these chemical conditions prevail and where the geothermal gradient is high (Muffler and White, 1969 ; Browne and Ellis, 1970) the same temperature-mineralogy relations seem to hold ; 100-120°C appears to be the upper limit of fully expandable smectite stability. However, R.O. Fournier (personal communication, 1974) feels that calcic montmorillonites will persist to higher temperatures. This opinion is based upon former (Honda and Muffler, 1970) and more recent work in Yellowstone Park, Wyoming in shallow drill holes. We will come back later to the interlayer ion composition-stability problem. However, if we consider for the moment the majority of available studies, it appears that fully expandable dioctahedral aluminous smectites disappear below 100°C at greater than two kilometer depths and slightly higher temperatures in more shallow series of rocks. It is possible that calcic smectite will be stable at 150°C at depths of 100-200 meters.

The existence and stability of expandable trioctahedral phases in sedimentary rocks is not well known, and little information which is available is not amenable to generalization at present.

d - Hydrothermal alteration

In zones of hydrothermal alteration it is apparent that the formation of dioctahedral smectites is limited by temperature. They almost never occur in the innermost zone of alteration, typically that of sericitization (hydro-mica or illite), but are the most frequent phase in the argillic-propylitic zones which succeed one another outwardly from the zone where the hydrothermal fluid is introduced into the rock. Typically, the fully expandable mineral is preceded by a mixed layered phase (Schoen and White, 1965 ; Lowell and Guilbert, 1970 ; Fournier, 1965 ; Tomita et al., 1969 ; Sudo, 1963 ; Meyer and Hemley, 1959 ; Bundy and Murray, 1959 ; Bonorino, 1959). However, temperature is possibly not the only control of expandable clay mineral occurrence ; the composition of the solution and the rock upon which they act might also be important. It is possible that high magnesium concentrations could form chlorite, for example, instead of expandable minerals.

e - Volcanic rocks

Fully expandable smectites are known to form from ferro-magnesium minerals in eruptive rocks during their late stage of cooling and have been substantiated to be in equilibrium crystallization product at thermal conditions above those of the surface (Velde D., 1971). This is strikingly apparent in certain basic extrusive rocks where smectites replace olivine in a glassy, unaltered matrix. The temperature of formation can only be guessed at by extrapolation of the stabilities of synthetic smectite of similar composition. The assemblage smectite-phlogopite-sanidine, noted to be in apparent stability in these rocks corresponds to the minerals produced in a study of celadonite compositions (Velde, 1972). These phases are stable below 400°C at 2 Kbars total pressure for a pure magnesian composition and lower temperatures as iron is introduced into the bulk composition. This occurrence, although interesting, is only locally important and would not contribute significantly to the clay composition of sediments or sedimentary rocks.

Bass (1971) has reported a smectite which forms a significant portion of a carbonaceous meteorite sample. This is again a rare occurrence and can be ignored as far as it would have any far-reaching consequences on the mineralogy of sediments on the earth.

f - Metamorphic rocks

As curious as it might seem, smectites can be form-ed during metamorphic processes. They do not crystallize at the thermal paroxysm, but during the latter stages of the cooling process. An instance reported by Studer and Bertrand (1981) gives a good description of the process. They have studied the metamorphic effect of basic dykes which intrude argillaceous carbonates. The highest grades of metamorphism reach grossularite-vesuvianite facies. Smectites and mixed layered minerals are found in various zones of the metamor-phic aureols which attain 80 meters in width. They obviously do not follow the general metamorphic pattern and therefore are not related to the metamorphic thermal gradient esta-blished by the intruding magma. They can be attributed to cooling processes and interaction between the gas-rich aqueous phases with the metamorphic minerals. These reac-tions produce minor quantities of clays but they are rather systematically present in the rocks. They appear to be tri-octahedral for the most part. We see then that clays can be present in high temperature rocks and be related to high temperature processes as a terminal phase.

This type of occurrence is most likely more common than one would assume from reports in the literature. The tendency of many geologists to attribute all clays to a weathering origin is certainly over-simplistic. It is proba-ble that many metamorphic rocks contain clays as granites do contain deuteric micas which are also due to low tempera-ture, cooling reactions.

2 - Synthetic dioctahedral smectites

Both sodium and potassium beidellites have been synthesized. However most studies have been conducted in such a manner that the results are somewhat unclear. Either the smectite was a by-product of another desired reaction, for example the synthesis of paragonite (Chatterjee, 1968), or the duration of the syntheses were not sufficient to obtain stable products. The resulting data are difficult to interpret and often contradictory. The pertinent information for Na-beidellite remains obscure although numerous studies have been published (Mumpton and Roy, 1956 ; Sand et al., 1957 ; Koizumi and Roy, 1959 ; Ames and Sand, 1958 ; Grandquist and Pollack, 1967 ; Eberl, 1971) to cite some. It is apparent that the relations of lattice charge to exchange capacity and swelling capacity are still unclear for these synthetic minerals. It is the experience of the author that experiments at 1 and 2 Kbars pressure between 200 and 400°C must be of one month's duration at minimum to determine with some measure of certainty the phase relations and crystal chemistry of clay minerals. In the studies cited, and most others, 14-day experiments are the longest performed, the average being closer to 5 days (Eberl, 1971, is an exception).

The study dealing with synthetic K-beidellite (Velde, 1969) is probably more valable in the sense that longer experimental durations were performed. However, there is undoubtedly a certain element of personal bias involved. Excluding the possibility of serious oversight for the moment, let us look at the results of this study. Figure 29 gives the phase relations for the expandable phase synthesized between muscovite and pyrophyllite bulk compositions at water pressures near 2 Kbars. The salient feature is the extent of mixed layering at low temperatures, most likely complete between muscovite and a montmorillonite. Another important point is the composition of the least K-rich phase produced which is not fully expandable. The charge on the basic 2:1 fully expandable structure will be significantly lower than the 0.33 value assumed ideal (Brown, 1961).

It is notable, in comparing the studies on potassium and sodium beidellites that the upper stability of the K^+ form is near 250°C at 2 Kbars while the sodium form is found at temperatures as high as 400°C. This is due to the fact that muscovite is stable to low temperatures, 25°C (according to Usdowski and Barnes, 1972) and paragonite only to 320°C or so (Chatterjee, 1968). Mumpton and Roy (1956), Eberl (1978, 1980), Eberl et al. (1978) and Roberson and Lahann (1981) show that smectites in the presence of a potassic aqueous solution are less stable, i.e. tend to form

micas, than in solutions containing Na, Ca, Mg or other divalent ions. A relatively high thermal stability is also
probable for calcic beidellite (Hemley et al., 1971). In the
potassium system, the interlayering between muscovite or the
illitic phase and the smectite beidellite is incomplete
above 250°C in the 10-25 % expandable layer range. The solid
solution (interlayering in this case) between mica and smectite is gradually decreased from the smectite end member
and, as temperature increases, only the 30 % expandable
layer form persists near 400°C.

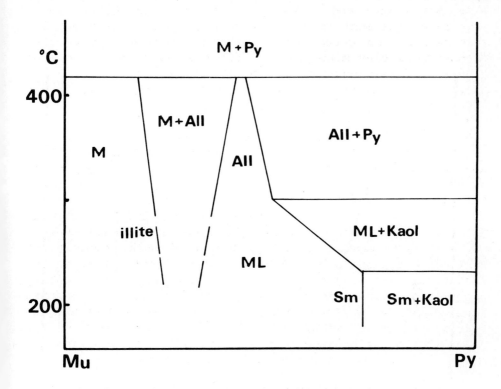

Figure 29 - Phases in the muscovite-pyrophyllite join.
M = mica like phase ; ML = mixed layered phase ;
Sm = fully expandable beidellite ; Py = pyrophyllite ;
Kaol = kaolinite ; Q = quartz ; All = ordered phase with a
superstructure reflection. The system is not binary.

Experimental work in the systems K-Mg-Si-Al-Fe-H_2O
concerning celadonites has also produced expandable minerals

120

(Velde, 1972 ; Velde, unpublished). In both the muscovite-MgAl celadonite and MgFe-MgAl celadonite compositional series, fully expandable phases were produced below 300°C at 2Kbars pressure. These expandable phases can coexist with a potassic feldspar (Figure 30). Their (060) reflection near 1.50 Å indicates a dioctahedral structure which can apparently be intimately interlayered with a trioctahedral mica, although this mica has just 2.5 Mg^{2+} ions present in the octahedral position. The potassic, magnesian, dioctahedral smectite appears to be stable up to 420°C at 2 Kbars pressure.

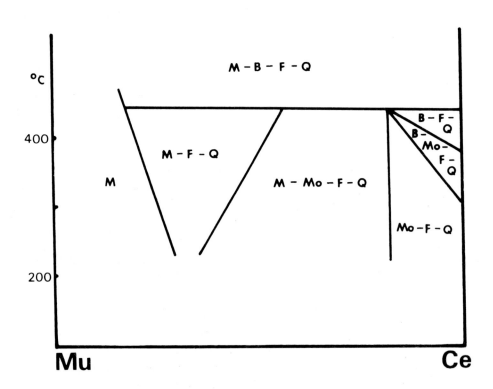

Figure 30 - Phase relations in the muscovite-MgAl
celadonite compositional join, 2 Kbars pressure
(Velde, unpublished data).
M = dioctahedral mica ; F = feldspar ; Q = quartz ;
Sm = expandable phase ; B = biotite.
As can be seen from the large number of phases,
the system is not binary.

Dioctahedral smectites with Mg^{2+} as an interlayer ion in the system $Mg-Si-Al-H_2O$ have been synthesized at 25°C (Harder, 1972) and 80°C, 1 atmosphere (Estéoule, 1965, 1969) and at 250°C, 1-2 kbars pressure (Velde, 1973). Their basic structure is that of a smectite which has magnesium instead of alkali or alkaline earth interlayer ions. The compositional range and charge on the structure are not totally defined in the studies. It is apparent, however, that the interlayer ions become better organized structurally at higher temperatures because the normal 17 Å swelling characteristic is decreased to 15.2 Å indicating the existence of one instead of two layers of polar molecules between the basic 2: units. This property is typical also of vermiculites and swelling chlorites. The analogy is maintained in that the basic interlayer distance of the mineral does not go below 14 Å upon heating to 400°C. There is no continuous solid solution series between the di- and trioctahedral expanding phases in the Mg-Al-Si system, either at low or high temperatures.

Harder (1976) has synthesized nontronite at room temperature also.

a - Experiments on natural dioctahedral smectites and mixed layered minerals

Velde and Bystrom-Bruzewitz (1972) have published the results of a series of experiments which treated natural expandable dioctahedral minerals under conditions of elevated temperatures and pressures for periods of one month (300-450°C, 2 Kbars pressure). Due to the slow reaction rates no reliable reaction temperatures could be determined but a general sequence of mineral transformations was established. Basically, the dioctahedral expandable minerals responded to increased temperatures as follows : the initial mixed layered structure decreased in expandability, evolving quartz. This continued until about 50-30 % expandable layers were present where further reduction in the expandability resulted in the production of chlorite. The assemblage allevardite (30 % regular interstratified layers, an ordered structure) - chlorite persisted until no expandable material was present, and only illite + chlorite + quartz remained.

Some studies have been made upon natural smectites (montmorillonites) in various aqueous solutions at atmospheric conditions (Kittrick, 1969, 1971). The principal observation made is that dioctahedral montmorillonite is stable under the chemical conditions which can be found in sea water, changing little as far as measurable physical parameters are concerned. One notable effect is the partial replacement of the interlayer ions Ca and Na by Mg^{2+}, a fact noted by Porrenga (1967.b) for smectites deposited in tropical ocean waters. The exchange of Mg for Na, and Ca is quite important in a consideration of the bulk composition of sediments and the development of diagenetic minerals.

b - Some properties of synthetic smectites

As we will see later, much attention has been paid to the composition and occurrence of dioctahedral smectites, especially in comparison with trioctahedral forms. This being the case, it is useful to try to understand the solid solution relations as one can attempt to understand them through a study of their physical and surface "chemical" properties. To this end the present author prepared by hydrothermal synthesis (300°C, 2 Kbars pressure) a sequence of magnesian smectites which covered the possibilities of charge variations from 0.20 to 0.50 per $O_{10}(OH)_2$. Lower or higher charge bulk compositions produced multiphase assemblages as determined by X-ray diffraction and infrared observations. The substitutions between beidellite and montmorillonite were considered in the range of charges mentioned. These samples were homogeneous according to their X-ray diffraction patterns (J. Sròdon, personal communication) and optical properties.

The major physical properties used to observe the smectites are cell dimension - b and c sin ß and their exchange properties. Figure 31 shows the b dimension of the synthetic smectites compared with their total charge and charge site (beidellite-montmorillonite). One sees that at high charge a definite inhomogeneity is apparent across the beidellite-montmorillonite series. It was observed that when the samples were immersed in Ca-Mg equimolar solutions (0.05 molar chloride salt concentration) little selectivity was apparent. A similar result was obtained by Levy and Shainberg (1972) and Levy et al. (1972) for natural montmorillonite. However, when Ca-K solutions were used, the clays showed a high calcium selectivity, as noted by Hutcheon (1966) and Inoue and Minato (1979) for natural montmorillo-nites. More striking is the relatively greater potassium-selectivity (although a modest 20 % in a Ca-K equimolar solution at 0.05 molar) of a low charge montmorillonite (Fi-gure 32). This selectivity approaches a normal distribution (K_D) for the 0.3 charge montmorillonite but other composi-tions show a strong non-regularity in their absorption cha-racteristics (Figure 33).

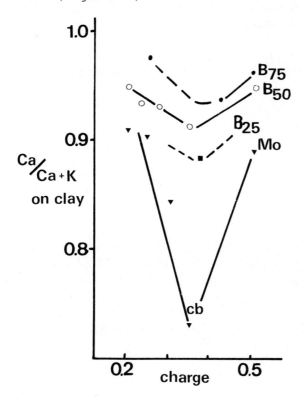

Figure 31 - Cation selectivity as a function of charge and site of charge on the structure. Mo = montmorillonite ; B_{25} = one quarter beidellite charge, etc. ; cb = Camp Berteau specimen. All other phases are synthetic minerals.

If we consider these data, it is apparent that high charge and beidellitic charge site tend to induce different physical behavior which suggests inhomogeneity of the struc-tures - as noted by other authors for natural clays (Maes et al., 1975 ; Tailburdeen and Goulding, 1983). Cation ex-

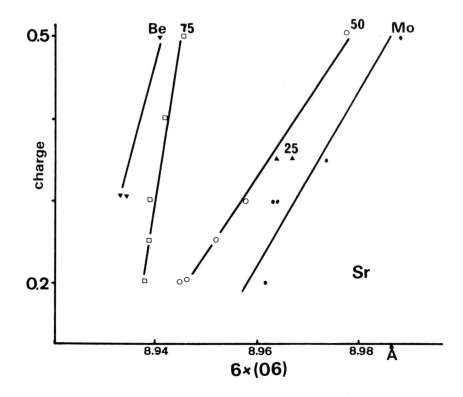

<u>Figure 32</u> - Cell dimension (<u>b</u> = c x 0,6 reflection) as a function of charge and charge site for air-dried, synthetic ; Sr = saturated minerals. Be = beidellite, Mo = montmorillonite charge site samples. 75 = 75% beidellite charge. Strontium is the interlayer exchanged ion on the synthetic smectites. Unpublished data of the author.

change capacities were determined using Sr as the exchange ion (Table 3). The results were not at all regular, a rather unpleasing thought when one assumes that clays should be a homogeneous substrate material. Actually, these same results were found for natural minerals (Chen and Brindley, 1976 ; Grim and Kulbicki, 1961) although the fact was not mentionned by these authors. This again points to non-regular behavior of smectites with either high or low charge. The one composition which seems to have a regular (predictable) behavior is the 0.3 charge montmorillonite charge mineral. It has the highest potassiphillic tendencies of the potassic smectites and an exchange capacity approaching that expected

of it. As it turns out this phase is the most common smectite found as a mono-mineral species in nature if the studies
of material used by clay mineral surface chemists mean any-
thing. Certainly this natural mineral is the most easily
procurred. This frequence in nature is probably an indication of a highly stable, or easily formed phase. One should
then keep in mind that synthetic studies indicate that a
regular structure occurs at the lower charge, montmorillonite compositions as opposed to higher charge and beidellitic forms.

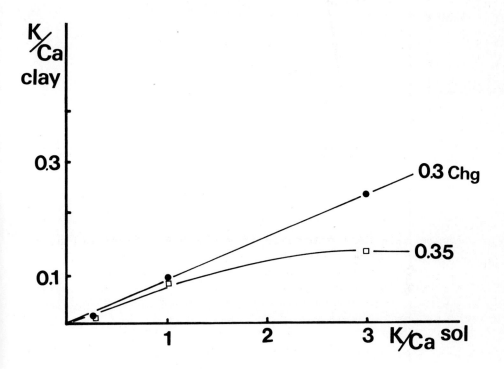

Figure 33 - Cation exchange selectivity for medium charge
synthetic montmorillonites. In this plot (K/Ca for clay and
solution) a linear relation shows ideal solid solution and
non-linear relations indicate non-ideal distributions. The
higher charge smectites and more beidellitic forms showed
very non-linear relations. It appears that only
montmorillonitic smectites approach ideal distributions.
Unpublished data of the author.

CHARGE	MONTMORILLONITE				BEIDELLITE
0.20	99		107		93
0.25	128				
0.30	128		118	99 103	93
0.35	99	114 117cb		98	
0.40	99			109	109
0.45	98				
0.50			131	131	106

Strontium Cation Exchange Capacity

Table 3 - Cation exchange capacities for Sr ions in 0,5 N chloride solutions. Minerals are synthetic magnesian forms when montmorillonitic (Mo), beidellites (Be) were synthesized as sodic phases. cb = Camp Berteau specimen. Double figures show duplicate determination. 30 mg of material were used. Unpublished data of the author.

c - Summary of the information from experimental studies

It can be concluded from these experiments that smectites are stable under most conditions between weathering and low grade metamorphism. Their appearance in a given natural system will be most often dependent upon the bulk composition or the chemical variables (extensive) which are operative. The great amount of chemical substitution in their structure makes them very sensitive to their chemical environment and thus very important in the equilibria between solids and solutions. It is also apparent from the experimental studies that the trioctahedral smectites or fully expandable phases are stable to higher temperatures and also present a greater range of solid solution than the dioctahedral equivalents. This is to a certain extent inherent in the structural form which permits more varied substitution in trioctahedral than dioctahedral coordinate sites. The occupancy is restricted to near two ions in dioctahedral minerals, the third site remaining vacant. By contrast trioctahedral minerals can contain between 3 and 2.5 ions giving a greater flexibility to the structure allowing, for example, very small ions, Li^+, and the relatively large trivalent iron to exist in the same mineral.

If we consider the three types of substitutions dioctahedral, trioctahedral and interlayer ion, we see that Na and trioctahedral minerals are stable to higher temperatures than others. This is logical when one considers that sodic trioctahedral magnesian minerals are unknown, paragonite is unstable below about 340°C (Chatterjee, 1968) and phlogopite is unstable below 250°C (Velde, unpublished). By contrast muscovite appears stable at low temperatures under high K_2O concentration (Velde, 1969) or appropriate H^+, K^+ and SiO_2 activities (Garrels and Howard, 1959).

Table 4 gives temperatures of smectite stability which are established by the experiments reported. The most important criteria used is reaction reversal ; this lacking, the length of the experiments and variety of starting material was taken into consideration. Two points are important among micas and other phyllosilicates - only kaolinite, serpentine and muscovite are stable to very low temperatures. All trioctahedral 2:1 structures break down to expandable phases at low temperatures (biotites) or to 1:1 structures plus expandable phase (chlorites).

THERMAL STABILITIES OF FULLY EXPANDABLE SYNTHETIC PHASES

Type	Elements in 2:1 lattice	Reference	1-2Kb pressure temp. °C
K dioct.	(AlSi)	Velde, 1969	230
K dioct.	(MgAlSi)	Velde, 1973	400
Na dioct.	(AlSi)	Sand **et al.**, 1957 Koizumi and Roy, 1958	350-450
Ca dioct.	(AlSi)	Chatterjee, 1969 Hemley **et al.**, 1971	300-500
Mg trioct.	(MgSi)	Esquevin, 1960 Velde, 1973	< 250
Mg trioct.	(MgAlSi)	Velde, 1973	430
Na trioct. beidellite	(MgAlSi)	Iiyama and Roy, 1963	550
Na trioct. hectorite	(MgAlSiNa)	Iiyama and Roy, 1963	800
K trioct.	(KMgSiAl)	Whitney, 1983	400

THERMAL STABILITIES OF MIXED LAYERED PHASES

K dioct.	(AlSi)	Velde, 1969	400
K dioct.	(AlSiMg)	Velde, 1972	430
Na trioct. beidellite	(MgAlSi)	Iiyama and Roy, 1963	780
Na trioct. hectorite	(MgAlSi)	Iiyama and Roy, 1963	800

Table 4

A special composition seems to be present at 0.3 charge montmorillonite-type substitutions. Other compositions are apparently more inhomogeneous.

3 - Chemical composition of natural fully expandable and interlayered dioctahedral minerals

Compiled data for aluminous dioctahedral smectites and mixed layered minerals are shown in Figures 34 and 35 (*). The field of illite composition is indicated in each figure. It is evident that these smectites designated as fully expandable phases by each author, cover a large field of compositions - from theoretical low charge smectite $(M^+)_{0.25} (R^{2+}R^{3+})_2 (SiAl)_4 O_{10} (OH)_2 .nH_2O$ to those near illite $(M^+)_{0.70} (R^{2+}R^{3+}) (SiAl)_4 O_{10} (OH)_2$. It is possible that some non expanding layers are present in the samples which were analyzed ; however it would be surprising that they could have been overlooked should they have represented as much as 40 % of the layers. This latter figure would be necessary if only low charge (0.3) and high charge (0.7) layers were considered as possible structures. The only conclusion which one can reach is that high charge to low charge dioctahedral smectites are quite common. Another aspect of these smectite compositions is their relative chemiographic position between the illite-beidellite and illite-montmorillonite composition (b and m in Figure 34). There is also a decided rarity of muscovite-beidellite.

If one considers the ideal formulas for the two end member minerals, beidellite and montmorillonite (Ross and Hendricks, 1945), it appears that the substitutions which create a net charge deficiency in the 2:1 structure are found more often in the octahedral site-montmorillonite $M^+_{0.25} (R^3_{1.75} R^2_{0.25}) Si_4 O_{10} (OH)_2 .nH_2O$. The compositions represented by b and m in the $MR^3 - 2R^3 - 3R^2$ system (Figure 34) obviously are rarely found in natural minerals. Thus natural montmorillonites appear to have other than ideal or theoretical mineral compositions.

(*) The coordinates are based upon calculated formulas for the 2 : A layers and subsequent assignment to the M^+ as equivalent to the total charge on the structure. This eliminates the problems of H^+ interlayer ions and others, which frequently arises in formula calculations for montmorillonites.

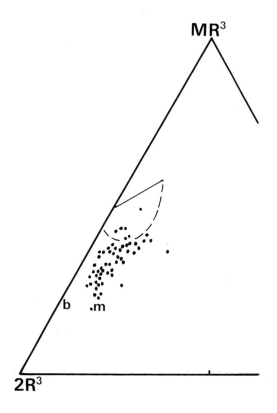

Figure 34 - Chemical compositions of natural fully expandable dioctahedral montmorillonites in the MR^3-$2R^3$-$3R^2$ coordinates. b = beidellite ; m = montmorillonite.

If we now consider the bulk compositions of the mixed-layered minerals which contain both expandable and non-expandable layers, two series are apparent, one between theoretical beidellite and illite and one between theoretical montmorillonite and illite (Figure 35). The intersection of the lines joining muscovite-montmorillonite and beidellite-celadonite (i.e., expandable mineral to mica), is a point which delimits, roughly, the apparent compositional fields of the two montmorillonite-illite compositional trends for the natural mixed layered minerals (Figure 36). That is, the natural minerals appear to show a compositional distribution due to solid solutions between each one of the two smectite types and the two mica types - muscovite and celadonite. There is no apparent solid solution between the two highly expandable (80 %) ends of the beidellitic and montmorillonitic smectitic series. The point of intersection

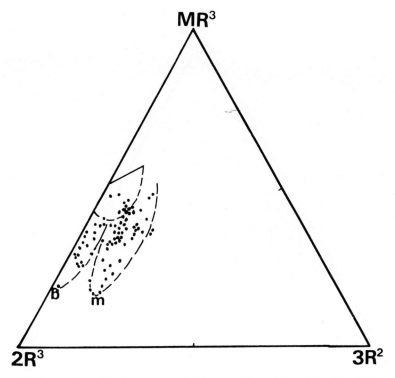

Figure 35 - Chemical compositions of natural mixed layered expandable phases (natural) in the MR^3-$2R^3$-$3R^2$ coordinates. ML_b= mixed layered beidellite series ; ML_m = mixed layered montmorillonite series ; I = illite compositional field.

of the theoretical substitutional series beidellite-celado-nite and muscovite-montmorillonite is located at about 30-40 % expandable layers - 70-60 % illite. This interlayering is similar to the "mineral" allevardite as defined previous-ly. It appears that as the expandability of the mixed layer-ed series decreases, the total range of solid solution (as a function of MR^3-$2R^3$-$3R^2$ components) increases.

Some interesting microprobe data given by Beaufort (1981) indicate that allevardites from hydrothermally alte-red rocks (porphyry copper-type alteration) have composi-tions which fall very close to this intersection point bet-ween the four phyllosilicate minerals. In further stages of alteration, more "argillaceous" or low alkali, the smectites present show lower contents of iron and magnesium, thus showing reduced solid solution compared to the less expanda-ble allevardite minerals.

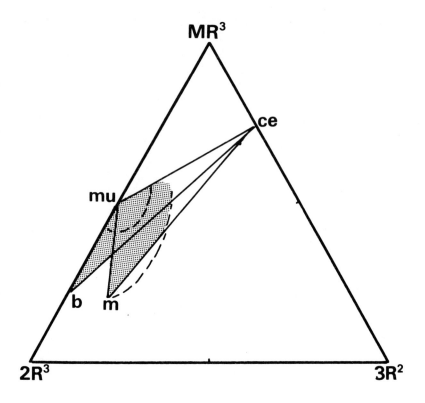

Figure 36 – Compositional fields of natural mixed layered
minerals compared with theoretical end-members (shaded area).
mu = muscovite ; b = beidellite ; m = montmorillonite ;
ce = celadonite

The general compositional dispersion of fully
expandable dioctahedral smectite bulk compositions is then
replaced by two substitutional trends as expandability begins to decrease (i.e., mixed layering is apparent). It can
be noted that there is a tendency toward apparent excess or
high $3R^2$ content evident for the mixed layered minerals as
was seen for the fully expandable montmorillonites. This is
again probably due to interlayer Mg^{2+} which is calculated as
octahedral ions. It is nevertheless quite possible that the
analyses of the fully expandable montmorillonites do show a
valid chemical variation and not just analytical error of
one sort or another. A remarkable point, in comparing the
mixed layered and fully expandable bulk compositions is that

the former defines two compositional series while the latter is found just between these two series. If indeed, this is the result of not only analytical errors, the relations would suggest that the fully expandable series are mixtures of the two extreme compositional types beidellite and montmorillonite. Since neither of these two forms are found alone, one would suspect the above deduction to be true. The possibility of the coexistence of two fully expanding phases of variable charge has important implications in the phase relations as we will see.

It is not easy to establish an upper limit for the smectite charges, however we can use the value of 0.5 charge per $O_{10}(OH)_2$ found by the present author for synthetic smectites at 250°C in non-alkali systems. This gives us a considerable range of beidellite and montmorillonite compositions. Now we must decide whether or not solid solution exists between the two smectite series. This question is not of fundamental importance in that if solid solution does not exist but the series are joined by a two phase field which forms a sort of tie-line series between them, the chemiographic result is essentially the same concerning relations with other phases, i.e., kaolinite, smectite, etc. Synthetic smectites show an apparent irregular continuum of solid solution, but this might just be due to inaccurate methods of identification. The rapid change in cell dimension with composition and irregular cation exchange capacity of synthetic and natural minerals suggests that segregation does exist. Exchange studies on natural minerals also indicate this.

For convenience, we will assume that there is a complete solid solution between the beidellite and montmorillonite smectites but we will not insist upon the accuracy of this statement. In the end the only point of interest is the chemiographic configuration. The fact that most natural dioctahedral smectite compositions fall in between the two series indicates that such a solid solution or possible two-phase field exists in natural geological environments. Scatter of some compositions to the $3R^{2+}$ side of the diagram probably reflects the presence of some magnesium exchange ions. However we cannot distinguish them using the data of the authors as presented.

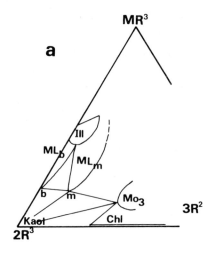

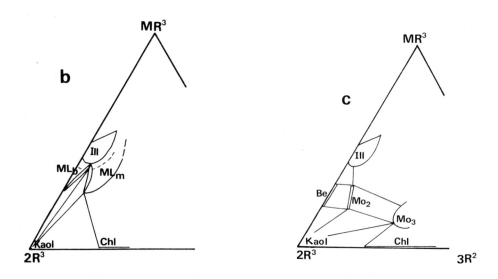

Figure 37.a - Phase relations in the $2R^3$ portion of the $MR^3-2R^3-3R^2$ system below 100°C where fully expandable smectites (b = beidellite, m = montmorillonite) coexist. ML_b, ML_m = corresponding mixed layered mineral series. Ill = illite ; Mo_3 = trioctahedral expanding phase ; Chl = chlorite ; Kaol = kaolinite.

b - Higher temperature phase relations where the kaolinite-illite tie-line occurs.

c - possible very low temperature relations where high charge smectites occur instead of mixed layered minerals.

4 - Phase diagrams for dioctahedral smectites (chemical components inert)

As we have seen, in the previous section, the bulk chemical compositions of smectites taken from the literature are dispersed over the field of fully expandable, mixed layered and even extreme illite compositions. Just what the limits of true smectite composition are cannot be established at present. We can, nevertheless, as a basis for discussion, assume that the ideal composition of beidellite with 0.20 charge per 10 oxygens and of smectite with the same structural charge do exist in nature and that they form the end-members of dioctahedral smectite solid solutions. If we recall the experimental data where a large range of charge is possible, we might assume that natural fully expandable phases will have a significant solid solution between the $2R^3-3R^2$ side of the coordinates in figure 37 and the MR^3- pole. Also, if we assume that the experimental data represent the smectite system at low temperatures where fully expandable phases occur, there is a certain inhomogeneity of the smectite layers as the charge increases. Cation exchange becomes less regular and cell dimension charge more drastic as one goes from beidellite to montmorillonite. One could suppose that in fact two smectite types exist and then could coexist for a given bulk composition. In this case, the composition of the natural minerals used, fall between the two series. However, it is almost impossible to distinguish the two minerals in the same specimen given their small grain size and similar physical properties, i.e., swelling cation exchange, etc... There is another argument for considering that two smectites exist, but this must follow a discussion of the composition of mixed-layered minerals. The important point to remember here is that there is apparently a significant range of charge (compositions between low charge $[0.2$ per $O_{10}(OH)_2]$ smectite and mica) for fully expandable minerals in nature as well as those produced in the laboratory (0.2 to 0.5 charge per 2:1 unit).

As has been deduced from the compositions of natural dioctahedral mixed-layered phases, two independent series of interlayered minerals are present based upon beidellite or montmorillonite end-members and illite. As the fully expandable phase becomes unstable, the coexistence of mixed layered phases and kaolinite will be possible. This assemblage is commonly observed in deep bore holes and other series of deeply buried sedimentary rocks. However, the assemblage kaolinite-mixed layered phase-illite is even more common in these rocks. In order for this assemblage to be stable, the chemical continuity of interlayered phases between illite and smectites must be interrupted at some point ; that is, the tie-line kaolinite-illite should exist. Looking again at the composition of natural mixed layered minerals the existence of this tie-line is not particularly evident, i.e., there is no obvious gap in the composition of the mixed layered minerals near the illite field (Figure 35). However, chemical analyses are not accurate enough to show such a discontinuity, nor are mineral separations normally precise enough to eliminate all foreign material. The only real indication of the existence of an illite-kaolinite tie-line is the common and persistent assemblage kaolinite-illite-mixed layered mineral in sedimentary rocks. Since these minerals are otherwise sensitive to physical change (Perry and Hower, 1970) it is unlikely that this assemblage would persist so often if it were metastable, especially since kaolinite is a mineral formed at low temperatures and, therefore, less likely than detrital phases to remain metastable under physical conditions of deep burial, as we will see in the following section. If one accepts these arguments, intuitive as they may be, a possible phase diagram for moderate temperatures and pressures can be drawn as in Figure 37b. The amount of solid solution (interlayering) between expandable and micaceous layers is continually restricted with rising temperatures. This was seen to be the case for synthetic, aluminous minerals (muscovite-K-beidellite) and natural Mg-Fe forms treated hydrothermally and it is known to be the case for those found in deeply buried sediments, as we shall see later.

The most important assumption used to construct Figure 37b is the existence of the kaolinite-illite tie-line. When illite-mixed layered series are no longer continuous in the 0-25 % mixed layered range (see Figure 39), two phase fields (compositional tie-lines) of illite-mixed layered phases appear, joining illite with an expandable phase in the mixed layered series. It is now necessary to fix the relations between kaolinite, illite and the restricted range of mixed layered minerals (allevardite-type structure). There are two possibilities : joining kaolinite to all mixed layered compositions by compositional tie-lines or joining only the most expandable phase stable to illite and kaolinite, thus having coexistence with the full range of expandable mixed layered minerals which are stable. The only basis available at present for choosing between the two alternatives is the assemblages found in nature. As we know illite is commonly associated with montmorillonite and highly expandable phases or with kaolinite. In the studies of deep bore holes, this situation persists as the maximum expandability of the mixed layered minerals decreases and eventually becomes the ordered mixed layered mineral, called allevardite here. This strongly suggests a full range of illite-expanding mineral tie-lines as shown in Figure 37b. An important result of such a geometric disposition is the gradual enlarging of the compositional zone where the three phases illite, kaolinite and mixed layered mineral assemblage will exist as P-T conditions increase (with burial depth). This three phase assemblage will contain the interlayered phase of maximum expandability which is stable under the P-T conditions prevalent.

The two series of phase relations deduced above result in, at a first approximation, two "facies" for the expandable dioctahedral minerals – that of low temperature where fully expandable minerals exist and where the tie-line or association beidellite-montmorillonite persists. More elevated conditions produce a kaolinite-illite tie-line characteristic of sequences of buried rocks.

In both figures 37a and 37b, we have assumed that a large range of mixed layered phases will exist for an appropriate composition. However, observations on the weathering of granite (surface conditions) suggest that dioctahedral smectites crystallize as well as illites but one does not find mixed layered minerals. It is possible then that at low temperatures no mixed layering occurs and one can form high charge smectites. In this case, a tie-line between illite and pure smectite should be present. This possibility is shown in figure 37c. There is then little difference between figures 37a and 37b for low alkali compositions but when alkali content is high, there will be a smectite-illite field at lowest temperatures and a mixed layered mineral field at higher temperatures. It is not possible at present to establish the temperature boundary between figures a and c.
The stability of dioctahedral smectites is, of course, not uniquely a function of P-T conditions acting

upon a given silicate mineral assemblage. Studies in the system $Na^+-H^+Al_2O_3-SiO_2H_2O-Cl$ (Hemley et al., 1961) show that a high activity of sodium ion at given silica and hydrogen activities can de-stabilize beidellite. Hess (1966) extrapolates this hydrothermal study to atmospheric conditions where the range of H^+, Na^+ and SiO_2 activities can determine the presence of an expandable phase. It is evident that such theoretical constructions find form in real situations, since the transformation of smectites to mica (potassic) or analcime has been reported in saline lakes and certain soil profiles (Jones, 1965 ; Hay and Moiola, 1963 ; Frankart and Herbillon, 1970). Thus the field composition phase diagrams constructed above (Figure 37) apply only to systems where montmorillonite is a stable phase under existing chemical and physical conditions and where the relative masses of the components permit the existence of montmorillonite.

We have seen that experimental data suggest high temperatures for dioctahedral smectite stabilities, especially the Na-Ca types with beidellitic substitution. Yet in most studies of smectites stabilities under natural conditions, the fully expandable phase is lost rather early, usually well below 100°C. This phase appears to be succeeded by an interlayered expandable-non-expandable mineral. Apparently two sets of information do not agree.

Cation exchange studies on smectites have shown a number of interesting relations regarding ionic distribution between aqueous solutions and the silicate (Deist and Tailurdeen, 1967 ; Hutcheon, 1966 ; Mitra and Prakash, 1957 ; Inoue and Minato, 1979). If the data concerning the pair K-Ca, show that Ca is favored in the montmorillonite at 25°C and this segregation is accentuated as temperature rises above 50°C. Increases of total ionic concentration in the fluid also favors calcium retention. During burial where temperatures are higher and fluids more saline, one would expect to produce calcic montmorillonites which would be stable well above 100°C if their stability is that of calcic beidellite. Again, the deductions based upon laboratory experiments do not appear to agree wholly with observations on natural minerals.

The apparent discrepancy could reside in the fact that if potassium ions are available at all, they will form a mica at temperatures near 100°C. Smectite structures below these conditions (pressure and temperature) need not contain potassium at all. However, at the correct physical conditions the 2:1 portion of the smectite must change greatly (increase of total charge on the 2:1 unit) in order to form a mica unit in a mixed layered mineral phase. Since neither Na nor Ca ions will form mica at this temperature, potassium will be selectively taken from solution. Obviously this does not occur below 100°C since cation exchange on smectites shows the reverse effect, i.e., concentration of calcium ions in the interlayer sites. If potassium is not available either in coexisting solids or in solutions, the sodi-calcic smectites will undoubtedly persist well above 100°C.

It must also be noted that the laboratory data is fragmentary in that not all types of expanding phases were investigated - beidellite to montmorillonite and low charge to high charge. The importance of chemical variations in the basic 2:1 unit of the expanding phase is in fact not well known. It is possible that as a function of temperature the cation selectivity will be different for different basic 2:1 structures. It is known for example that selectivity between Ca^{2+} and Mg^{2+} can be inversed for vermiculite and montmorillonite (Levy and Shainberg, 1972). Further, the natural mica-beidellite interlayered minerals (rectorite) are sodi-calcic while the mica-montmorillonite minerals (allevardite) are sodi-potassic in nature. Quite possibly, the site of charge imbalance changes the selectivity coefficients for exchangeable ions. Cation selectivity experiments by the present author using magnesium as the structural R^{2+} component show that there is a greater tendency for montmorillonite to attract potassium than there is for beidellites (Figure 32). The medium charge montmorillonite is the only phase which effectively selects potassium. We must remember that natural montmorillonites normally also contain iron which might further affect the potassium selectivity. Nevertheless only about half of the exchange sites will be filled by potassium in the most optimistic estimate. However, there is not enough information available to determine the effect of montmorillonite 2:1 layer compositions on ion selectivity. We can only base our analysis upon the observation that in rocks where potassium is available, an interlayered illite-montmorillonite phase appears near 100°C at depths greater than 2 km.

The mechanism of interlayering has been mentioned briefly in the introduction chapter. It might be useful to recall here that the homogeneity of the 10 Å, 2:1 unit layer is not really an established fact. It is not certain that both tetrahedrally coordinated layers maintain the same surface charge transmitted to the interlayer "site" where alkali or calcium ions will be found in dioctahedral minerals. If some smectite compositions (montmorillonite) are more potassiphillic than others, it is possible that certain tetrahedral units will create a tendency to increase the interlayer concentration of this element while they remain low charge in character. By contrast, other layers become beidellitic in charge and are calciphillic when expandable layers but potassic when they are high-charge (> 0.6 per $O_{10}(OH)_2$).

If we consider the illitization process described by Hower and Mowatt (1966) and Hower et al. (1976), it seems that some portions of an expanding-non expanding mixed layered mineral become aluminous in forming mica-like layers, while others remain low charge and fully expandable, containing Mg and Fe. It would seem then that two types of layers are formed, calci-sodic montmorillonites and aluminous potassic illites, in the pelitic series with a significant $3R^2$ component.

Although there is little classical mineralogical data available (bulk chemical analysis accompanied by detailed X-ray diffraction) in the highly expandable portion of the mixed layered beidellite mineral range, some new microprobe data exists at the low expandability range which suggests that the two mixed layered mineral series do not really respond to temperature in the same way. This suggests that although the two series have parallel chemical trends, they will not be found in the same stage of development at the same temperatures. Microprobe analyses by Paradis et al. (1983) indicate that the chemical composition of new clays give in some cases a composition of a sodic beidellitic mixed layered mineral (in this case, rectorite or a mixed layered mineral with less than 50 % expanding layers) which occurs well into the illite-chlorite metamorphic zone just before the presence of chloritoide. These rocks are very aluminous, containing pyrophyllite. X-ray diffraction traces of clays extracted from these sandstones show that they contain mixed layered minerals with a higher proportion

of expanding layers than do adjacent shales (I/S allevardite-type versus ISII-type). The chemical (microprobe) evidence shows that the new minerals show an inverse K-Na relation
with total alkalis in the range of 0.4-0.7 atoms per formula
(Figure 38). The striking point in this study is that the
new sodic phases occur when the mixed layering of the
"groundmass" phases, potassic almost exclusively, contains
very few expandable layers (less than 10 % using Reynold's
curves, in Brindley and Brown, 1980). The sodic phases are
almost strictly alumino-silicate where as the groundmass or
other illitic phases analyzed contain some iron and
magnesium.

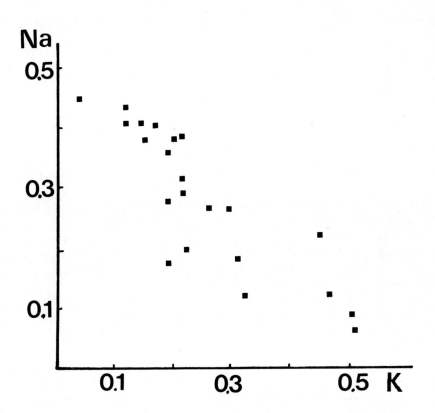

Figure 38 - Relative content of Na and K in secondary mixed
layered minerals of metamorphic rocks of the illite-chlorite
facies (Paradis et al., 1983). These phases contain almost
no Mg or Fe and are therefore mica-beidellite
interlayered minerals.

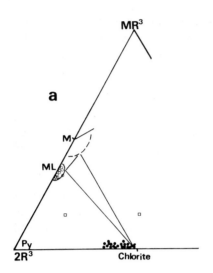
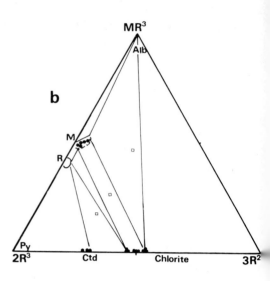

Figure 39 - Representation of microprobe analyses for
highest grade diagenesis zone to contain expandable
minerals in pelites.
Lower temperature facies (a) with mixed layered, ML (< 10 %
expandable layers) and chlorite.
Higher temperature facies (b) with chlorite-chloritoid
(Ctd)-pyrophyllite (Py), rectorite (R) and illite (M).
Dots and circles show microprobe analyses for phases.
Squares show assemblages present where minerals were
analyzed. Data from Paradis et al. (1983).

It is possible that previously mentioned assemblages of allevardite-pyrophyllite might in fact be rectorite-
pyrophyllite. Eberl (1978) noted that synthesis experiments
with sodic interlayer ions in aluminous systems tended to
produce rectorite which persisted to much higher temperatures than potassic minerals. The difference in thermal stability of the two mineral series - beidellite mixed layered
and montmorillonite mixed layered, which have different
interlayer ions in the mica portion of the structure, is an
important possibility which might explain certain anomalies
found in natural rock series. These points will be brought
up in the discussion of the natural mineral facies based
upon mixed layered mineral types. For purposes of simplici-

ty, we will assume that the mixed layered series are pene-contemporaneous at lower temperatures in temperature-depth space, at least as far as the facies phase diagrams given in figure 37 are concerned.

Figure 39a & b show the phase relations in the rec-torite facies where chlorite and chloritoid coexist. These are preceeded by illite (< 10% expandable)-chlorite-albite facies (a). Dots show chlorites and circles rectorite, based on microprobe data.

A word should be added concerning the interstrati-fied minerals kaolinite-aluminous smectite which are found in nature, mainly in soils (Herbillon et al., 1981) and which have been synthesized (Sròdon, 1980). The synthesis seems to be restricted to temperatures above 25°C, in that Kittrick (1969) produced only kaolinite under the same che-mical conditions. One can say that we do not have very much information about the kaolinite-smectite mixed layered pha-ses but their existence will certainly modify the phase relations of the phase diagrams proposed here.

5 - Nontronite

The existence of a ferric dioctahedral smectite is important to consider since again we must face the choice of keeping all R^{3+} ions together in a chemiographic plot or being obliged to give another dimension to our phase analy-sis. Therefore, we will consider nontronites as a special case.

It is evident from natural occurrences that ferric iron-bearing smectites are not similar to aluminous ones. This has been summarized briefly in the discussion of the difference between illite and glauconite. There are essen-tially two groups of nontronite, one calcic and one potas-sic. The potassic series tends to become a mica by increas-ing potassium content in a mixed layered series. Aluminum is always in very low abundance (glauconite series and deep sea basalt celadonite series). The calcic nontronites on the other hand can contain aluminum in varying proportions (Sei-bertz and Vortisch, 1979 ; Mevel, 1980). It seems that there are in fact two evolutions - one toward an iron-rich potassic mica-like phase and another with varying Fe/Al contents which remains expandable. The chemical or structural reasons for the two series are not clear at the present time. One thing is certain however, when Fe^{3+} nontronite exists in a mixed cation environment it is always potassic (see sections on deep sea basalts and on glauconites).

The chemiographic evolution of the two series is thus different and neither corresponds to that of the aluminous minerals (smectite-illites). Again, Fe^{3+} is not the complete chemical analog of Al in clay mineral structures as also seen by changes in cell dimension (Eggleton, 1977 ; Russell and Clark, 1978). It seems that nontronites are basically low temperature phases. Their composition does not seem to evolve as a function, physical conditions affecting the rock in which they form. Therefore, we will not discuss nontronitic substitutions in the evolution of the smectites as a function of burial metamorphism. Their composition is a function of the chemistry of the system in which they form.

A microprobe study of serpentinized basic rock weathering by Fontanaud (1982) shows that oxidizing conditions favor nontronite genesis. The resulting dioctahedral smectite concentrates potassium as an exchange ion by a factor of six compared to its magnesian saponite (trioctahedral smectite) predecessor. It appears that even in a potassium-poor environment, the ferric smectite has a strong selectivity of potassium.

The stability of nontronites can be affected by chemical conditions. Eswaran and Sys (1970) and Elias et al. (1981) have noted that nontronite is no longer stable in the uppermost weathering horizons of serpentinite rocks. In both cases nontronite is replaced by kaolinite as the phyllosilicate and the iron present forms either hematite or goethite. One can deduce that strong oxidation conditions favor iron as a free oxide. The reverse reaction was observed by Pédro et al. (1978) where an assemblage of quartz and iron oxide was transformed into nontronite at the bottom of lake Chad. Slightly reducing conditions were invoked by these authors as the motor for the reaction even though the iron remains in the trivalent state when in the silicate phase. Thus it appears that the reaction nontronite = iron oxide + silicate or silica is reversible at one atmosphere and surface temperatures. The control is the Eh or oxidation potential of the environment, and here we must consider an intensive variable other than pressure, temperature or the chemical potential of a constituent element in the phase equilibria of nontronite.

The importance of nontronite resides in its role as a trivalent ion clay mineral, and thus dioctahedral, in systems which are originally R^{2+} dominant. The shift from tri- to dioctahedral clays indicates a loss of the R^{2+} component, some by physical removal from the system (Mg notably) and a gain in R^{3+}. Since nontronites tend to be little aluminous, we see them on the R^{3+} side of a chemiographic projection, but they do not represent a continuum with aluminous minerals but rather a discontinuous shift across chemiographic space. The abrupt change in composition between saponites and nontronite (see section on weathering) show a sharp immiscibility which is less evident when going from dioctahedral aluminous phases to aluminous saponites (see Trauth, 1977) in the evaporitic mineral sequence. Mg-Al solid solutions is much greater than Mg-Fe^{3+} substitution. We find Mg and Fe^{3+} together only in celadonite or glauconitic micas.

c - Trioctahedral Expanding Minerals

We will treat in this section three mineral groups which seem to be related in a phase-equilibria sense but which are normally considered as being quite different minerals. These include saponites, which are the trioctahedral smectites ; vermiculites, which are quite variable in origin, physical properties and composition ; and corrensite which defines essentially a type of mixed layering between expanding and non-expanding trioctahedral structures. In all probability, the well known "type" occurrences of each of the materials are uppermost in the minds of clay mineralogists instead of the similarities in chemical composition and structural properties of the different minerals found in more common geological environments.

The most difficult mineral is vermiculite. This phase has been studied many times where its origin is the hydrothermal alteration of biotites.

As a result, many laboratory studies of biotite

alteration have been performed in order to understand vermiculite of this origin (Basset, 1963 ; Harward et al.,
1969 ; Mammy, 1970 ; Barshad and Kishk, 1970 ; Leonard and
Weed, 1970 ; Robert, 1970, 1971 ; Hoda and Hood, 1972 ;
Robert and Pédro, 1972, among others). However, vermiculitic
materials are well known in soils and weathered rocks (Fontanaud, 1982 ; Rich, 1958 ; Meunier, 1980 ; Ildefonse et
al., 1979 ; Ildefonse, 1980, among many others). It has been
noted that these materials can be di- as well as trioctahedral. Since, this section concerns the latter form we will
retain only these mineral types here. A mineral of vermiculitic composition and physical properties has also been
found in low grade metamorphic rocks at various pressures
(Velde, 1978). Thus the origin of vermiculites can be quite
varied and one should consider all geological occurrences
instead of just the material which has been formed from the
hydrothermal alteration of biotites.

Essentially, the saponite-vermiculite-corrensite
mineral groups show a decrease in expanding properties in
the sense as listed. This being the case, we must consider
them in their geological and chemiographic relations as a
function of this variable. But perhaps one should define
what will be used as criteria to distinguish the various
mineral types by X-ray diffraction, saponites are fully
expanding upon glycollation to a 17 Å spacing. Air-dried
samples are closer to 14 Å and they collapse at > 300°C to
< 10 Å. Vermiculites have a 15 Å spacing in the air-dried
stage, expand only slightly upon glycollation (< 16 Å) and
collapse to less than 14 Å but greater than 10 Å at about
300°C. Corrensite shows the characteristics of expansion for
only part of its layers indicated by a super structure reflection at > 26 Å. These criteria allow one to place many
phases in the categories which are not strictly acceptable
on a mineralogical basis, but it allows us to consider many
phases which would otherwise go nameless, and thus out of
intellectual reach in the natural sciences.

1 - Studies in synthetic systems

Experiments by Siffert (1962) showed that the precipitation of trioctahedral smectite (saponite) could be
effected at high pH (9 to 10) for low concentrations of
Mg^{2+}, SiO_2. Chemical analysis of the synthesis products

showed a high Ca content due to a calcium buffer used to control pH. The temperature of the experiments was 25°C. Lower pH, near 8, formed sepiolite and still lower pH's gave no precipitate. Estéoule (1965, 1969) demonstrated that there is a discontinuity between dioctahedral and trioctahedral expanding phases in the $MgO-Al_2O_3-SiO_2$ system under conditions of one atmosphere pressure and 80°C. It was found that the trioctahedral phase had a variable alumina content which was the result of variations in the composition of the chemical system of the experiment. Variations in pH (4-6) and the additions of Na or K ions did not seriously affect the phase relations of the saponites. Decarreau (1981) has synthesized the series of smectites between magnesian stevensite (non aluminous) and the lithic phase hectorite in the trioctahedral-dioctahedral substitutional series. This was done at atmospheric conditions and up to 90°C over periods of several weeks.

Velde (1963) synthesized several types of smectites in the $Si-Al-Mg-H_2O$ system at 2 Kbars pressure near 300°C. The trioctahedral forms have a substitutional series as follows :

$$(Mg_{3-x} Al_x)(Si_{4-(x+0.34)} Al_{x+0.34})(Mg_{0.17})O_{10}(OH)_2 . nH_2O$$

The substitutions creating a charge deficiency are located in the tetrahedrally coordinated ionic position exclusively. This substitutional series is distinguished by two types of apparent structural habits, a 17 $\overset{\circ}{A}$ and 15 $\overset{\circ}{A}$ expanded structure (upon glycollation). The 15 $\overset{\circ}{A}$ form at low temperature is found to be present at the high alumina end of the series. Its composition is :

$$(Mg_{2.20}Al_{0.80})(Si_{2.87} Al_{1.13})(Mg_{0.17})O_{10}(OH)_2 . nH_2O$$

It can be assimilated to the mineral vermiculite. Adjacent, but separated from this composition the 17 $\overset{\circ}{A}$ series begins and it continues to a very nearly non-aluminous end-member. It is assumed that the series is incomplete in this direction (i.e., at the stevensite composition which is more silica rich, $(Mg_{2.85} Si_4)(Mg_{0.15})O_{10}(OH)_2 . nH_2O$. This is deduced from experiments in the system $MgO-SiO_2-H_2O$ which do not produce a smectite at high pressure above 250°C (Johannes, 1969 ; Velde, 1973). Increasing temperature and pressure increase the compositional range of the 15 $\overset{\circ}{A}$ (vermiculitic) expanding phase in the series. The relations between the different phases are shown in a Mg-Al-Si plot for physical conditions of 350°C, 2 Kbars pressure (Figure 40).

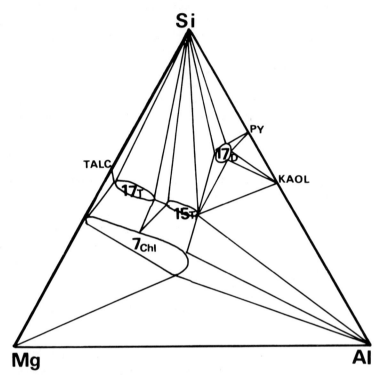

Figure 40 - Phases found in the Mg-Al-Si-H$_2$O system at 350°C, 2 Kbars pressure (from Velde, 1973). Expanding phases are 17T = fully expandable trioctahedral saponite ; 15T = low expandability trioctahedral aluminous phase, similar to vermiculite or expanding chlorite ; 17D = dioctahedral fully expandable montmorillonite with magnesium as the interlayer ion. KAOL = kaolinite ; PY = pyrophyllite ; 7Chl = aluminous serpentine solid solution. Note that 14 Å chlorite is not present and thus we have expandable phases in equilibrium with serpentines which occurs in low temperature environments in nature.

Iiyima and Roy (1963), Koizumi and Roy (1959) performed experiments which delimit the solid solution and stability of sodic montmorillonoids in the Na$_2$O-MgO-Al$_2$O$_3$-SiO$_2$-H$_2$O system. At temperatures of 400-500°C, the extent of solid solution is rather great covering 60 to 80 % of the composition between talc and Na phlogopite depending upon the pressure. Both increase in pressure and temperature restrict the smectite compositional range. Above 600°C the composition of the fully expandable phase shifts to the Na-hectorite series where Na^+ enters into the octahedrally coordinated position. This is not possible for potassic phases because the K^+ ion is too large to fit into this structural site. At 800°C, a 30 % Na-hectorite smectite coexists with cordierite and anthophyllite. These experiments demonstrate the great range of thermal stability possible for sodic magnesian smectite. The data on cation exchange capacity shows that the higher the interlayer charge, the greater the exchange capacity of the structure.

2 - Relative stabilities of synthetic trioctahedral smectites

If we consider the substitutions in the trioctahedral smectite structure which give rise to a charge imbalance on the basic 2:1 structure, they can be considered as being two in kind :

1) deficiency of ions in the octahedral site
2) Al^{3+} in the tetrahedral site

Synthesis has produced phases of type (1) at low temperature (80°C). Experiments in the $MgO-SiO_2-H_2O$ system demonstrate that type (1) is not stable at high temperatures (250°C). The smectites contain neither Na, Ca or trivalent ions, such as aluminum. In contrast, substitutions of type (2) were effected at both low and high temperatures, 80-600°C and to 1,000 atmospheres pressure. The interlayer ions in type (2) smectites were Na, Ca or Mg. It appears then that a distinction is possible between the trioctahedral smectites ; the non-aluminous form (stevensite) being restricted to low temperatures, aluminous forms can be stable to temperature in the range of metamorphism. They behave as vermiculites at higher temperatures.

3 - Chemical composition of natural trioctahedral smectites

Figure 41a gives the chemiographic relations of the

bulk compositions of natural expandable trioctahedral phases, 14 of which can be plotted as a function of the MR^3-
$2R^3$-$3R^2$ coordinates. However 16 vermiculites and all stevensite, ghassoulite and hectorite analyses (8) from Foster
(1963), Faust et al. (1959) and Trauth (1977), would be
found in the more alumina-poor sector of the larger M^+-$2R^3$-
$3R^2$ system. The minerals which can be plotted in the restricted coordinates, all of which are reported to be fully
expandable, cover a large range of MR^3 content indicating a
rather variable interlayer charge. A similar situation
exists for the natural dioctahedral smectites.

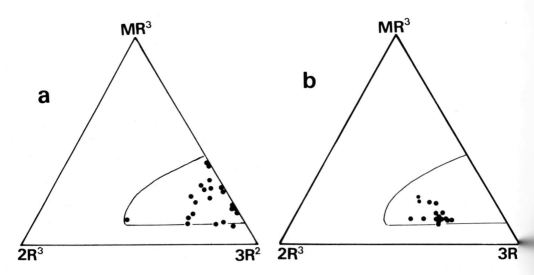

Figure 41 - MR^3-$2R^3$-$3R^2$ plot of expanding trioctahedral
smectites (stevensite, vermiculite and saponites).
MR^3 coordinates based upon 2 Ca + Na + K in the analysis.
Fig. 41.a shows a classical analyses and Fig. 41.b shows
electron microprobe results for minerals formed in a
serpentinized ultrabasic rock (Fontanaud, 1982). All iron is
calculated as Fe^{2+} in these formulae.

Several recent studies on the weathering products
of crystalline (coarse grained) rocks and alteration of deep
sea basalts have given an insight into the type of
trioctahedral phases which can be found to form under surface conditions. As has been mentionned earlier, iron-rich

rocks tend to form the dioctahedral mineral nontronite. However, very magnesian rocks - dunites, peridotites and serpentines can produce trioctahedral minerals (Fontanaud, 1982). Most of the chemical data for these mineral was obtained using an electron microprobe which does not allow one to determine the Fe^3-content of the mineral. Thus a plot in $MR^3-3R^2-2R^3$ coordinates is not very precise. If we assume that oxidation of iron is highly probable under alteration conditions, we can plot these data assuming $Fe_{total} = Fe^{3+}$. The data, plotted in $MR^3-2R^3-3R^2$ coordinates (Figure 40b) coincides well with the sparse data for other trioctahedral minerals. In these analyses, excess octahedral Mg was assigned to an interlayer position. Iron content is less than 20 % of the octahedral ions but in half of the analyses there is a deficit of aluminum and Fe^{3+} must be added to fill all of the tetrahedral sites. This represents however less than 10 % of the sites. Since the mica tetra-ferri-phlogopite is well known both in nature as well as synthesis studies (D. Velde, 1971) one should not be surprised to see it in saponites.

The point which is probably the most pertinent is that within the same weathering profile, much of the area of saponite composition is covered by newly formed clay minerals. This area extends from the $3R^2$ corner of the diagram much of the way towards the $2R^3$ side. This means that saponites will occur when there are alkali or alkaline earth elements present, relegating chlorites to an Mg-Fe-Al compositional range at low temperature conditions. This fact explains, in part, the low frequency of chlorite occurrence at surface conditions where saponite and dioctahedral smectites will coexist instead of the mica-chlorite assemblage of metamorphic rocks.

Despite the small number of analyses, it is apparent that the range of solid solution for expandable trioctahedral minerals is very great. One can expect an equally large if not larger extent of chemical variation in the mixed-layered phases because they can be interlayered with mica (trioctahedral) as well as chlorite - either towards alkali-rich or alkali-poor mineral compositions. Given such possibilities, the phase relations of these minerals will certainly present at least two series of solid solution through mixed layering. In addition it is possible that mixing of expandable and talc layers also exists (Veniale

and van der Marel, 1968) or expandable and kerolite (Eberl
et al., 1982) giving a third series. Certainly the phase
equilibria of such minerals will be complex. However, expandable trioctahedral minerals do not have a great frequency
in argillaceous rocks of pelitic (aluminous) composition.
Their major reported occurrences are in soils, hydrothermally altered rocks associated with vein mineralization and
evaporite or magnesian carbonate deposits. These phases do
not seem to persist through sedimentation or diagenesis.

4 - Vermiculites

These minerals are often considered to be high
charge saponites although Suquet (1978) seems to demonstrate
that no distinction of this kind should be made. A large
part of the problem appears to be one of identification
methods. It is claimed (Suquet et al., 1980) that all low
(less than mica) charge trioctahedral minerals are expandable when enough care is taken in the introduction of organic
homopolar molecules between the 2:1 unit layers. However,
classical definitions, based upon poor or incomplete expandability as well as collapse of the layers (in fact this is
the introduction and expulsion of water or other polar molecules) seems to find substance in natural mineral identifications, especially those materials coming from soils (Rich
and Obershain, 1955 ; Rich, 1958) or weathering rocks (Meunier, 1980 ; Proust, 1982 ; Ildefonse, 1980).

In the present discussion, we will consider the
older definition (Grim, 1968 ; Brown, 1961 ; Brindley and
Brown, 1980) as indicating a mineral with a high charge
$(0.4 < x < 0.8)$ mineral which contains magnesium, iron (Fe^{3+})
or aluminum hydroxy complexes inbetween the 2:1 layers which
results in the often unclear X-ray diffraction properties
observed. This is not just an arguement over terms but it in
fact represents a compositional and physico-chemical mineralogical reality in many instances. A very good demonstration
is given by Proust and Velde (1978) in a weathered amphibolite. These authors show that a succession of minerals formed from either plagioclase or amphibole. The first phyllosilicate formed is what can be called a vermiculite according
to the "classical" definition. Its composition is either
more magnesian or aluminous than the phases which it replaces. At the same time the vermiculite reflects the composi-

tion of the altering fluids which contain elements from destabilized plagioclase and amphibole, and the immediate composition of the phase concerned. The vermiculite forming from plagioclase is more magnesian than plagioclase, yet is a dioctahedral phase while the vermiculite forming from the amphibole is decidedly more aluminous than its precursor. The vermiculites are replaced in their turn by smectites which are less marked by the general fluid composition and thus reflect the local chemistry (within the old mineral grain) to a greater extent. Ildefonse (1979) and Ildefonse et al. (1979) show that vermiculite can form from other clay minerals in the highly argillaceous portion of a weathering profile developed on an amphibolite. The presence of this phyllosilicate phase undoubtedly reflects the short and long range equilibria of soil phases and fluids percolating in the profile. The vermiculite finds its greatest development when the old mineral grain limits of the initial rock are destroyed and solifluction occurs. The result is a tendency to form a single phase instead of phases dependent upon amphibole or plagioclase precursors. It seems that the interlayer site of the soil vermiculite is the area most adapted to the charges in chemistry. Here one sees the excess magnesium or aluminum and iron hydroxides which characterize the mineral. Further weathering (upper levels in the profile) tends to destroy these soil vermiculites. Experiments by Kittrick (1973) represent these chemical conditions where the aqueous solutions are more dilute than those which were in long term contact with the silicate minerals lower in the alteration profile.

The composition of vermiculites is difficult to assess for two reasons : one is that little data is available for single phase material which could be separated for both X-ray and wet chemical analysis methods (where Fe^{2+} and Fe^{3+} are determined). The second problem is that when more data is available, by electron microprobe, one cannot determine Fe^{3+} content, and thus the importance of R^3 in the structure is not assessed. Further, Ildefonse et al. (1979) have shown that individual vermiculite grains vary from one another in composition and therefore a classical mineral chemical analysis shows only an average value. For these reasons, we will not show the vermiculite composition in $MR^3-2R^3-3R^2$ coordinates since the value of $Al-Fe^{3+}$ cannot be determined. Certainly some iron is divalent in these minerals even though they are predominantly ferric. It can be

said however that vermiculites found in weathering environments tend to be more R^{2+}-rich than the dioctahedral smectites and more R^{3+}-rich than the trioctahedral smectites with
which they are associated.

    a - Experiments on natural vermiculites

        Experiments at atmospheric and room temperature
conditions by Kittrick (1973) demonstrate that vermiculite
is not stable compared to the alternate assemblage montmo-
rillonite-magnesite-silica. A great number of recent experimental studies in a number of different laboratories in
various countries demonstrate the possibility of producing
vermiculite or an expanding trioctahedral mineral from biotite. The chemical conditions under which this transformation takes place indicate the necessity of solutions having
a very low alkali content.

        Roy and Romo (1957) and Boettcher (1966) performed
high pressure experiments on natural vermiculites. They
observed the production of a 14 Å chlorite between 300 and
550°C, talc + enstatite and an unidentified phase above
650°C. The experiments on natural minerals indicate that
vermiculite will occur when alkali content or activity in
solution is low. This trioctahedral expanding phase is relatively stable at high pressures and temperatures as are
interlayered minerals which are composed in part by such
layers. It is not stable relative to smectite at low temperature under conditions of dilute aqueous solutions.

    b - Metamorphic vermiculites

        A mineral group, called metamorphic vermiculite by
the present author, has been identified by several authors
(Black, 1975 ; Kendall, 1976 ; Kerrick and Cotton, 1976 ;
Velde, 1978 ; Mc Dowell and Elders, 1980). Unfortunately
these minerals have not been clearly defined by the normal
X-ray diffraction methods in several different geological
occurrences where they have been found. This is due in part
to their accessory character. They are often found in rocks
of pelitic composition, where most phases are not phyllosi-
licates-granites, sandstones and so forth but can be found
in rocks which contain glaucophane. They are identified op-

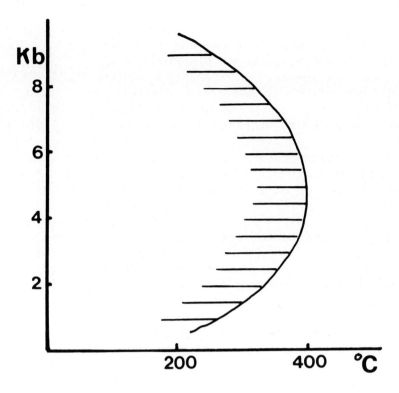

Figure 42 - Shaded area indicates approximate conditions
where the metamorphic vermiculite mineral has been found to
form (Velde, 1978). The lower stability range of this
mineral or mineral group is not known. It is found
at the upper boundaries of clay mineral facies.

tically mainly by a character which is other than either
chlorites or biotites and chemically (mainly by microprobe
analyses) by their similarity to chlorites (high alumina
content as opposed to stilpnomelanes) but by a persistent
but low alkali or calcium content, about 0.1 to 0.3 ion per
unit of $O_{10}(OH)_2$. The geological occurrences of these minerals seem to form the outer limits of the clay mineral facies (Figure 42). Normally, they occur as separate grains in
the rocks and do not seem to be associated with a specific
pre-existing phyllosilicate. They can, apparently, coexist
with chlorites and biotites and thus seem to form a transition phase between expanding minerals and chlorites or biotites. They often contain potassium, suggesting a possible
relation as a low temperature replacement of biotite but can
also be calcic and slightly sodic, thus showing no relation

whatsoever to a higher temperature phyllosilicate.   At the
moment, these minerals are enigmatic as to their role in the
evolution of phyllosilicate mineralogy.

        Vermiculites have been reported as forming from
hydrothermal processes on or below the Red Sea floor (Singer
and Stoffers, 1981). These phases are found with normal sedimentary minerals (illite, chlorite, palygorskite, sepiolite) and thus their classification as to geological occurrence is difficult.

    c - Composition of vermiculites

        The available data on vermiculites is highly weigh-
ted toward the hydrothermal alteration products due to biotite destabilization.   Most other data from diverse geological environments is that gathered by electron microprobe
and thus does not distinguish between Fe^{2+} and Fe^{3+} . This
is of course a great handicap since normally much iron is
present and the role of R^2 and R^3 are very important in distinguishing the phase relations of the minerals.   It is possible, however, to distinguish between chlorites and vermiculites on the basis of Al_2O_3-SiO_2 content (Velde, 1978).
Most often, metamorphic vermiculites contain more silica
than chlorites of the same R^2-Al^{3+} content.   They tend to be
silica-rich compared with the high temperature chlorite substitution of Al^{VI} Al^{IV} = MgSi. However, soil vermiculites are
more difficult to categorize since they may contain alumina
or magnesium hydroxy-complexes in interlayer sites thus
altering the Si-R^2-R^3 balance.   It is not possible at present to estimate whether or not the interlayer Mg and Al
should be attributed to an alkali site (M^+).   It is possible
that the Mg or Al present is in fact a response to the chemical activities of these ions which thus produce an R^2 or
R^3 phase instead of a calcic or alkali-bearing one.   It does
seem that soil vermiculites do occur when alkali activity
decreases, leaving R^3 and R^2 ions in the system. In this way
there is no reason why vermiculite would not coexist with a
trioctahedral smectite ; however we have no evidence. Numerous authors have reported vermiculite-smectite interlayered
minerals which were identified by X-ray diffraction in multiphase assemblages.   These phases could represent a solid
solution between end members similar to smectite-illite.

It is not possible to distinguish between the different vermiculite-type phases, their possible interlayering and their chemical compositions with the data available at present. The problems are more difficult when dealing with the less well defined soil forming phases. As a result we cannot attribute a definite chemical role to the vermiculites with respect to other trioctahedral phases. They do seem in most cases to be chemically different from the other phyllosilicates with which they are associated - saponites or chlorites. In the section on weathering, the vermiculitic minerals are found to be distinct from the smectitic precursors or those smectites which replace them. The study on metamorphic vermiculites (Velde, 1978) showed that they had compositions distinct from chlorites which accompany them, therefore vermiculites form a distinct mineral group, but their role is not easily determined.

d - Importance of vermiculites

Considering the information presented, it seems that two types of vermiculites occur in nature - a low temperature mineral which plays an intermediate and possibly ephemeral role in weathering, one which bridges the long range and short range equilibria established during the hydrolysis of rock forming minerals. The first stage is that of the destabilization of high temperature minerals ; the second is that of the destruction of microsystems in the weathered rock (argillization). The vermiculites are formed in equilibrium with an aqueous solution which contains significant dissolved material, flowing slowly through the silicate matrix. The vermiculites are most often reaction products due to the destabilization of soil phyllosilicates as they equilibrate with a profile scale chemical system instead of a mineral by mineral replacement. More dilute solutions destroy the vermiculites in favor of smectites.

The second vermiculite mineral is one of high temperature-either metamorphism or hydrothermal alteration, where as the classic vermiculites are formed from biotites. These minerals occur at the upper limits (pressure and temperature) of the clay mineral facies and thus represent phases which react to form metamorphic phyllosilicates under yet higher metamorphic conditions, either biotites or chlorites.

As yet we have no evidence that vermiculite-type phases persist under diagenetic or burial metamorphism conditions. This would lead one to believe that the compositions and structures of the phases are not at all the same, since their phase relations are not the same. Due to a lack of data, especially the Fe^{3+} content of the phases in question, it is not possible to distinguish between the two mineral groups at present. One hopes that future studies will elucidate the problem further.

d - Corrensite

This regularly interstratified trioctahedral mineral (see Lippmann, 1956 ; Martin Vivaldi and MacEwan, 1960) is a rough equivalent of rectorite or allevardite-like minerals. However, corrensite is less frequent in sedimentary rocks and sediments than the dioctahedral mixed layered minerals. It is possible that corrensite has been overlooked and is more common in argillaceous rocks than so far reported. It is nevertheless evident that corrensite occurs in a variety of geologic environments. This is somewhat in opposition with the conclusion reached by Millot (1964). Corrensite occurs in sediments rich in basic volcano-clastic rocks or sandstones (Ataman and Gokien, 1975 ; Almon et al., 1976 ; Kübler, 1973 ; Kossovskaya, 1972 ; Kimbara and Sudo, 1973), quartzitic sandstones (Early et al., 1953 ; Kulke, 1969 ; Becher, 1965), carbonates (Kastner, 1971 ; Maurel, 1962 ; Dreizler, 1962 ; Echle, 1961, 1974) as well as its supposed typical association with gypsum salt deposits or other evaporites (Millot, 1964 ; Lippmann and Savascin, 1969 ; Schlenker, 1971 ; Ataman and Baysal, 1978 ; Furbish, 1975 ; Kopp and Fallis, 1974). Corrensite is a frequent mineral in hydrothermal alterations or epi-metamorphic zones acting upon basic (basaltic) rocks (Sigvaldason, 1962 ; Tomasson and Kristmannsdottir, 1972 ; Kossovaskaya, 1972 ; Kübler, 1968, 1970 ; Fujishima, 1977 ; Kimbara et al., 1971) and other pyroclastics (Yoshimura, 1971 ; Kimbara and Sudo, 1973) or pelitic sediments (Vergo and April, 1982 ; Blatter et al., 1973 ; April, 1980). It has also been identified as a product of weathering in soils developed on meta-basalts (Johnson, 1964 ; Nichols, 1970). Essentially phyllosilicates associated with corrensite do not differ in the various rock types described. The following three-or-greater phyllosilicate phase assemblages have been reported :

- Corrensite-chlorite-illite
- Corrensite-mixed layered illite smectite-illite
- Corrensite-chlorite-illite-trioctahedral smectite
- Corrensite-chlorite-illite-dioctahedral smectite - talc.

Two phase assemblages of any of these minerals are known. It should be noted that aluminous phases, such as kaolinite, have never been reported with corrensite ; neither have sedimentary phyllosilicates such as 7 Å chlorite or glauconite. Non-phyllosilicates in association with corrensite frequently include diagenetic quartz, albite, calcic zeolites and dolomite. Pelitic rocks, specifically associated with those containing corrensite, contain the allevardite-type mixed layered mineral and fully expanding smectite (dioctahedral).

From the above observations, it is certain that corrensite is a mineral which will form in normal sedimentary rocks and weathering environments during diagenesis and low grade metamorphism or hydrothermal alteration. Thus it will be stable throughout the full range of clay mineral physical environments. It forms in sedimentary rocks which contain important quantities of iron (divalent) or magnesium but is not necessarily related to evaporite deposits and thus alkaline conditions of formation. The data of Schlenker (1971) indicate that corrensite is not specifically related to the occurrence of gypsum in evaporites although this mineral is present in the sedimentary sequence where corrensite is found. We can assume then that corrensite occurrence is a factor both of chemistry and physical conditions acting upon a sediment or rock.

Although little information is available on the stability of corrensite in pelitic sedimentary rocks, some specific observations can be made. It obviously can form at low temperatures just above the alkali zeolite zone (Tateyama et al., 1970 ; Kimbara, 1973 ; Kimbara and Sudo, 1973 ; Sawatski, 1975) and can persist into the allevardite zone of P-T conditions (Kübler, 1973). More information is available on corrensite occurrence in magnesian-rich environments. Such studies are concerned with basic volcanic rocks which have undergone either regional metamorphism or been subjected to an elevated geothermal gradient producing "hydrothermal alteration". The best documented occurrences are in the low grade calcic zeolite facies rocks in the "exterior zones" of Iceland (Thomasson and Kristmannsdottir, 1972 ; Sigaldason, 1962) and the Alps (Kübler et al., 1974). Because the compositions are basic, the expanding minerals are trioctahedral and they are apparently associated in all facies with chlorite. The occurrence of a regularly inter- stratified montmorillonite (saponite)-chlorite mineral, cor- rensite, is typified by an association with calcic zeolites and albite. Temperature measurement in the "hydrothermal" sequences at several hundred meters depth indicate that the ordered, mixed layered mineral succeeds a fully expandable phase between 150-200°C and this ordered phase remains pre- sent to about 280°C. In this interval calcium zeolites dis- appear, being apparently replaced by prehnite. The higher temperature assemblage above corrensite stability typically contains chlorite and epidote.

The apparent coexistence of corrensite and chlorite under diagenetic conditions has been observed by the present author in several samples of "volcanic" sandstones, rocks with fine grained particles of volcanic rocks of the ande- site-basalt type. They come from the Tertiary of Alaska. Typical in such rocks is a phase forming at the pore edges which is alumino-magnesian, usually a chlorite. This phase is followed by a calcic zeolite forming in the pore centers. Certain rocks contain pore wall coatings of two different trioctahedral phases. Figure 43 shows the compositions of one, a chlorite and the other which is a calci-corrensite. The R^{2+} component of both phases is almost identical (Fe/Fe + Mg = 0,39 for corrensite and 0,41 for chlorites). It is not possible to establish the genetic relations bet- ween magnesian phases and the zeolites. It should be noted that both the chlorite and corrensite are rather alumina- poor. One can compare this composition with that typical of chlorites which occur with potassic micas (Figure 50, chlo- rite chapter) according to Velde and Rumble (1977). It seems that there is a difference between calcic and potassic alu- minous phases concerning the tie-lines with magnesio-alumi- nous phases corrensite or chlorite. The partitioning of aluminum in Ca-Mg systems is strongly toward the zeolite whereas in K-Mg systems much more aluminum enters the chlo- rite-corrensite phyllosilicates.

Pelitic rocks investigated in the same areas where corrensites are formed during alpine metamorphism (Kübler, 1970, 1973 ; Kübler et al., 1974) revealed the absence of both montmorillonite and kaolinite but the illite or mica fraction was well crystallized as evidence by measurement of the "sharpness" of the (001) mica reflection (Kübler, 1968). This observation places the upper thermal stability of the expandable and mixed layered trioctahedral mineral assemblages at least 50°C, above their dioctahedral correlevants. This is valid for rocks of decidedly basic compositions where no dioctahedral clay minerals are present.

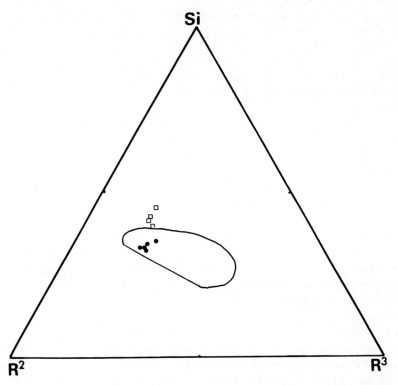

Figure 43 - Si-R^2-R^3 plot of corrensites (squares) coexisting with chlorites (dots) at edges of pore-fillings of a volcanic sandstone. Calcium is the interlayer ion of the corrensites. The pore center is filled with an alkali zeolite. Outlined area shows maximum 14 Å chlorite composition range.

Experimental work (Velde, 1973) helps to establish the relation between dioctahedral and trioctahedral or aluminous and magnesio-ferrous mixed layered minerals. Essentially, the initial material is composed of expanding clays which contain some alkalis, aluminum and divalent ions. These phases then become, upon diagenetic reorganization, potassic mica chlorite and an ionic aqueous solution (containing mainly Ca^{2+} and Na^+). The most important problem is to understand how this evolution proceeds so that we might identify the different steps and use them to trace the paleo-history of a sedimentary rock.

Using the model proposed for the dioctahedral minerals, the phase changes in the trioctahedral minerals can be investigated by choosing mineral assemblages intermediate between those two types and subjecting them to various experimental pressure and temperature conditions. This allows the observation of the interaction of the two mineral types as they re-equilibrate and such an investigation permits one to establish phase relations which are a result of varying composition.

The results of experiments (Velde, 1977) using seven different natural minerals and mineral assemblages is summarized in Figure 44. We can deduce that when the expandability of the dioctahedral interlayered minerals decreases, a trioctahedral expanding phase is produced. This phase rapidly becomes ordered, and could then be called corrensite ; that is a 14 Å-trioctahedral smectite interlayered structure with an ordering reflection due to repetition of two units. The phase relations in the simplified diagram indicate an incompatibility of kaolinite and illite as the corrensite or trioctahedral expanding phase appears. The most important point is the possible coexistence of two ordered mixed layered minerals both showing an ordering reflection. In a glycollated specimen this would mean reflections near 27 and 31 Å or 31 and 37 Å, depending on whether the dioctahedral phase has two or three layer ordering.

From the experiments it seems that the corrensite-type mineral is converted to 14 Å chlorite when a four layer dioctahedral ordered mineral is produced. The experiments show that the corrensite can coexist with 7 and 14 Å chlorite also. This possibility is due to the non-equivalence of Mg^{2+} and Fe^{2+} which segregate into corrensite and chlorite respectively. This effect is discussed further in the chlorite chapter. Thus four major phyllosilicate phases could be

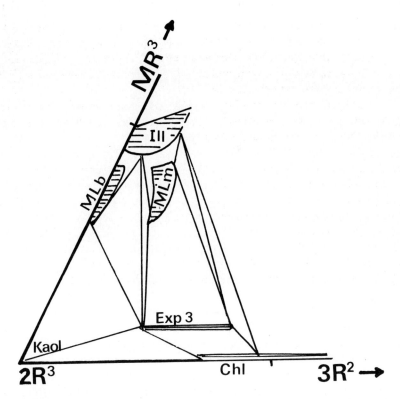

Figure 44 - Results of experiments on natural minerals are schematically shown in MR^3-$2R^3$-$3R^2$ coordinates.
Kaol = kaolinite ; ML_b = mixed layered beidellitic mineral ; Ml_m = mixed layered montmorillonitic mineral ; I = illite compositional field ; Chl = chlorite ; Exp_3 = trioctahedral expandable-chlorite mixed layered mineral (expanding chlorite and corrensite). Shaded areas are two-phase fields, lined areas are one-phase fields.

present at equilibrium. It should be noted that the expanding trioctahedral phase is or can be more aluminous than chlorite. This might lead one to think that some of the layers might in fact be dioctahedral such as those in sudoite. The importance of the differentiation of the two types of mixed layered minerals lies in the segregation of alumina and potassium in one (the dioctahedral mixed layered mineral) and of the magnesium and iron in the other (the corrensite type mineral). Specific mineral identification is not important beyond the designation illite-smectite mixing and chlorite-expanding layer mixing. One leads towards mica, the other towards chlorite (as described in natural samples by

Dunoyer de Segonzac, 1970). When the corrensite type phase is no longer stable, it is possible that the illite-kaolinite or illite-pyrophyllite tie-line will occur again in the $MR^3-2R^3-3R^2$ diagram.

The stability conditions of corrensite then cover the low grade clay mineral facies (near 100°C) and extend well into the calcium zeolite-prehnite, muscovite-chlorite facies (above 200°C). In pelitic rocks the upper limit will be somewhat lower near the illite-chlorite zone. It is evident that composition of a rock governs the occurrence of corrensite. It can be found in very aluminous, alkali-rich as well as magnesian evaporites and metamorphic rocks.

e - Relations between trioctahedral expanding phases

The relationship between chlorite, saponite and corrensite must now be considered. If corrensite is a mixed layered mineral composed of saponite (aluminous one imagines) and chlorite, it must occupy an intermediate position in P,T,x space with respect to its two component layers. We must then define the compositional range of these layers. First, the existence of ferrous saponites in nature is not at all well documented, however, the magnesian form is common. Next, the existence of ferrous-ferric chlorites is well documented (berthierine-chamosites, see chlorite section). It would seem that ferrous iron forms a 7 Å chlorite phase instead of a ferrous saponite at low temperatures. Serpentine (Mg-Al) is not stable either, forming a saponite during weathering (Fontanaud, 1982). We can then suggest a compositional diagram for low temperature trioctahedral phases as in Figure 45. The Mg, Fe^{2+}, $Al-Fe^{3+}$ coordinates can be used to describe the phase compositions. This is not a complete phase diagram in that we do not see alkali or alkaline earth ions -K, Na, Ca- which determine the presence of micas, smectites and possibly most vermiculites and corrensites since the last two phases always contain some of these ions in their natural occurrences.

The microprobe data presented by Velde (1978) coincides with that from later studies (Summarized by Meunier, 1982 ; Parneix and Meunier, 1982) concerning corrensites of hydrothermal alteration origin. Given the imprecision of the

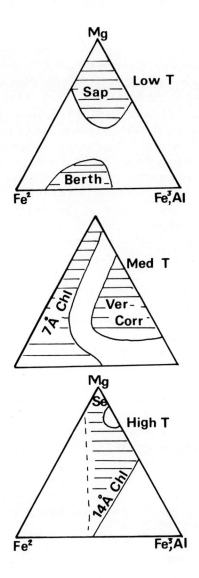

Figure 45 - Indication of possible major triotahedral mineral associations in Mg, Fe^{2+}, Al-Fe^{3+} coordinates as a function of temperatures. Low T = less than 100°C ; Med T = 100-230°C ; High T = 230-500°C. Minerals are :
Sap = saponites ; Berth = berthierine and possibly chamosite ; 7 Å chl = chamosite-berthierines, aluminous 7 Å chlorites ; Se = serpentine ; 14 Å chl = chlorites in equilibrium with an aluminous mica ; Ver-Corr = vermiculite-corrensite minerals which are grouped here for chemical convenience and due to a lack of data.

$Fe^{2+}-Fe^{3+}$ ion ratio determination ; we can place vermiculites and corrensites in a central position of the $Mg-Fe^{2+}$-
(Fe^{3+},Al) coordinates. The corrensite represents medium temperatures (probably 100-250°C) while the metamorphic vermiculites occur toward the higher temperature limits of this
range. Iron-rich chlorites can still persist and now we find
magnesian serpentine occurring. In fact it is probable that
one could have all compositions of chlorites in the low R^3
range. We assume that true saponite is no longer stable and
a mixed layered-type phase occurs as suggested in the experiments of Velde (1973) for the magnesian system at temperatures above 350°C. Here there is a continuous solid solution
between saponite composition and chlorites similar to that
of the dioctahedral smectite-mica series. These trioctahedral phases are aluminous and probably also to a certain
extent ferric.

The range of solid solution in R^2-R^3 variables of
chlorites becomes rapidly fixed in the presence of micas as
we will seen in the chapter on chlorites, and therefore the
high temperature facies above corrensite stability is one of
serpentine - 14 Å chlorite.

Regional studies of tuffaceous sandstones by Kimbara and Sudo (1973) and Kimbara (1973) indicate that loss of
saponite occurs as alkali zeolites are no longer stable in
the assemblages, being replaced by laumontite which typifies
the corrensite zone. The corrensite-laumontite assemblages
have also been noted by Kübler **et al.** (1974) as a systematic
occurrence in basic rocks which have experienced low grade
metamorphism. Corrensite is apparently replaced by chlorite
in the laumontite-epidote zone.

The experiments on natural, pelitic (aluminous)
compositions by Velde (1977) indicate that corrensite follows an iron-rich, 7 Å chlorite and is no longer present
when the illite facies is attained which then becomes the
illite-chlorite facies. It is evident then that corrensite
persists to higher temperatures in basic rocks than in pelitic rocks. It certainly occupies an intermediate position
between saponite and chlorite, both in terms of chemistry as
well as in terms of physical conditions of stability. Corrensite in diagenesis must be expected to contain significant quantities of iron, magnesium and aluminum. Undoubtedly
its alumina and Fe^{3+} content (R^3) will be at a maximum when

it occurs with dioctahedral clay minerals or alkali zeolites. It could contain more R^2, probably magnesium in more R^{3+}-poor environments such as salt deposits and hydrothermally altered ultrabasic rocks.

168

SUMMARY

It is evident that a summary of this section on expanding phases, smectites, must be immediately divided into a discussion of the two major families - di- and tri-octahedral. The first group is based upon an evolution in the presence of alkalis. Dioctahedral smectites tend to concentrate potassium in their interlayer sites under diagenetic conditions of temperatures between 60°C to 200°C for aluminous varieties as they are transformed gradually into micas or illites. Ferric smectites appear to form potassic phases, eventually also mica-like layers, at low temperature conditions. The more dilute the aqueous solutions with which these smectites are in contact, the lower their charge and the fewer R^{3+} ions they will contain.

Sufficient data is available to establish two mineral types - those with octahedral and those with tetrahedral charge imbalance. We cannot determine whether there is solid solution between these two types of structures, i.e. random substitutions of the differont ions in each 2:1 unit layer. However, it seems clear that no tie-line between illite and kaolinite exists at very low temperatures where fully expandable smectites exist. However, this tie-line does exist when mixed layered minerals occur above 60°C. Further, it is probable that each mixed layered mineral series follows a parallel evolution of mixed layering at high expandabilities but the beidellites, when sodic, appear to form a rectorite (smectite 50 %-mica 50 %) structure which persists to highest temperatures (Eberl, 1978). Allevardite-type minerals (potassic, montmorillonitic) show all stages of mixed layering between micas and smectite. Thus, it is not sufficient to use X-ray diffraction to establish the existence of mixed layered minerals, but one should have some idea of their composition by electron microprobe.

The trioctahedral phases are more difficult to deal with at present. It seems that there are a series of stevensite-aluminous saponites which form at low temperatures as precipitates from solution. A vermiculitic phase can form in situations of restricted water flow (weathering in early stages) which might be due to solution with higher ionic concentrations, than those which produce saponites. A similar case probably exists for dioctahedral minerals. These fully expandable smectites and the vermiculites most likely disappear at early burial. The mixed layered trioctahedral minerals - corrensite and possibly metamorphic vermiculites - in general appear toward the upper limits of the clay mineral facies conditions. They are not necessarily restricted to basic rock compositions but will be only of minor importance in pelitic rocks. These minerals will ultimately be transformed into chlorites or biotites, but can coexist with both minerals over a certain, undefined, range of P-T conditions. These partially expanding minerals are stable well above those of a dioctahedral nature, probably up to 300°C or so. However, exact temperatures have been established.

It seems that in the case of di- and trioctahedral vermiculites, they extend the range of solid solution more toward the other octahedral type than do fully expandable minerals. Vermiculites appear to attempt to fill in the gap of bulk composition between the two series by a concentration of either R^2 or R^3 ions as the case might be in their interlayer sites instead of alkali or calcium ions. These elements are not easily exchangeable. However, it does seem that the di- trioctahedral immiscibility remains. The shift from one type to another can only be accomplished through a total reorganization of the crystalline structure.

5 - Chlorites

Relatively little is known about the chemical composition of chlorites found in soils, sediments or sedimentary rocks compared with those formed under metamorphic conditions. It is generally admitted that authigenic chlorites in low temperature environments are iron-rich (Grim, 1968) but their exact Fe^{2+}, Fe^{3+}, Mg and Al content cannot be determined by the most common indirect means such as X-ray diffraction or infra-red adsorption (Brown, 1961 ; Velde, 1973). Other classical methods cannot be used since chlorite can rarely be separated from its clay mineral environment. Chemical analyses are therefore not readily available. One exception to this statement is the 7 Å pelletal chlorites called berthierines. It is known however that chlorites are the minerals which eventually concentrate the iron and magnesium in pelitic rocks upon their metamorphism in the greenschist facies.

a - Natural Occurrences

1 - Weathering

Generally speaking the 14 Å chlorites found in rocks are not stable in weathering profiles. This is especially true under oxidizing conditions (Jackson et al., 1952 ; Millot, 1964 ; Tripplehorn, 1970 ; Adams et al., 1971 ; Harrison and Murray, 1959 ; Bain, 1977 ; Herbillon and Makumbi, 1975). In fact all chlorite polytypes - 14 and 7 Å - seem to be unstable in upper levels of weathering profiles. Magnesian, low aluminum serpentines weather rapidly to smectites (Fontanaud, 1981 ; Wildman and Whittig, 1971) although berthierine, ferrous-ferric 7 Å form, is still present in an antarctic soil (Kodama and Foscolos, 1981). However, since the chlorite structure contains no alkali ions, it frequently remains present as a relict phase in soils and sediments where it is less easily altered than are biotites during intermediate stages of the leaching process. There is evidence, however, that normal 14 Å chlorite can form during weathering in a temperate climate (Quigley and Martin, 1963 ; Ducloux et al., 1976). The apparent insertion of a gibbsite layer (hydrated alumina) in the interlayer position of a degraded mica can produce a chlorite-like phase (see Rich and Obershain, 1955). The 2:1 portion of these "chlorites" can be either di- or trioctahedral in character -something not generally admitted for 14 Å chlorites found in sedimentary and metamorphic rocks. Experiments by Coulter (1969), Brydon and Kodama (1966) and Coulter and Tailburdeen (1968) demonstrate that aluminum ions in solution are greatly favored over others as the interlayer ion in dioctahedral smectites. It is apparent that once alumina in solution reaches a high enough level, any expanding phase will become what is called a soil chlorite. The alumina becomes nonexchangeable in the interlayer position of the structure. It is usually necessary to have low pH values to allow significant quantities of Al^{3+} to enter an aqueous solution and thus soil chlorites would be found preferentially in "acid soils". The fate of these materials in the transportation and sedimentation processes is unknown. In many instances, the soil chlorites are closely related to vermiculite-type minerals.

2 - Sedimentation

There are numerous arguments for the formation of chlorite upon sedimentation of materials in sea basins (Millot, 1964). There are also numerous mechanisms proposed to accomplish this. Many workers have insisted upon the existence of a clay mineral transformation in sea water which effects the reconstitution of a degraded phyllosilicate structure to chlorite by reaction with the ions in solution. Chlorite is common in deep-sea sediments (Biscaye, 1965 ; Heath, 1969 ; Griffin et al., 1968) where it is generally considered to be associated with detrital terriginous materials. Rex (1967) reports the probable formation of chlorite from smectite on the deep sea bottom itself. Copeland et al. (1971) report the formation of a 14 Å iron chlorite from a metamorphic rock precursor on the ocean bottom ; Swindale and Pow-Fooung (1967) report the formation of chlorite from gibbsite in this environment and Carroll (1969) reports the formation of 14 $\overset{o}{A}$ chlorite in deep sea sediments up to 150 cm depths.

Chemical analyses of sediment pore solutions from deep sea cores commonly show a decrease in Mg^{2+} content with depth which has led certain authors to propose the formation of chlorite in this environment (Bischoff and Tehlung, 1970 ; Degens and Chilingar, 1967). However, Chamley et al. (1962) describe the development of expandable phases from chlorite with increasing depth (to 34 cm) in a Mediterranean sea-bottom core.

The crystallization of berthierine, i.e., 7 $\overset{o}{A}$ chlorite or aluminous serpentine, on shallow ocean shelves and estuaries at the sediment surface is well known in recent sediments. There are also instances where this material is found in sedimentary rocks (Velde et al., 1974 ; Leone et al., 1973).

3 - Sedimentary 7 $\overset{o}{A}$ chlorites

Two names are commonly applied to sedimentary 7 $\overset{o}{A}$ minerals ; chamosite and the more general term berthierine. Both contain variable quantities of R^{3+} ions, but Fe^{3+} seems to predominate in the chamosites. The term chamosite is generally applied to minerals in ironstone deposits which frequently contain both 7 and 14 $\overset{o}{A}$ chlorite. Berthierine is a term which can be used to indicate a uniquely 7 $\overset{o}{A}$ iron-rich phase. Two modes of occurrences have been reported for these minerals - as transformations of oolites in ironstone and other deposits (chamosite) and biogenically induced transformations of detrital silicates in pelletal form through interaction with sea water (berthierine). The oolite occurrence is typified by a very high iron content (FeO and Fe_2O_3) in the rock. The exact time of chamosite formation is generally considered to be after the initial sedimentation of an essentially amorphous iron oxide oolite and quartz (Millot, 1964 ; Schellmann, 1966, 1969). These chlorites have thus a diagenetic or post-sedimentary origin. The berthierine occurrence, best known in modern sediments, is apparently due to (the action of) chemical migrations between sea water and sediment at or very near the sediment-sea interface (Porrenga, 1966, 1967.a, 1967.b ; Rohrlich et al.,

1969 ; Gaertner and Schellmann, 1965 ; Leclaire, 1968 ; Giresse and Odin, 1973) at fairly shallow depths (< 80 meters). These reactions take place under saline or estuarine conditions. The transformation of sediment into berthierine is apparently progressive ; the initial sedimentary material found in shell tests or fecal pellets becomes gradually transformed into a single phase, 7 Å chlorite structure (Carmouze et al., 1978).

One aspect of sedimentary 7 Å chlorite formation which is particularly interesting is the fact that these minerals are never found forming at depths greater than 80 meters in recent sediments. Porrenga (1967.b) thinks that they are characteristic of tropical sediments and their formation is thus temperature dependent. This appears invalid since they are known to form in recent sediments in a Scottish loch (Rohrlich et al., 1969). Nevertheless there does seem to be a bathymetric control on their occurrence. This is probably not a pressure effect but more likely some sort of factor related to organic activity in the sediments which is controlled by the biotic factors of sea depth, temperature, nutrients, etc.

In addition to proper biotic factors, it appears that the oxidation state of the iron in the sediment is critical to the formation of sedimentary 7 Å chlorites ; these conditions are more reducing than those which form glauconites (Porrenga, 1967.b ; Leclaire, 1968). As is the case for glauconite, iron mobility is a key factor in forming the berthierine mineral. Under reducing (non-oxidizing) conditions Fe^{3+} becomes Fe^{2+} in combined or ionic form. The solubility of Fe^{2+} at pH above 7,5 is very great while ferric iron, especially the oxide, is virtually insoluble. This has been seen in interstitial waters of marine sediments (Brooks et al., 1968). Since, Mg^{2+} has a high concentration in sea water ($\simeq 1300$ ppm), and SiO_2 (aqueous) can be important at the sea-sediment interface ($\simeq 15$ ppm), it is obvious that all of the components necessary to form chlorite are readily available in solution using Al_2O_3 or an aluminous silicate as a starting material (inert component). If Mg^{2+}, Fe^{2+}, SiO_2 concentrations are controlled by sediment-sea water equilibria, they can be considered as intensive variables in a local clay-aqueous solution system. Experiments by Battacharyya (1983) show that kaolinite can be transformed into berthierine at room temperature conditions. The tendency to

form a monomineralic product in the pelletal 7 Å chlorites
can be explained as being due to a system attaining equilibrium with one inert and several perfectly mobile components
(see glauconite section-micas).

4 - Sedimentary rocks

Chlorites are known as major phases in sedimentary
rocks throughout the geologic column (Weaver, 1959). The
typical assemblage in evolved or old sedimentary rocks is
illite + 14 Å chlorite + quartz (Millot, 1964 ; Dunoyer de
Segonzac, 1969 ; Weaver, 1959). Generally speaking, the
importance of chlorite increases in a sequence of rocks to
the detriment of expanding phases (van Moort, 1971 ; Dunoyer
de Segonzac, 1969). Chlorite has been produced under experimental conditions of 2 Kbars pressure, 300-400°C from natural illites and expandable mixed layered minerals, both dioctahedral and trioctahedral types (Winkler, 1964 ; Velde
and Bystrom-Brusewitz, 1972 ; Velde, 1977). The experiments
reinforce the observations made on sedimentary rocks which
lead to the conclusion that chlorite can be an early product
of diagenetic or epimetamorphic change in pelitic rocks.
Although the gradation between sedimentary and metamorphic
rocks can be defined by the polymorph and composition of the
illite-muscovite association, no such distinction can be
made for chlorite. The 14 Å polymorph is present in association with diagenetic or authigenic illite and remains present into medium grades of metamorphism.

The change between 7 and 14 Å has been noted to
occur at incipient diagenesis (Schoen, 1964 ; Mitsui, 1975 ;
Frey, 1970) for the chamosite-chlorite series containing 60%
Fe^{2+} in the octahedral position. There is apparently a
slight enrichment in iron during the 7-14 Å transformation.
Less is known for compositions which are more magnesian. 14 Å
chlorite has been noted as the first diagenetic mineral in
an undeformed turbidite (Lovell, 1969). Iron-rich 14 Å chlorite is found in the analcime-albite zone in a series of
tuffs and pillow lavas in Puerto Rico (Otalora, 1964) and as
an early diagenetic phase in tuffs of the Wairakei area New
Zealand (Steiner, 1968) and Japan (Kimbara, 1973). Present-
day temperatures of 100°C and coexistence with smectite
attest its precocity. The 7-14 Å polymorphic transition pro-

bably occurs at rather low temperatures, somewhere near 100°C (Velde et al., 1974 ; Mitsui, 1975) for berthierines, i.e., chlorites isolated from other phyllosilicates in the rocks.

Chlorite has been reported as a pore cement in quartzitic sandstones (Hutcheon et al., 1980 ; Almon and Davies, 1979 ; Land and Dutton, 1978) as well as volcanic sand arenites (Dickinson, 1962 ; Davies et al., 1979 ; Ota-lora, 1964 ; Surdam and Boles, 1979 ; Stanley and Benson, 1979). Such an occurrence indicates that magnesium as well as aluminum are transported and precipitated in pore spaces at depth. In the case of the quartzitic sands, the transpor-tation has certainly occurred over distances of at least centimeters if not meters. We cannot explain the chemical reasons for the decrease in solubility of these elements in pore spaces of sands but it is interesting to note that the pore filling material is usually only of one species of phyllosilicates.

The present author has made microprobe analyses of chlorites from several volcanic sand sandstones (Tertiary age rocks from Alaska). The most striking observation is that the pores are lined with a chlorite and a vermiculitic phase both of which have very much the same composition in all of the pores (Fig. 43, Vermiculite section). The compo-sitions vary slightly from one rock to another but both rocks show chlorites with a relatively low alumina content. This is true of the vermiculites also. This undoubtedly reflects the overall chemistry of the rock to a certain extent, but when one realizes that the pore centers of these rocks are filled with calcic zeolites, the assemblage is even more interesting. It appears that the first phase to precipitate is magnesian and alumina-poor while the second is an alumi-no-silicate. Considering the normal conceptions of elemental solubility one would predict the reverse sequence of events. It is generally assumed that magnesium silicates will be more soluble than alumino-silicates. It is possible that the sequence of pore filling is due to differential solubility rates of the constituent minerals in the volcanic sand mate-rial. One can suppose that olivines and pyroxenes will be less metastable that plagioclase and therefore they will release abundant magnesium to the solution at an early sta-ge. The zeolites would then show the slower solubility of plagioclase - the major source of alumina in these volcanic sandstones. However this explanation is purely hypothetical at the moment.

The occurrence of chlorite as a possible cementing material in sandstones is of great importance in that it is a mineral which is easily destroyed by changes in its chemical environment - such as the weathering cycle - and thus it will be a "mobile" mineral in the diagenetic sequence compared with a mineral such as kaolinite which persists frequently throughout the weathering sedimentation and diagenetic cycles.

b - Experimental Studies

1 - Iron chlorites

Little work has been done on the stability and compositional variation of iron-rich chlorites. This is largely due to the problems of controlling the oxidation state of the iron which is actively available to form a silicate mineral. Harder (1978) has succeeded in forming the minerals nontronite, greenalite and chamosite at atmospheric conditions depending upon the Fe/Si ratio and Mg/Fe ratio of dilute solutions which keep the iron in the ferrous state using dithionite. In Harder's experiments, the ionic species are usually present in the 5-10 p.p.m. concentration range. These experiments are of great importance because they demonstrate that one can form clay minerals in short periods of time (several months) even though the elemental concentrations are low in the aqueous solutions. Further, there is a definite chemical control of the species which forms, which demonstrates a definite approach to a chemical equilibrium. The crystallization process is not haphazard nor is it controlled by surface activity phenomena.

Flascher (1957) has synthesized greenalite (Fe^{2+}, Fe^{3+}, 7 Å chlorite) in the system $FeO-Fe_2O_3 - SiO_2$ at temperatures near 470°C. Below 250°C they obtained X-ray amorphous materials. He concludes that chert-hematite-greenalite should not be stable because of the persistence of the mine-mine pair greenalite-magnetite. Unfortunately this type of experimental work was not continued into alumina and magnesium-bearing experimenal systems.

2 - Magnesian chlorites

Synthetic magnesian chlorites have been studied by numerous workers. The complete range of compositions investigated by Yoder (1952) ; Roy and Roy (1954) ; Nelson and Roy (1958) ; Gillery (1959) and Velde (1973) in the magnesian-aluminous chlorite series have the following characteristics : the range of solid solution for 7 Å chlorites is large in $Al^{VI} + Al^{IV} = Mg + Si$ substitutions but rather restricted in the variation of silica content and octahedral site occupancy. The range of solid solution for 14 Å chlorites is greater in Si-content than for 7 Å phases but it does not extend as far toward the magnesian end-member (serpentine composition, Figure 46). Estimations of the 7 Å-14 Å conversion in P-T space give a slope of about 40°C/Kb giving temperatures of 360°C at 1 Kbar and 320°C at 1 atmosphere using linear extrapolation (Velde, 1973). Experiments reviewed by Caillère et al. (1957) and those performed by Estéoule (1965) at 1 atmosphere and 80-100°C show that addition of alumina to a divalent transition metal-silica system increases the range of chemical conditions under which the 7 Å phases can exist. The experiments also demonstrate that 7 Å chlorites can be precipitated from solutions containing the necessary relative quantities of Mg^{2+}, Al^{3+} and SiO_2 at pH between 6 and 8. According to Hostetler and Christ (1968), chrysotile is stable at earth surface P-T conditions ; this is based mainly upon mineral solubility data and thermodynamic considerations. It can thus be concluded that a 7 Å polymorph of chlorite can be stably formed at near earth-surface conditions. This polymorph can persist to high pressures and temperatures (2 Kbars, near 400°C). Although the magnesian 7 Å mineral might be stable at its own bulk composition this is of course not the only factor which will affect its geologic occurrence. Work by Wollast et al. (1968), using sea water and varying pH and SiO_2 (aq) at atmospheric conditions indicates that the first silicate to precipitate will be sepiolite in a low-alumina solution such as sea water. Consequently 7 Å chlorite would not be expected to be found as a precipitate per se in sea sediments coming from a sea water solution. However reaction between sea water and aluminous sediments apparently can form 7 Å chlorite minerals since they have been observed in nature (the berthierine occurrence) as well as in the laboratory.

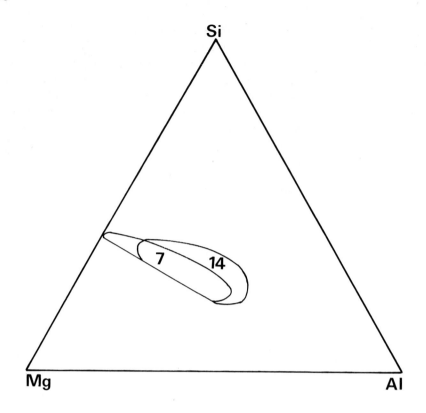

Figure 46 - Compositions of 7 Å and 14 Å chlorites in synthetic magnesium systems (After Velde, 1973).

In the magnesian system, 7 Å chlorite can coexist with talc, magnesian trioctahedral and dioctahedral montmorillonite, boehmite and brucite. A 14 Å chlorite can coexist with magnesian montmorillonite, talc, quartz, kaolinite, boehmite and brucite. It is important to note that 7 Å aluminous chlorites do not coexist stably with quartz or a free silica phase.

Although experiments indicate an instability of 7 Å magnesian chlorite and quartz, it is common to find chamosite pellets with a quartz grain at their center (Schellmann, 1969). Does this mean stability due to a high iron content, poor experimental data, or a metastable association ? If we consider that quartz is effectively not the mineral which controls the silica activity in low temperature solutions, due to its low solubility and the fact that it apparently

does not precipitate from solution, it is possible to consider that the crystallization of 7 Å chlorite around a quartz
grain is due to the initial solution of SiO_2 which acted as
a source of silica for the chlorite. Successive layers of
chlorite would have taken silica from solution below the
levels of silica saturation, i.e., where there would be precipitation of a silica phase such as opal. Thus the chlorite
is formed at conditions below silica saturation, those where
a free silica phase is precipitated. The persistence of the
quartz grain is due to its low solubility in solution. When
the sediment is buried and temperature increases, the quartz
will become the phase which controls silica concentration in
solution and the chlorite polymorph should become 14 Å enlarging its compositional range. This is commonly the case
in chamosite mineral deposits.

c - Chlorite Chemistry and Iron-magnesium Distribution among Phyllosilicates

An important feature of the chemistry of natural
chlorites is their relative Fe,Mg and Al content. The
available information for 7 Å chlorites indicates that the
Fe^{2+} + Mg + Al content is decidedly variable, ranging from
4 % Fe^{2+} to 82 % Fe^{2+}. Carroll (1969) reported 14 Å chlorites as forming in sediments (up to 150 cm depth) in Pacific
Ocean red and grey clays which had variable Mg-Fe contents.
14 Å chlorites from consolidated sediments and metamorphic
rocks have a complete range of iron content.

Microprobe analyses of some berthierine pellets
from sedimentary rocks (Velde et al., 1974 , Leone et al.,
1975 and new data, Figure 47) indicate that these minerals
have compositions close to those of 7 Å chlorites delimited
by synthesis studies, and here there is a more restricted
range of silica substitution in the structure than is found
in 14 Å chlorites. This is confirmed by Brindley (1982)
using classical chemical analyses. Thus the two polymorphs
have at least different limits in tetrahedral substitutions.
A review of some 200 chlorite analyses from the literature
(Velde, 1973) indicated that Fe-Mg-Al ranges for 7 and 14 Å
chlorites overlap to a large extent. Moreover, both 7 and
14 Å chlorites are considered to be iron-rich when found in
low temperature environments. However, if we consider the

composition of all 7 Å chlorites, two groups appear : the magnesian serpentines and the iron rich chamosite-berthieri-nes. Figure 47 shows the distribution of magnesian serpenti-nes (crysolite, antigorite and lizardite) compared to ber-thierine-chamosites. There appears to be no overlap. Thus one can find identical compositions of low temperature, 7 Å chlorites and 14 Å metamorphic chlorites, but the high tempe-rature 7 Å forms (serpentines) seem to form a chemical group of their own. The role of ferric iron must be important in stabilizing the 7 Å aluminous-ferrous form, however we do not know just why at present.

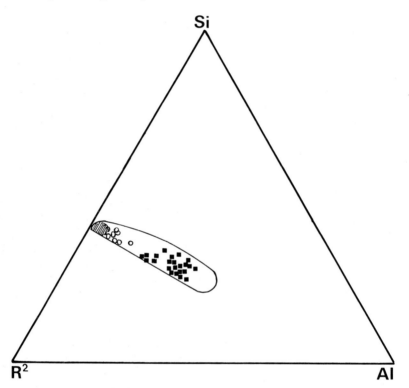

Figure 47 - Microprobe analyses of berthierines (squares) and magnesian serpentines (circles). Outlined area shows synthetic 7 Å phase limits.
All iron is calculated as Fe^{2+} (R^2).

Why are the diagenetic or authigenic chlorites found in sedimentary rocks ferrous ? The answer can be found in the phase relations of the minerals common in sedimentary rocks. Basically, 14 Å chlorite is formed either through the destabilization of the montmorillonite-illite mixed layered mineral or kaolinite in the majority of argillaceous sedimentary rocks (Dunoyer de Segonzac, 1969 ; van Moort, 1971 ; Perry and Hower, 1970 ; Muffler and White, 1969). The increase in chlorite content is frequently observed in the presence of illite or a mixed layered mineral with a high non-expandable layer content.

It is well known that two silicate minerals, simultaneously stable, will have a specific distribution of homologous ions between them, depending upon the temperature and pressure conditions prevalent. This is especially evident for Fe^{2+}-Mg. Generally, as temperature increases the segregation of one species in each mineral will become less evident until, for example, the $Mg-Fe^{2+}$ distributions become equal between two mineral species in equilibrium (Ramberg and de Vore, 1951). However, at low temperatures segregation is often highly developed, Mg tending to be found in one phase and Fe^{2+} in the other. If we consider some information for potassium mica (phengites) and chlorites used by Velde (1967) and Brown (1967), it is apparent that chlorite tends to be relatively more iron-rich than mica ; 50 to 100 % more than the coexisting phengite. Although phengite is not illite nor mixed layered illite-smectite, the structures and compositions are similar. It can be argued that the sedimentary dioctahedral mineral illite behaves as a phengitic mica, concentrating Mg in preference to Fe^{2+} in the presence of chlorite. Conversely, chlorite concentrates Fe^{2+} in preference to Mg. The higher the iron content of the rock, the higher the iron content of the chlorite will be. In this way 14 Å chlorites, in equilibrium with the bulk composition of the rock and its micaceous constituents would tend to be more consistently iron-rich compared with 7 Å pelletal chlorites. These are formed under localized equilibrium conditions in a system containing essentially one silicate phase where variations in total available Mg and Fe^{2+} will be directly reflected in the mineral's composition.

d - Composition of Some Natural Chlorites Formed in Various Physical Environments in Pelitic Clay Mineral Suites

Although previously mentioned, the information on the chemical composition of natural, low temperature chlorites in sedimentary rocks is limited, some new data has been gathered using microprobe analysis of grain mounts or rock thin sections. The samples studied come from rather different geographic areas - western Montana, Algeria and the Franco-Italian Alps and African off-shore Atlantic coast shelf sediments.

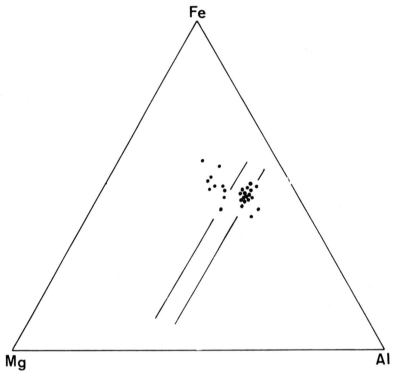

Figure 48 - Berthierine compositions in
Fe-Al-Mg coordinates.

First, we will consider the chlorite known as berthierine. These are the pelletal ocean bottom 7 Å chlorites. Those reported in the literature (Velde **et al.**, 1974 ; Leone **et al.**, 1975) and several new analyses from Alpine samples indicate a homogeneous composition throughout the pellet. The samples have undergone metamorphism and the minerals now have a 14 Å polymorph. This may well explain their relative compositional homogeneity. The analyses of many single grains (with microprobe) show some scatter of compositions but they all lie within the 7 Å chlorite range determined experimentally. Figure 48 shows the compositional range in Fe-Al-Mg coordinates for grains in ten rock samples. It is evident that these berthierines are iron and alumina-rich minerals. Similar results were obtained for berthierines from coal measures (Iijima and Matsumoto, 1982).

Samples reported by Schellmann (1969) from the sediments in the Gulf of Guinea were analyzed at grain edges and centers. These pellets have not completed the evolution toward a single-phase 7 Å mineral. They are iron-rich, containing no other detectable phyllosilicate than berthierine but they contain goethite. Grain edges are variable in composition whereas grain centers tend to group near a berthierine composition comparable with those of the meta-berthierines. The grain center compositions tend to lie close to those of synthetic 7 Å chlorites in the Si-Al-R^{2+} coordinates.

The process of berthierine formation appears to be similar to that described for glauconites. Initial sedimentary pelletal material is chemically transformed into chlorite at the sediment-water interface. Figure 49 shows microprobe compositions of grain edges and grain centers of berthierine pellets and oolites from which they are forming. The plot shows all iron as R^2 which is certainly not correct but since microprobe results cannot give a Fe^{2+}/Fe^{3+} ratio we will use such a plot as an expedient. Two sets of samples were used, those described by Schellmann (1969), from a sedimentary rock deposit and those from a surface sediment of Tertiary age off the coast of Gabon (samples supplied by G. Odin). In the first instance (Fig. 49a), the edge-center vector is toward a composition in the compositional area where berthierines are found. It appears that the initial oolites are composed of a wide range of oxide mixtures, some more iron-rich than chlorite - others more silica-rich. The grain edge remains outside the chlorite range while the center becomes chloritic in composition. One can conclude that the cortex zone maintains an intermediate composition between the outside environment from which material is taken and the inner chlorite core. This is typical of systems which have a chemical gradient within them. Each grain seems to behave as an independent system while the edge compositions vary and the centers tend to be of a general composition. The cortex reflects the difference between outside environment and the initial composition of the oolite. The samples represent the diagenetic formation of 7 Å chlorites or the chamosite mineral.

184

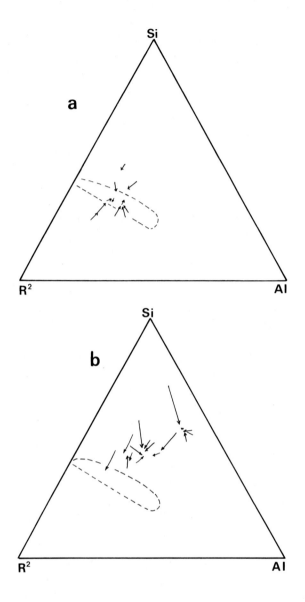

Figure 49 - Center-edge microprobe compositions of
berthierine and oolite (chamosite) materials in Si-Al-R^2
coordinates where all iron is considered to be R^2.
a - Ironstone oolites reported by Schellmann (1969).
b - Berthierine pellets in recent sediments.
Arrows indicate edge to center chemical vectors.
Dashed line shows 7 Å chlorite compositional range.

A second example, sediment-surface berthierine pellets from shallow (< 100 m) marine sediments, shows a different evolution : we see (Fig. 49b) a series of grain center-grain edge compositions which tend to define a local chemical vector as well as a general, rather well defined trend. Mineralogically, the initial sediments are mixtures of kaolinite-quartz and iron oxide. If we assume in our plot that all iron is ferrous (R^2), it appears that the grain centers form average compositions which fall on a tie-line kaolinite chlorite. Successive changes modify the ratio of aluminous to iron-rich phase both of which have the 7 Å form. Again, as in the case of chamosites, the outside edge of the grain behaves as an intermediate buffer zone which separates two end members of the compositional system. The cortex zone represents the area of chemical transport. The major chemical change in the silicate material is an increase in the R^2 (Fe) component. This brings the pellets towards a berthierine composition. Here we find the same problem as encountered in glauconites or the sedimentary nontronite pellets (Pédro **et al.**, 1978). Iron is a major mobile component. In most sediments one finds most iron to be the highly insoluble Fe^{3+} form. Yet, if we assume that time is of little importance (a geologist can well afford one million years) it should be possible to transfer iron from aqueous fluid to solid even though its concentration is only several parts per million of the solution : chemical migration in aqueous solution is undoubtedly rapid compared with the distances involved (several centimeters at the most). Odin (1975) has shown that glauconite pellets are rather porous, thus we can envisage the chemical transfer through liquids and need not worry about the much slower diffusion rates in solids. The critical factor then becomes the crystal growth rate (glauconite, berthierine or nontronite) and the rate of dissolution of iron oxides. The speed with which one attains saturation of the aqueous liquid is not at all pertinent. If the rate of crystallization exceeds that of diffusion in the liquid, the controlling factor will be the rate of dissolution of the iron-bearing phase. If the crystallization rate is not great enough to exhaust the solution or undersaturate it, crystal growth will control the process. The concentration of iron in solution is then only an indication of which part of the process is controlling it.

The two examples of berthierine and chamosite origin shown here are of course only isolated cases and they then cannot be used as a general case. However, it is interesting to note that the chamosite example studied shows both iron increase and iron decrease depending upon the local system, while the berthierine shows an increase in iron from outside the pelletal system.

It is possible that the mechanism of berthierine formation in this example is one of accretion, i.e., the grain would accumulate material at the exterior and this is eventually transformed into a chlorite composition. None of the grains was noted to have the form of a shell test as is often noted in glauconite pellets. However the metamorphic berthierine pellets reported by Velde **et al.** (1974) were often found inside foraminifera tests. Those found in shells would indicate elemental migration into and out of the pellet which maintains a constant volume.

The most important character of all of the berthierine compositions is their low silica content. The variation of compositions found for pellets from the recent sediments appears to be the result of the crystallization of a chlorite structure with full octahedral occupancy. The meta-berthierines fall within the limits deduced for synthetic magnesian 7 Å chlorites ; limits which are also near full octahedral occupancy. The samples studied are richer in iron than in magnesium and they show a limited variation in relative content of these two ions.

Figure 50 gives the compositions of berthierines, and 14 Å chlorites from sedimentary rocks. Examples are from sandstones which contain mixed layered smectite-illites in the 30-40 % smectite range (french Alps, Velde unpublished) in the 30-20 % range (North Sea drill core samples) from the illite-chlorite facies of the Montana pre-Cambrian (Nicot, 1981) and from pyrophyllite facies rocks in Brittany (Paradis, 1981). All of the data are electron microprobe results which are plotted as total iron against magnesium and aluminum.

If we can consider these argillaceous sandstones to be typical of sedimentary rocks in general, one can see in the figure that berthierines are set apart from the other chlorites. This is probably due to the fact some of the iron present is trivalent, and thus it has the same function as aluminium. If all R^{3+} ions were grouped at one pole, it is

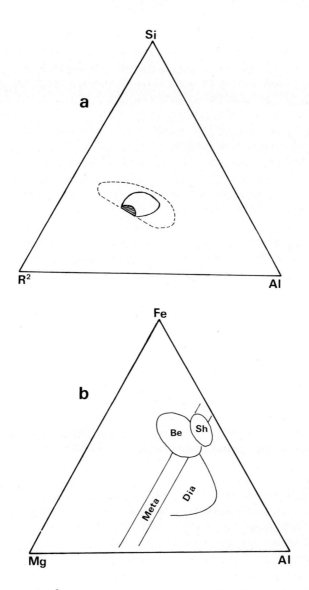

Figure 50 - Si-R^2-Al plot and Fe-Mg-Al plot of microprobe analyses of chlorites from some sediments and sedimentary rocks. Figure 50a shows the metamorphic or high grade diagenetic mineral compositions in the shaded area, the full line gives the compositional zone of sedimentary rocks (containing expanding minerals) and the dashed line shows maximum 14 Å magnesium chlorite range. Figure 50b shows metamorphic (Meta), diagenetic (Dia), berthierine (Be) and black shale (Sh) facies zones for several samples studied as they plot in Fe-Mg-Al coordinates.

probable that berthierines would overlap with other low temperature chlorites. Next one sees that as metamorphic grade
increases, the alumina content decreases. There is no great
tendency to concentrate iron in the earliest chlorites compared with those in the illite-chlorite grade rocks. However,
the amount of alumina does decrease. If we compare these
analyses on an $Si-R^2-R^3$ plot, we can see how the alumina
content decreases towards a tight span of compositions typical of chlorites found in metamorphic rocks of all grades
which contain potassic white micas (Velde and Rumble, 1977).
This "magic" composition has a strict alumina content with a
complete range of Fe-Mg ratios as shown in figure 50.

The composition of individual chlorite grains in a
single thin section are more variable in sedimentary rocks
than they are in their metamorphic counterparts. One finds
variations of ± 5 ionic percent Si or Al and more than this
for Mg and Fe. Nevertheless the compositions determined from
grain to grain in one sample do not exceed the limits defined for synthetic 14 Å chlorites (Velde, 1973). Those chlorites associated with mixed layered clay minerals are most
silica-rich and have the greatest compositional variations
for grains in a single thin section ; they tend to be iron-
rich and aluminous. One chlorite vein was found to transect
a glauconite pellet. This chlorite was quite iron-poor, indicating attainment of a local chemical equilibrium between
chlorite and iron mica upon its crystallization.

It appears, using a limited number of samples, that
low "metamorphic" or diagenetic grade in the clay mineral
facies produces chlorites of variable composition within a
sample. This variability diminishes with higher grade of
metamorphism or diagenesis and a decrease in alumina and
silica contents. Microprobe data of Brown (1967) and Nash
(1973) from rocks of moderate physical conditions of
crystallization indicate small scatter in the composition of
individual grains from the same sample. This has been confirmed in the present study for chlorites from six rocks
from the Belt series in northern Montana (Harrison and
Jobin, 1963) analyzed by Nicot (1981) three samples from the
outer zones in the Alpine chain and sandstones from the
North Sea. From these analyses, it is apparent that metamorphic chlorites which have crystallized with muscovite have
low silica contents and a rather limited alumina content (27
± 3 % Al ions). The relatively large variation in chlorite

Fe-Mg ratio from rock to rock suggests that bulk rock composition is more important in determining the chlorite composition than is the case of chlorites from clay mineral facies. This is confirmed by the analyses of chlorites from black shales in the rectorite-pyrophyllite facies (Paradis, 1981) which contain highly reduced silicate mineral compositions (all iron is Fe^{2+}) and as a result the chlorite is very iron-rich.

There appears to be less grain-to-grain variation in metamorphic chlorites than in chlorites from clay mineral assemblages.

e - Chlorite Polytypes and Polymorphs

Bailey (1969) and Bailey and Brown (1962) have shown that each of the chlorite polymorphs, 7 Å and 14 Å, can have various stacking arrangements which creates different polytypes described by Smith and Yoder (1955) for micas. Polymorphs are changes from 7 to 14 Å phases where the types of units change - we go from a 1:1 structure to a 2:1 + hydroxide structure. Earlier it was mentioned that the 7 → 14 Å polymorph transition was observed to take place somewhere near 100°C in burial sequences. Hayes (1970) has estimated that there is a similar temperature dependence for the polytype transformation from type Ib to type IIb. He finds several type I polytypes which he attributes to phases in the diagenetic grades below 150-200°C. Type II structures are 14 Å metamorphic chlorites. However, as we mentioned before, other authors have found the 7 Å → 14 Å transition to occur in very early diagenesis. Most authors seem in fact to note chlorite when a 14 Å peak is present on X-ray diffractograms. This being the case, the 14 Å polymorph is certainly present near or below 100°C (see Hower et al., 1976, for example). In fact then we would expect to see the following sequence of chlorite forms as a function of burial metamorphism : 7 Å chlorite → 14 Å chlorite type I → 14 Å chlorite type II.

The first reaction occurs near 100°C and the second above 150-200°C.

According to Hayes (1970) the type I sequence is I disordered → Ib(ß97°) → Ib(ß90°). However, if one looks closely at the diagrams calculated by Bailey (1969) and Brown and Bailey (1962) one finds that type Ib (ß90°) is similar to type D of the 7 Å chlorites and that type Ib (ß97°) is not too different from the A type of 7 Å polymorphs. There could then be some overlap in the sequence proposed by Hayes where the early polytypes are those of the 7 Å polymorph while the later ones (higher temperature) could be of the 14 Å polymorph. The problem is possibly complicated further by the apparent fact (Bailey, 1969) that some polytypes are found more frequently in chlorites of a given compositional range. Thus, one could be seeing an effect of initial bulk composition of a sample as well as one of changing chlorite chemistry as metamorphism progresses.

SUMMARY

Although the information available from synthetic studies strongly indicates a P-T control of the chlorite polymorph, natural minerals appear to exhibit both polymorph, 7 and 14 Å, at low temperature. Most diagenetic chlorites correspond to a 7 Å polymorph. However, there are occurrences especially in deep ocean sediments of a 14 Å phase. The contradiction cannot be resolved with the information available at present. It is probably reasonable to assume that the 7 Å polymorph is stable for all chlorite compositions (i.e., various Fe^{2+}, Mg, Al ratios) and that the 14 Å forms are metastable at low temperatures. However, this is certainly not definitive.

In summary, one can say that 14 Å trioctahedral brucitic chlorite is largely unstable in most weathering environments, but aluminous soil chlorites are common under acid conditions. The bulk of chlorites found in sediments is certainly detrital in origin ; 7 and 14 Å chlorites can be formed from 50°C upward in temperature until above 100°C where 14 Å chlorite becomes one of the most common minerals in sedimentary rocks. The compositional variation from grain to grain is greater in low temperature 14 Å chlorites and this scatter decreases as metamorphic grade increases. Low temperature chlorites tend to be ferrous and aluminous.

It appears that increasing metamorphic grade tends to give a 30 % aluminum atomic content in chlorites and often decreases the iron content.

6 - Zeolites

This complex mineral group has been studied from different aspects for many years, but remains essentially enigmatic where questions of the physical-chemistry of zeolite genesis are concerned. Zeolites are chemically simple, being composed essentially of Ca, Na, K, Si and Al cations. The more common chemical substitutions for the alkali and calcic series are $(Na, K)Al = Si$ and $CaAl_2 = SiO_2$. The increase of SiO_2 in a zeolite series is generally accompanied by additional H_2O in the bulk mineral analysis. Calcium zeolites normally fall between anorthite and SiO_2 anhydrous compositions. Alkali zeolites can be less silica-rich than the corresponding feldspar and can range to compositions significantly richer in silica than feldspar. Anhydrous compositions appear to be continuous between the two series themselves (Hay, 1966 ; Deer **et al.**, 1962 ; Sheppard, 1970). Two types of substitutions are possible $Ca = 2 (Na, K)$ or $CaAl = (Na, K) Si$.

It is this large and continuous variability in bulk composition coupled with the fact that crystal structures may be different for the same anhydrous or hydrous bulk composition which makes zeolite identification so difficult (see Breck, 1970, for example and Deer **et al.**, vol. 4, 1962). The factors determining which species of zeolite will crystallize are undoubtedly complex, involving such variables as the chemical activity of dissolved ionic species, crystal growth rate and ease of nucleation ; however, certain patterns of mineral paragenesis can be discerned through a survey of the literature.

Natural calcium zeolites are known to remain stable at higher temperatures than their alkaline counterparts. They are found to exist under conditions which produce obviously metamorphic rocks (Coombs, 1970). The calcic zeolite stabilities will be strongly dependent upon the activity not only of Ca^{2+} but also CO_2 (Liou, 1970, 1971b ; Zen, 1961) and thus their presence will not reflect uniquely silicate equilibria but also those of carbonate systems. For these reasons calcic zeolites will not be considered in detail here, but it should be noted that they give useful information about the global parameters of chemical activity and physical conditions under which a given assemblage of minerals was formed.

Alkali zeolites (especially the more common species natrolite, analcime, phillipsite, erionite, scoleite, heulandite, clinoptilolite and mordenite) are found to form in most low temperature environments. Hay's summary of zeolite occurrence (1966) demonstrates the relative importance of several chemical parameters. High activity of silica in solution is certainly a primary requisite for zeolite formation, and it probably also controls the composition of the crystallized zeolite. Of course alkali chemical potential is also important but it is obviously inversely related to that of silica, since higher alkali content necessitates lower silica in zeolite substitutions. Because these minerals contain large quantities of water, the chemical potential of H_2O is also important (Hess, 1966). In surveying the literature it is apparent that zeolites, more than most mineral groups, are suspected of metastable crystallization and slow attainment of equilibrium (Hay, 1964) and thus discussion of their mineral equilibria are necessarily tentative. However an attempt can be made to clarify the major phase relations of the natural minerals.

a - Natural Occurrences

We will briefly consider the major mineral associations found in the various low temperature environments where zeolites are present.

1 - Weathering

A large variety of zeolite species crystallize from volcanic glasses under weathering conditions and several can be associated in the same sample. The process seems most pronounced for acid eruptive rocks (Hay, 1963 ; Iijima and Harada, 1969 ; Harada **et al.**, 1967) but does occur in basalts also (Hay and Iijima, 1970). In some African soil profiles, zeolites (analcime) are found to develop at the expense of dioctahedral smectite and sodium carbonate ; their occurrence is apparently a function of local drainage.

They grow in more stagnant situations at the expense of smectite (Frankart and Herbillon, 1970). K-spar and alkali zeolites have been found to form along with smectite in first-cycle transformation of desert alluvium (Walker **et al.**, 1978).

2 - Sedimentation (Continental, Shallow marine)

A wide variety of zeolites are known to form in saline lakes where the species present is dependent upon the chemistry of the solutions. Rapid zeolite formation is aided by the existence of the volcanic glass and high water salinities. Potassium feldspar occurs with the common alkali zeolites (Hay and Moiola, 1963 ; Hay, 1964 ; Hay, 1966 ; Sheppard and Gude, 1969, 1971 ; Walker **et al.**, 1978), however, albite is not evident as a diagenetic mineral in saline lakes.

So far as is known, near-shore marine sedimentary environments do not frequently produce zeolites. They have nevertheless been reported in a Florida bay (Huang and Goodell, 1967) in Naples bay (Muller, 1961) and in a neritic Texas sandbar along with opal, glauconite and smectite (Wermund and Moiola, 1966). The fact that zeolites occur in these very different environments which contain varied materials (terriginous sediments, volcanic debris and sorted sand and clays) leads one to believe that the presence of zeolites in shallow water marine sediments has gone undetected in many previous investigations. This is undoubtedly due in part to the size of zeolite crystals which is most often greater than two microns. Since most clay mineral studies are concerned with only the finer fractions, authigenic zeolites will go unnoticed in the unused coarse fraction which includes the detrital minerals of the sediment.

3 - Deep sea sediments

Many investigators have reported the presence of zeolites at the deep ocean bottom (Biscaye, 1965 ; Heath, 1969 ; Bonatti, 1963 ; Sheppart and Gude, 1971 ; Jacobs, 1970 ; Morgenstein, 1967 ; Hoffert, 1980 ; Couture, 1977 ; among others). Most of the alkali zeolites are represented except the silica-poor species natrolite and analcime. Rex and Martin (1966) indicate that detrital potassium feldspar is not stable under ocean floor sediment conditions. Zeolites are found in most ocean basins where wind-carried volcanic ash predominates over detrital river-born clay mineral sediments. In these sediments phillipsite is particularly evident and it is known to continue to grow in the sediment column to depths of more than a meter (Bernat et al., 1970). Stonecipher (1976) finds phillipsite to be the most common zeolite in non-palygorskite bearing sediments.

A common form of basalt alteration in sequences found on the ocean bottom is one which contains alkali zeolites. These most often occur in hyaloclastite rocks, i.e., a brecciated basalt which is largely recrystallized and cemented. The zeolites commonly occur in concentric zones around the basalt clasts (see section on deep sea basalt alteration). Besse et al. (1981) found that a zonation can occur where Na-K phillipsite is found in the upper zone, clinoptilolite and mordenite in mid-range and analcite-clinoptilolite in the lowest zone of a 500 meters thick section ; these materials were volcanic lapilli and hyaloclastic rocks. They show a continuous sequence of decrease in Si/Al with depth until one finds a calcic clinoptilolite associated with analcime at the bottom of their sequence. Couture (1977) and Nathan and Flexer (1977) have observed that palygorskite-bearing deep-sea sediments frequently contain the silica-rich alkali zeolite clinoptilolite. Aluminous smectite is also frequently present. This seems to be a very general, world wide assemblage. Hoffert (1980) has established that the dominant clays in Pacific Ocean red clay oozes are comprised of aluminous smectite and phillipsite.

4 - Sedimentary rocks

Most commonly, zeolites are found in series of sedimentary rocks which contain pyroclastic material and are formed during the devitrification of this material. The type of zeolite formed, alkali-rich and siliceous or more calcic and aluminous, seems to be influenced by the type of sedimentary material involved, especially eruptive volcanic sands and tuffs (Davies et al., 1979 ; Surdam and Eugster, 1976 ; Boles and Coombs, 1975 ; Reynolds and Anderson, 1967 ; Moncure et al., 1980 ; Read and Eisbacher, 1974 ;

Morgenstein, 1967). If the rocks are silica-rich, the zeolite species formed seems dependent upon the bulk composition and burial depth or temperature of formation (Hay, 1966). They are most frequently accompanied by silica in an amorphous or cryptocrystalline form (opal, chalcedony). Analcime and all other compositional intermediates up to the silica-rich clinoptilolite are found in this association. The most common clay mineral in such tuffs is smectite. Zeolites are sometimes found with glauconite (Brown et al., 1969) or celadonite (Hay, 1966 ; Iijima, 1970 ; Read and Eisenbacher, 1974) in pelitic layers or acidic eruptive rocks and with celadonite in basic tuffs (Hay, 1966). Sequences of deeply buried acidic tuffaceous rocks are observed to contain progressively less silica-rich zeolites, as temperature (and pressure) increases (Iijima, 1970, 1975 ; Iijima and Utada, 1966 ; Moiola, 1970 ; Boles and Coombs, 1975 ; Aoyagi and Kazama, 1980 ; Read and Eisenbacher, 1974 ; Besse et al., 1981). Basic rocks present more ambiguous associations indicating that bulk composition can also be important (Coombs and Whetten, 1967). Analcime is the most common zeolite known in coals where it is associated with a definite rank in the coalification process (80 % C, 40 daf). More silicic zeolites are found in less evolved coal measures (Kisch, 1969).

Summary of Natural Occurrences

Natural occurrences in hydrothermal areas show that the replacement of analcime + quartz by albite probably takes place near 150-180°C (Coombs et al., 1959) at several hundred meters depth. The observed upper limit of analcime appears to be 100-125°C in deeply buried tuffaceous rocks ($\simeq$ 5 km depth) (Iijima, 1975 ; Reed and Eisbacher, 1975 ; Merino, 1975 ; Coombs et al., 1959). In other rocks for which no temperature data are available analcime can be found to coexist with sodium feldspar (High and Picard, 1965 ; Iijima and Utada, 1966 ; Iijima and Hay, 1968 ; Otalora, 1964 ; Callegari and Jobstribitzer, 1964 ; Gulbrandsen and Cressman, 1960 ; Iijima, 1975). Several authors have indicated that analcime replaces other zeolites in buried sequences of rocks (Moiola, 1970 ; Sheppard, 1970 ; Iijima and Hay, 1968 ; Iijima, 1970 ; Gude and Sheppard, 1967) but this is certainly not the rule since analcime is frequently associated with other zeolites as a primary mineral in soils sediments and sedimentary rocks (Hay, 1966 ; Singer and Stoffers, 1980).

From the clay mineral-zeolite associations found at low temperatures, it is apparent that kaolinite as well as potassium mica occur rarely with alkali zeolites. Such assemblages are known for highly alkaline waters in continental lakes (Hay, 1966 ; Sheppard and Gude, 1969) where smectite is nevertheless the predominant clay mineral. At higher temperatures, where most alkali zeolites become unstable but analcime persists, smectite will be present up to 100°C and a mixed layered mineral above this temperature.

It can be seen that alkali zeolites, those predominantly sodi-potassic, are most often found in low temperature, low pressure environments. Frequently two or more species are found together in the same geologic sample. As pressure-temperature conditions become more severe, the mineralogy becomes more simple, feldspar appears and finally within the limits of clay mineral stabilities only calcic zeolites are found. However, the calcic minerals are generally confined to rocks of basic compositons, i.e., andesitic or basaltic volcano-clastics, and are not often found with aluminous clay minerals in pelitic rocks.

b - Zeolite Synthesis and Stability

It is not our purpose here to analyse the voluminous literature dealing with synthetic zeolites, suffice it to say that the subject is vast and as yet incompletely explored. However, citations from several recent summary papers allow the general trends of observed stability and crystallization to be outlined in a reasonably accurate fashion.

The most important factor in zeolite synthesis in the laboratory, or factory, is the rate of crystallization. Composition and concentration of the liquid solution acting on the solids is important to the process, as is the absolute necessity of maximum disorder of the Si-O-Al bonds in the initial solids reacted (Zhdanov, 1970). It is thus evident that not only bulk chemical (equilibrium) factors are important in the initial crystallization of zeolites, but also the relative free energies of the reactants. It is apparent that zeolite equilibria are essentially aqueous ; i.e., that silicate equilibrium or approach to it is attained through reaction with solutions, and thus the solubilities of the solids present are of primary importance. If materials are slow to enter into solution they are essentially bypassed in the rapid crystallization sequence (Schwochow and Heinze, 1970 ; Aiello et al., 1970). In most studies the zeolites precipitated from solution appear to respond to the laws concerning chemical potential of solutions (Zhdanov, 1970). However reaction time can control even H_2O content of analcime (Arima and Edgar, 1980).

One important aspect of experimental studies is the ease with which alkali or other ions are exchanged in a given crystal structure (Zhdanov, 1970 ; Breck, 1970 ; Taylor and Roy, 1964 ; Hayhurst and Sand, 1975). However, these operations are usually effected at high pressure and temperatures over short periods of time. These conditions go well beyond those of natural zeolite stability. One might suspect the creation of metastable phases which would be unstable under normal natural zeolite environmental conditions. This point is fundamental to the discussion which follows. Further, although no formal evidence can be presented for all zeolite species, it is likely that the extensive cation exchange effected at several hundred degrees centigrade and hundreds of atmospheres would be the result of abnormally high energy factors, more than those found at equilibrium conditions. This is well demonstrated by the mineral analcime found to be strictly sodi-calcic at low temperatures in nature but capable of extensive alkali cation exchange in the laboratory at temperatures of 250°C (Balgord and Roy, 1970).

Experimental phase equilibria studies by Campbell and Fyfe (1965), Thompson (1971) and Liou (1971a) indicate an approximate 180°C, lower stability for albite in the presence of quartz and analcime from 12 to 2000 atmospheres pressure. A calculated stability for analcime at 3 Kbars is about 120°C (Campbell and Fyfe, 1965), conditions equivalent to rock pressures at 7.5 Km depth. However, if water pressure is lower than total, lithostatic pressure, the thermal stability of a very hydrous, low-density mineral such as analcime can be significantly lowered (Greenwood, 1961). The experimental transformation of alkali zeolites to analcime at 100°C and 2-3 atmospheres pressures was demonstrated by Boles (1971). The alumina content of the alkali zeolites used in this latter study was found to influence that of the analcime produced, and this independently of the amount of crystalline quartz added to the initial materials.

Probably the only general statement which can be made about the experimental studies on zeolites is that the majority of published data is directly inapplicable to natural minerals. This is due either to the excessively high temperatures under which the experiments are performed, outside of the physical limits of zeolite stability, or to short time spans of observation which do not allow the silicates to come to equilibrium with the fluids of the experiments. The importance of time in experiments is well demonstrated by Arima and Edgar (1980). Those studies designed to determine zeolite stability indicate that the most silica-poor alkali zeolite, analcime, is unstable above 180°C. More silica-rich species will be found below this temperature. However, the reasons for the crystallization of one or another of the silica-rich alkali zeolites are not yet elucidated.

c - Chemiographic Analysis

1 - Zeolite compositions

Although much information is available on this subject, it is not plentiful enough to draw conclusions with any certainty. The major problem with natural zeolites is that they occur frequently in multiphase assemblages, at least on the scale of a hand specimen sample, making mineral separation difficult and thus identification and chemical information unsure. Only X-ray diffraction allows a proper mineral identification, but this is also not certain due to the complexities of structural variation in zeolites which arise through chemical substitutions. In fact, ideally, one would need electron microprobe and X-ray diffraction of single crystals in a rock. Wise and Tschernich (1976.b) have shown the usefulness of such types of studies. In summary, chemical analyses of so-called single-phase zeolites are likely to be unreliable.

On the assumption that adequate numbers of mineral analyses have been made and that these analyses represent single-phase zeolites, a certain compositional pattern can be discerned from the alkali zeolite compositions (using the compiled data of Deer **et al.**, 1962 ; Boles, 1972 ; Nahon et **al.**, 1981 ; Passaglia, 1970 ; Iijima and Hay, 1968 ; Gude and Sheppard, 1967 ; Sheppard and Gude, 1971 ; Iijima, 1970 ; Wise and Tschernich, 1976.a ; Rinaldi, 1976 ; Wise and Tschernich, 1976 b; Passaglia, 1970 ; Besse **et al.**, 1981 ; Gottardi, 1978 ; Gude and Sheppard, 1981). First of all, low temperature analcime is strictly sodic or possibly sodi-calcic (Surdam, 1966). This is true to a somewhat lesser degree for natrolite. This distinguishes these two minerals from the other alkali zeolites where sodium and potassium are apparently interchangeable. Most important is the observation that neither pure K nor Na end members of other alkali zeolites have been reported in nature. This point is fundamental to the following analysis.

The identification of a specific zeolite species with a particular genesis or environment of formation is very difficult if natural mineral occurrence is used as the sole criteria. Most alkali zeolites are found at one place or another in most low temperature geological situations. Various authors have cited various physical and chemical factors which would control the sequence or particular species of alkali zeolite found in nature. Silica and alkali activities in solution are of great importance in surface and buried deposits (Sheppard and Gude, 1971 ; Honda and Muffler, 1970 ; Hay, 1964 , Coombs **et al.**, 1959 ; Read and Eisbacher, 1974) as is pH (Iijima, 1975). Temperature is also of great importance, apparently decreasing the Si-content of the zeolites as it increases. Temperature and time, or approach to equilibrium, appear to determine the type of zeolite assemblages found and thus an understanding of these factors permits the tentative establishment of two alkali zeolite "facies" subdivisions ; the diagenetic and analcime type (Hay, 1966 ; Moiola, 1970 ; Iijima and Utada, 1970 ; Iijima, 1970 ; Studer, 1967 ; Coombs, 1970 ; Seki, 1969 ; Miyashiro and Shido, 1970).

2 - Phase diagrams for zeolite - Clay mineral systems
   (Systems with fixed chemical components)

        The major aluminous clay minerals, alkali zeolites
and feldspars which are most commonly associated in nature,
can be considered as the phases present in a simplified chemical system. Zeolites can be chemiographically aligned between natrolite (Na) and phillipsite (K) at the silica-poor,
and mordenite-clinoptilolite at the silica-rich end of the
compositional series. Potassium mica (illite), aluminous
smectite, kaolinite, gibbsite and opal or amorphous silica
are the other phases which can be expected in a system containing the chemical components most common in alkali zeolites. We will assume that equilibria are effected through the
fluid media by precipitation or solution of the chemical
constituents. Quartz, because it is relatively inert, will
not control the concentration of SiO_2 in solution and consequently the silica phase critical to effective equilibria
will be opal or precipitated amorphous silica. In order for
equilibrium to be attained, rates of dissolution and crystal
growth must be unimportant with regard to the length of
time over which near constant physical and chemical conditions reign in a given geological system.

        Using the most simple expression of the chemical
formulae for the minerals cited above, a chemical system can
be constructed using the components Na-K-Al-Si-H_2O. Initially we will assume that hydrogen and oxygen are always combined in a 2:1 ratio. This is a valid approximation for zeolite structures but not for phyllosilicates, a point to be
discussed later.

        Since the major chemical reactions take place
through the agency of an aqueous fluid, the system can be
considered to be saturated with respect to water. H_2O is
always the major component of an omnipresent fluid phase
during the attainment or approach to equilibrium and it is
therefore considered a component in excess. We are left with
a four component system, Na-K-Al-Si where, for unspecified
P-T conditions over a short range, there will be a maximum
of four phases coexisting. Figures 51 and 52 indicate the
compositions alkali and calcic zeolites as a function of
alumina and silica content.

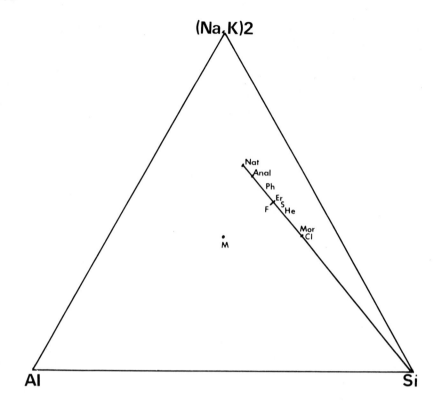

Figure 51 - Alkali zeolites as a function of their compositions in Al-Si-(Na,K)2 coordinates assuming Na-K end-members. Nat = natrolite ; Anal = analcite ; Ph = phillipsite ; Er = erionite ; F = feldspars ; S = stilbite ; He = heulandite ; Cl = clinoptilolite ; Mor = mordenite ; M = mica.
Solid solution or continuous compositions are assumed present between analcite and mordenite-clinoptilolite.

a - Alkali zeolites

Using observations from the literature made upon zeolite-bearing rocks and using the available pertinent experimental data, it is possible to construct a tentative phase diagram based on the general physical and chemical environment of their formation. It must be pointed out however that this attempt at systematization can only be considered as superficial at the moment due to the large gaps in the knowledge of zeolite and phyllosilicate assemblages for certain geologic environments, and due to the fragmentary experimental information on zeolite stabilities and solid solutions. It is also unfortunately rare to find attention paid to both zeolites and clay mineral suites in the same study.

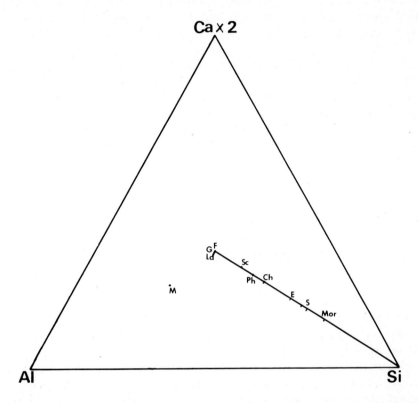

Figure 52 : Calcic zeolites as a function of their compositions in Al-Si-Cax2 coordinates assuming calcium end members. F = feldspar ; G = gismondine ; La = lawsonite ; Sc = scolectite ; Ph = phillipsite ; Ch = chabazite ; S = stilbite ; E = epistilbite ; Mor = mordenite ; M = mica (margarite).

The two major sources of information available are quite different and, as a first approximation, require different interpretations. We will first consider the composition and chemiographic relations of the silicate phases involved as they can be deduced from analyses of natural minerals. Then we will look at the mineral assemblages reported in soils, sediments and sedimentary or altered rock sequences. As has been previously mentioned, the problem of metastability is of prime importance in the study of zeolites, both in the laboratory and in nature. Since we cannot assess at present the kinetic factors involved in the crystallization of zeolites in nature, we must assume that unless demonstrated to the contrary, natural mineral assemblages formed over hundreds or thousands of years will represent a closer approach to the stable situation than laboratory experiments performed for shorter periods of time under identical physical conditions. Nevertheless one must bear in mind, as Hay (1966) has insisted, that even tens of thousands of years' "reaction time" have possibly not produced stable mineral assemblages in certain cases ; Dribble and Tiller (1981) propose 10^7 years. The utility of experimental studies lies in the fact that the chemical and physical variables are known and do not have to be deduced, contrary to most geologic studies.

Chemiographically the alkali zeolites are found below the K-Na-Si plane in the K-Na-Si-Al tetrahedral volume. Generally, as alkali content increases, Al increases, so that zeolite phases form a surface of compositions which plunges toward the common phyllosilicates as alkali content increases. This can be seen more clearly on Al-Si-(Na,K)^2 projection (Figure 51). If their Al content is ignored momentarily, alkali zeolite compositions can be considered as a function of Na-K-Si components, a useful step in attempting to see the spatial relations in the larger tetrahedral system. This simplification is possible because a variation in solid solution never places a zeolite spatially between or below (i.e., toward the Al pole) two phyllosilicates phases, engendering tie-line crossing or superposition of subtetrahedral volumes.

Natural zeolites and feldspars can be divided into two types - those showing almost no Na-K solid solution such as the low temperature feldspars, low temperature analcime and natrolite and those phases showing extensive Na-K solid solution. In the Na-K-Si projection, the zeolites showing extensive solid solution are considered to form a continuous series of compositions in the center of the triangle. Surdam and Parker (1972) have remarked that alkali zeolites in analcime rocks have an Si/Al ratio greater than those in potassium feldspar-bearing samples. This leads us to a non-symmetric high silica face of the zeolite polygon (Passaglia, 1976 ; Surdam, 1966). The most alkali-rich member in phillipsite, the most alkali-poor, clinoptilolite (Figure 53). Low temperatures give maximum solid solutions where all of the so-called "diagenetic" zeolites are stable. This forms the initial zeolite paragenesis (Figure 53a).

As has been pointed out in the first part of this section, it is common to find an association between two or more high-silica zeolites. This could be considered an example of metastable association but, equally, this could be considered an indication of a tendency toward a stable assemblage representing incomplete solid solution between Na and K poles in natural alkali zeolites. It is instructive to note that the associated zeolites quoted by Hay (1966) in his summary of zeolite occurrences represent, usually, minerals typically sodic, sodi-potassic and calcic indicating possible compositional gaps in the solid solution. For example, analcime is associated with sodi-potassic phillipsite and a calcic zeolite such as gonnardite. There are examples known, however, where two minerals of identical anhydrous composition such as clinoptilolite and mordenite are reputed to coexist, an association which certainly indicates metastable crystallization. Furthermore, Sand and Regis (1966) report alternating bands of four zeolites of identical anhydrous composition in a series of altered basic extrusive rocks.

Reported assemblages in sedimentary rocks containing analcime and potassic feldspar plus an alkali zeolite (Hay, 1966 ; Sheppard and Gude, 1968, 1969 ; Moiola, 1970 ; Iijima, 1975) lead to the construction of an intermediate paragenesis which denotes a more restricted range of alkali zeolite solid solution, notably the instability of the alkali-rich phase phillipsite. It is also probable that albite becomes stable when this restricted solid solution exists, since analcime-albite and alkali zeolites of restricted composition have been reported together (Hay, 1966). The existence of albite implies a decreased silica content in analcime and such a variation is commonly reported in rocks having experienced moderate temperatures. At this point analcime can no longer coexist with amorphous silica, or albite can be considered to characterize intermediate physical conditions of pressure and temperature (Figure 53b).

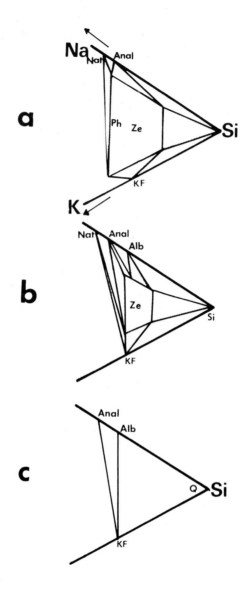

Figure 53 - Alkali zeolites projected into a portion of the Na-K-Si coordinates. Anal = analcime ; Ph = phillipsite solid solution ; Ze = alkali zeolites undifferentiated ; Alb = albite ; KF = potassium feldspar ; Q = quartz ; Si = amorphous silica.
a) low, b) medium, and c) high temperature facies. Shaded areas are two-phase fields.

Finally, when analcime is the only stable alkali zeolite, one finds the association analcime-albite-potassium feldspar (Figure 53c). This is the highest temperature zeolite paragenesis. It might be added that natrolite may also be stable but one cannot decide, using the available data, how it fits into zeolite parageneses. From experimental studies, the analcime-albite-K feldspar paragenesis exists up to 180°C at low pressures ($P_{H_2O} = P_{total}$). However, Iijima (1970, 1975) indicates that its limit can be 180-190°C at 1.1 Kbars lithostatic pressure in volcanic sediments of Japan or as low as 65°C in alkaline sedimentary deposits. Lower temperatures are indicated by Merino (1975). Although Campbell and Fyfe (1965) predict a negative slope for analcime stability [confirmed experimentally by Thompson (1971) but contradicted by Liou (1971a)], their 120°C analcime stability requires significantly higher pressures than even 3 Kbars (lithostatic pressure at 10 km depth). It is possible that the fluid pressure acting upon the rocks studied by Iijima was less than total pressure, $P_{H_2O} < P_{Lith.}$; thus reducing the thermal stability of this hydrous mineral. In the same studies, Iijima reports an observed upper thermal limit of the alkali zeolites to be near 90°C at about 1 kbar lithostatic pressure. Experiments by Boles (1971) give a 100°C value at 2-3 Kbars.

Due to the conflicting experimental results, we will rely upon natural occurrence and we will place an 80°C limit on the initial alkali zeolite paragenesis where solid solution is maximum. An intermediate stage exists up to temperatures near 100°C at high water pressure where analcite, potassium feldspar and alkali zeolite can coexist as can analcime and albite. Analcime persists up to 180°C where the upper limit of the alkali zeolite facies is reached when fluids are essentially pure H_2O (Iijima 1975).

The first two parageneses described above, where alkali zeolites are stable, correspond to the "diagenetic" zeolite facies of Coombs (1970). The latter, according to Coombs, is an analcime-heulandite facies which contains other calcic zeolites in more basic rocks. The disappearance of analcime would occur near the heulandite-laumontite transition for calcic zeolites. Thus, calcic zeolites can continue to be stable at higher grades of diagenesis or epimetamorphism than alkali zeolites.

b - Phase relations concerning zeolites and aluminous clay minerals

Let us now combine the zeolite phases related in figures 54a & b with those phyllosilicates commonly found in the larger K-Na-Al-Si system. Representation of the clay minerals associated with zeolites can be made in K-Al-Si and Na-Al-Si compositional planes to a good approximation of their compositions. The phases kaolinite, illite (mica) and smectite (beidellite) are all common in zeolite assemblages. The mica will show little K-Na solid solution when both end-members are stable (Velde, 1969 ; Koizumi and Roy, 1959). Paragonite (Na mica) is not stable below about 300°C (Chatterjee, 1968). The solid solution between mica and aluminous smectite, mixed layering, has not been established for all Na-K compositions but it can be assumed to be complete. It has been established experimentally from muscovite to K-beidellite (Velde, 1969) and paragonite to Na-beidellite (Eberl, 1971). Solid solution (as interlayering) probably becomes incomplete near the mica end of the muscovite-beidellite series at temperatures of 100°C or so.

The division of the zeolite facies assemblages is made in three groups : low, medium and high temperature and pressure for "closed" systems where the mass of the elements K, Na, Al and Si determines the presence of the different phases for a given P-T range. The initial low temperature facies will be denoted by the stable coexistence of analcime-kaolinite-smectite in the Na-Al-Si plane. Amorphous silica or opal-chalcedony will be present with smectite, feldspar and analcime (Figure 53a). Addition of the alkali zeolite solid solutions gives the possible assemblages natrolite-analcime-zeolite ; analcime-zeolite(**)-silica(*) ; feldspar-zeolite-silica which, in combination with the phyllosilicates, gives the following four phase associations :

1 - natrolite-analcime-zeolite-kaolinite
2 - natrolite-analcime-zeolite-illite, smectite s.s.(***)

(*)   amorphous SiO_2 or opal, chalcedony
(**)   alkali silicite zeolite in the phillipsite-erionite-stilbite-faujasite-clinoptilolite-heulandite-mordenite group.
(***) s.s. = solid solution as mixed layering between aluminous, dioctahedral smectite interlayered with illite.

    3 - analcime-kaolinite-illite, smectite s.s.-zeolite
    4 - analcime-smectite-zeolite-silica
    5 - feldspar-smectite-zeolite-silica

Two, three or four of the minerals in these assemblages have
been reported for assemblage (1) by Dzotsendidze and
Skhirtladze (1964), Moiola (1970), High and Picard (1965)
Bellis et al., (1967), Singer and Stoffers (1980) and
Davies et al. (1979) ; (2) by Jacobs (1970), Loughnam
(1966), Wermund and Moiola (1966), Anderson and Reynolds
(1966), Huang and Goodell (1967) and Reynolds and Anderson
(1967) ; (3) and (4) by Hay (1966), Watton (1975), Pevear et
al. (1980), Murata and Whiteley (1973), Nathan and Flexer
(1977) and Singer and Stoffers (1980) ; (5) by Moiola
(1970) ; Brown et al. (1969), Hay and Iijima (1970), Iijima
(1970), Reynolds and Anderson (1967), Reynolds (1970), Heath
(1969), Morgenstein (1967), Surdam and Parker (1972), and
Couture (1977).

    The geological environments for these assemblages
are those of weathering, deep-sea floor sediments and continental shelf sediments, or shallow burial of these materials
as sedimentary or tuffaceous rocks.

    The second division of the zeolite facies is based
upon the appearance of albite as a diagenetic mineral,
usually coexisting with analcime in the initial stages of
its development, and also with the widespread development of
smectite-illite mixed layered mineral (30 to 90 % expandable
layers) coexisting with illite. The phase relations of this
facies are indicated by Figure 54b. Assemblages can contain
natrolite as above. They are :

    1 - analcime-albite-illite-kaolinite
    2 - albite-kaolinite-illite-smectite s.s.(*)
    3 - analcime-albite-zeolite-kaolinite
    4 - albite-zeolite-kaolinite-smectite s.s.
    5 - albite-smectite s.s.-zeolite-illite
    6 - albite-smectite s.s.-zeolite-silica

(*) smectite solid solution = 30 to 90 % expandable layers
    interlayered with illite.

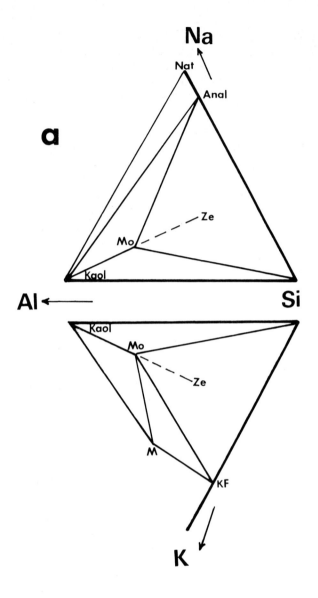

Figure 54.a - Clay minerals and zeolites in K-Al-Si and
Na-Al-Si systems at less than 100°C.
Kaol = kaolinite ; Mo = beidellitic smectite ; M = muscovite
(or illite) ; ML = mixed layered minerals ;
Anal = analcite ; Nat = natrolite ; Ze = alkali zeolites.
Alkali zeolite tie-lines for specific species are not given.

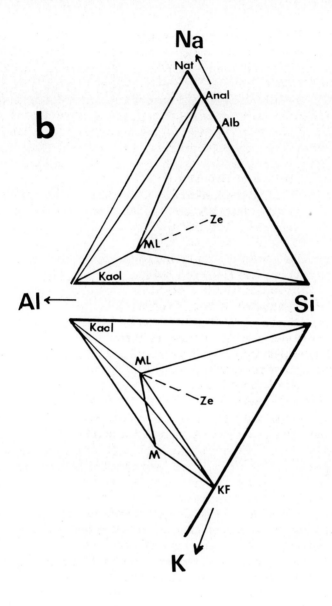

Figure 54.b - Clay minerals and zeolites in K-Al-Si and Na-Al-Si systems at greater than 100°C.

These associations are noted by Hay (1966) as being found in sequences of sedimentary rocks or altered pyroclastics buried to depths greater than 3,000 meters and generally less than 10,000 meters. However, the limits are actually vague and the identifications imprecise. The relatively frequent occurrence and persistence of albite or potassium feldspar and alkali zeolite in such rocks leads one to believe that they can coexist stably in nature. This could be, however, a misleading conclusion based upon too few observations. The elimination of the silicic, alkali zeolites and the persistence of dioctahedral smectite is known to exist in series of deeply buried rocks (Iijima, 1970 ; Moiola, 1970 ; Iijima and Hay, 1968).

Elimination of the "diagenetic" zeolites in the higher temperature associations give :

1 - analcime-albite-K feldspar-illite
2 - analcime-albite-K feldspar-smectite s.s.
3 - albite-kaolinite-K feldspar-smectite s.s.
4 - albite-smectite s.s.-K feldspar-silica

Assemblages (1) and (2) have been noted by Moiola (1970), Callegari and Jobstribizer (1964), High and Picard (1965), Hay (1966) and Iijima (1970) from rocks either deeply buried by stratigraphic determinations or rocks of Mesozoic or older age. Assemblages (3) and (4) are those common to sedimentary rocks up to the point of obvious instability of smectite solid solution (mixed layering).

In each of the different parageneses outlined here, the instability of a mineral can be denoted by its replacement with one or usually several minerals. The rocks in these facies are typified by multi-phase assemblages which can be placed in the K-Na-Al-Si system. This is typical of systems where the major chemical components are inert and where their masses determine the phases formed. The assumptions made in the analysis up to this point have been that all phases are stable under the variation of intensive variables of the system. This means that at constant P-T the minerals are stable over the range of pH's encountered in the various environments. This is probably true for most sedimentary basins, deep-sea deposits and buried sedimentary sequences. The assemblage albite-potassium feldspar-mixed layered-illite smectite and albite-mixed layered illite smectite-kaolinite represent the end of zeolite facies as found in carbonates and sedimentary rocks (Bates and Strahl, 1957 ; Kastner, 1971).

c - Systems with variable chemical potentials

There are zeolite-bearing rocks in which one mineral is apparently being replaced by another mineral under constant P-T conditions. This indicates a system in which certain chemical components appear to be perfectly mobile ; a system in which the total number of phases that can co-exist at equilibrium is reduced as a function of the number of chemical components which are internal to the system. Two examples of this type of equilibrium concerning zeolites can be cited : saline lakes and analcime-bearing soil profiles (Hay, 1966 ; Hay and Moiola, 1963 ; Jones, 1965 ; Frankart and Herbillon, 1970 ; Surdam and Eugster, 1976 ; Singer and Stoffers, 1980). In both cases a smectite bearing assemblage becomes analcime or zeolite-bearing at the expense of the expandable phyllosilicate. Other phases remain constantly present. If one considers the fluids in these soils and ter-restrial lakes as having variable alkali activities, the instability of smectite can be assumed to be a function of increasing alkali activity in the fluid. Due to the relati-vely low alkali content of smectite, it becomes unstable under conditions of high alkali activity and is replaced by an alkali zeolite in saline lakes. This action is nicely demonstrated in analcime-bearing soils where variations in drainage determine the stabilities of smectite and analci-me ; more stagnant conditions produce analcimites, better drainage results in zeolite-free, smectite-bearing soil pro-files. The source of Na in solution depends upon Na carbona-te-sulfate stabilities in the soils. Stagnant waters become more concentrated in sodium ions which favor the formation of analcime. Thus sodium chemical potential in solution is independent of the silicate equilibria and the system is characterized by a "mobile" component and internal variable of the system. Probable phase relations for a system with Al and Si fixed as inert or components and the chemical poten-tial of sodium independently variable are shown in Figure 55. Bulk compositions between kaolinite and silica show a progression from kaolinite to smectite to analcime-bearing assemblages as the activity of sodium increases in the sys-tem. Thus soils which contain kaolinite in well-drained profiles will be smectite-bearing in stagnant zones. This evolution is accounted for by a movement towards higher sodium activity in Figure 54.

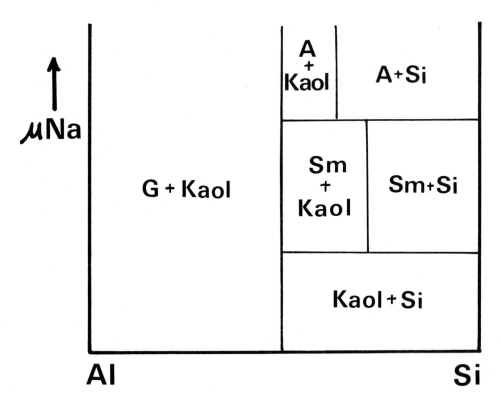

Figure 55 - Representation of zeolite-clay mineral assemblages found in a system at 25°C and atmospheric pressure where Na is an intensive variable (perfectly mobile component) whereas Al and Si are extensive variables or inert components of the system.
G = gibbsite ; Kaol = kaolinite ; Sm = smectite ;
Si = amorphous silica ; Anal = analcime.

A detailed study of zeolite paragenesis in an "alkali" lake can be used to illustrate the use of phase diagrams to explain an observed sequence or series of zeolite-clay mineral facies. Sheppard and Gude (1969) describe the mineralogy of a small desert basin lake which has been filled by pryoclastic deposits, mostly acidic in composi-

tion. The conditions of zeolite and silicate mineral formation are assumed to be dictated by the evaporitic concentration of run-off water in the lake, which increases in alkalinity and dissolved alkali content toward its center. This
lake water, in contact and within the underlying sediment,
has progressively altered the largely uncrystallized volcanic material to phyllosilicate-zeolite-opal-feldspar assemblages. Detailed mineralogical identifications and mapping
reveal that the parageneses become more feldspar-rich toward
the lake center while near the lake shore the glass is largely undevitrified. Potassium feldspar, on the basis of tex-
tural evidence, is thought to replace pre-existing alkali
zeolites. The potassic, boron zeolite, searalsite, is commonly associated with the feldspar.

These observations are confirmed in a list of the
minerals encountered in each sample investigated. In this
list, it is striking to see that almost all samples contain
three "authigenic" minerals, and frequently four are present.

Chemical analyses of the pyroclastic material indicate that the major oxides present are K_2O, Na_2O, Al_2O_3,
SiO_2, CaO and H_2O. If we assume Na and Ca to play equivalent
roles in zeolites, as well as K, and if we consider Al and
Si as the major variables combined with K and Na in the
phyllosilicates, we can adequately represent the phases in a
(Ca,Na)-K-Al-Si system where H_2O is in excess in the fluid
phase. If the system has four chemical variables and the
natural assemblages are frequently found to contain four
authigenic minerals, we must assume that most chemical
variables are inert or extensive variables of the chemical
system which controlled the crystallization of the zeolite-
clay mineral containing sediments.

Let us assume for the moment that a tetrahedral
representation is adequate. For the case in hand, it can, in
fact, be solely represented by a triangular face of the system (Ca,Na)-K-Al-Si. These coordinates contain the phyllosilicates reported by Sheppard and Gude, mica, illite and a
smectite as well as potassium feldspar. Alkali zeolites are
found towards the fourth pole where Ca and Na are present
(Figure 54).

The bulk composition of the sediments must normally be near the potassium-rich side of the zeolite facies

since analcime is not reported in these sediments and potassium feldspar apparently coexists with or replaces the alkali zeolites.

Sheppard and Gude report two types of assemblages : those where zeolites are dominant, towards the lake edge ; and those where feldspar is dominant, towards the lake center. There are two groups of assemblages of diagenetic minerals which characterize these two zones :

1 - mica-smectite-feldspar-zeolite
    mica-smectite-zeolite
    smectite-opal-zeolite
    smectite-zeolite-feldspar

2 - mica-feldspar-opal
    mica-feldspar-zeolite-opal

Zone two can be defined by the absence of smectite and by the tie-line mica-opal (Figure 56). Zone one, which contains smectite shows the coexistence of feldspar and smectite (Figure 56a). Trona and halite found in the sediments are considered to indicate higher alkalinity and alkali content of the pore fluids that effected the crystallization of the feldspar "facies" in zone two at the lake center. Here the evaporated fluids became more concentrated.

The difference in the two assemblages of facies (lake edge and lake center) can be accounted for by a change in the tie line feldspar-smectite to the tie line mica (illite)-opal. The authors Sheppard and Gude suggest that the change in facies (and thus tie lines) is due to an increased alkalinity in the pore waters. Since the variations in sediment depth are less than 100 meters, one could hardly evoke change in P-T conditions in order to account for the reaction. If we recall that high pH increases silica solubility dramatically, it might well be that an assemblage mica-feldspar-smectite will not be in equilibrium with a highly alkaline solution. The assemblage "needs" the presence of amorphous silica in order to be in equilibrium with the solution. Thus the field where silica is present is enlarged. Thus assemblages in Figure 56a are those of lower pH than those in Figure 56b, the reaction is pH dependent due to the higher solubility of silica in the amorphous form. This general effect has been observed by Wirsching (1976) in experiments on rhyolitic glass alteration.

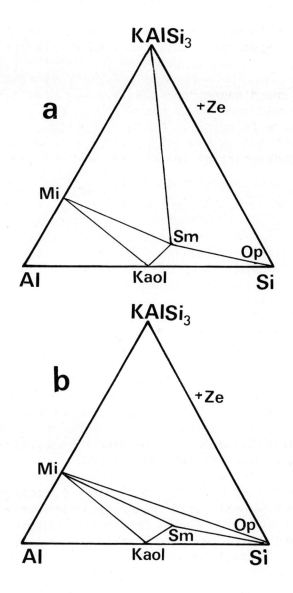

<u>Figure 56</u> – Phases found in zone one of alkali lake (a) and
in zone two of lake (b). Reaction relation is evident from
diagrams feldspar (F) + smectite (Sm).
Mi = mica ; Kaol = kaolinite ; Op = opal ; Ze = zeolite can
be present on alkali-silica side of diagram.

In this analysis we have assumed that alkali zeolite is present, or can be, in all cases. This assumes that Na-K ratios in the solids will not provoke the presence of a new phase assemblage. In the cases where potassic feldspar and zeolite are present, the alkali zeolite will be predominantly sodic.

d - Na-K speciation in zeolites and associated phases

Several authors have indicated that Na-K ratios in solutions can influence zeolite stability (Hawkins, 1981 ; Taylor and Surdam, 1980). Singer and Stoffers (1980) demonstrate the existence of the reaction smectite + alkali zeolite ⇀ illite + analcime in East African lake sediments. Again we see that smectite is destabilized when evaporite solutions become concentrated in dissolved salts. What is striking in the described relation is the shift in alkali species between phyllosilicate and zeolite. In the first assemblage potassium is present in the zeolite while the second assemblage contains a purely sodic zeolite and a potassic phyllosilicate. Figure 57 shows these relations. We see that the phase tie lines cross indicating that a reaction must take place. This reaction appears to occur under increasing brine concentration ; higher pH, alkali content and silica activity in the aqueous solution ; Sindam and Eugster (1976) describe highly alkaline environments in Lake Magadi where neither feldspar nor phyllosilicate occur.

Let us go back to the study of Sheppard and Gude (1969) where the tie lines smectite-potassium feldspar and mica-opal cross (Figure 56) indicating chemical reaction between the minerals. When we consider this reaction deduced from the mineral assemblages encountered it would appear that the potassium content of the silicate increases as one approaches the basin center, i.e., when facies two is reached. The existence of mica-K feldspar-opal assemblages to the exclusion of those containing alkali zeolites would indicate a relative decrease in Na and Ca in the solids. Chemical analyses of the pyroclastic glassy (and thus little altered) sediments indicates that the initial material was predominantly potassic with subordinate amounts of calcium and Na present. Since there is no reason to assume that the glass composition was initially different in different parts of the basin, how then does the silicate assemblage become almost entirely potassic ? How do the sediments concentrate potassium to the exclusion of Na and Ca ?

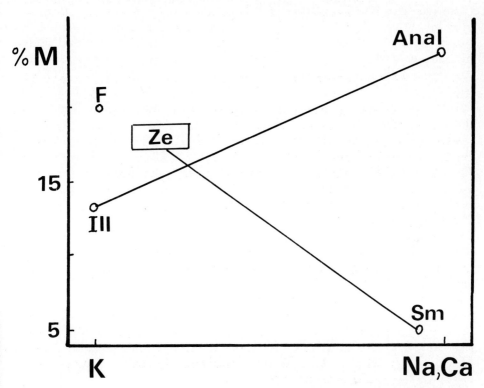

Figure 57 - Schematic representation of the phyllosilicate-zeolite chemical relation described by Singer and Stoffers (1980) for alkali lake sediments. Destabilization of the smectite results in a shift of sodium, calcium from the phyllosilicate to the zeolite when mica replaces the smectite. Sm = smectite ; Ill = illitic mica ; Ze = alkali zeolite (potassic) ; Anal = analcime ; F = potassium feldspar ; % = atom percent M^+ ions in mineral.

Our original observation of the existence of three or four authigenic phases in a four component system should indicate a "closed" system with few perfectly mobile components and would change the relative proportions of chemical components present through elemental migration or diffusion. Thus we must explain the potassium enrichment of the silicate aggregate by another process. If we assume variable alkali content of the solutions represented in Figure 58, and if we place the silicate phases on a parallel line, it is evident that the assemblage smectite-zeolite-solution represented by point A must have a more potassic solution than a feldspar-mica solution assemblage of the same bulk composition at point A. The exchange of potassium between solution and solids is necessitated by the instability of a sodicalcic smectite which is replaced by uniquely potassic phases mica and K feldspar. Potassium enrichment of the silicates could be explained by a concomitant enrichment of the solution. Sheppard and Gude did observe that alkali zeolites were replaced by potassium feldspar in the rocks of zone two. This corresponds to the destabilization of smectite which produced potassium-rich silicates and accordingly sodium and calcium-rich solution.

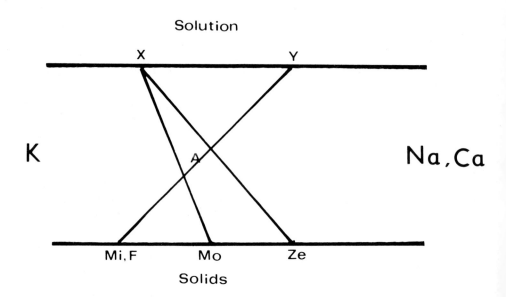

Figure 58 - Possible compositional relations between fluid and solids concerning K, Na and Ca ions.
Mi = mica ; F = feldspar ; Mo = montmorillonite ; Ze = zeolite. x and y are fluid compositions for assemblages one and two (see text). A is possible bulk composition for the two assemblages.

It is important to note two things in this analysis : first, the reactions which govern silicate phase equilibria occur in a system closed to large-scale chemical migration. This corresponds to a pore-water sediment system of local equilibrium. Second, the most striking mineralogical change - the crystallization of feldspar - is, in fact, the result of the instability of another phase, smectite. The use of a general phase diagram, which accommodates the number of co-stable phases allows a full analysis of the mineralogical relations.

The importance of a change in the fluid composition reacting with silicates to form zeolites can be seen in other respects. For example, the zeolites found in potassium bentonites by Reynolds and Andersen (1967) coexist with potassium feldspar which indicates that the whole system is close to the K-Al-Si face of the diagrams 53a, and 53b. In zeolitic soils, sodium is the main alkali ion, and analcime is formed at surface conditions. The system is near the Na-Al-Si face of these figures. The same is true for most closed sedimentary basins where zeolites form. The effect of pore water compositions has been emphasized by Iijima (1975) who observed the presence of analcime-clinoptilolite and analcime-albite in saline lake sediments at temperatures 60°C below those of normal pyroclastic sediments in a sequence of burial metamorphosed rocks. The shift to a sodic system eliminates the alkali zeolite facies much earlier in diagenesis compared Na-K systems. As a result, the use of zeolites to estimate paleo-pressure - temperature conditions must be done with precaution. If the whole assemblage is uniquely sodic one could well find the apparent high temperature assemblage of figure 53 when in fact more general chemical conditions would allow one to see the medium temperature facies.

d - Silica Content of Zeolites

As has been noted above, the silica content of zeolites appears to decrease as temperature increases. Thus, one expects that the most silica-rich zeolite will form as the first phase under low temperature conditions. However, this is not always the case, and one can find several zeolites present in the same rock sample. Hay, in his many pa-

pers, usually concludes that metastable crystallization of
zeolites is the rule in natural environments. However, this
may not be the general case. Local variations in chemical
potentials could possibly explain the multiphase zeolite
rocks. It might be that zeolites are in fact sensitive to
chemical variation and they reflect such fluctuations
through rapid readjustments in their composition. One example can be given.

In deep sea sediments, often of volcanoclastic
type, one finds that phillipsite is the phase present at the
surface in the most recent material. The next layers down
(several centimeters) contain the more silica rich form of
zeolite, clinoptilolite (Stonecipher, 1976 ; Besse et al.,
1981). As one goes to further depth, the silica content of
the alkali zeolites decreases. This appears to be rather
systematic. How can one explain the increase then decrease
in silica content of zeolites in volcanogenic sediments ?

If we consider the geological environment of sedimentation, it is well known that compaction takes place
rapidly with depth in a sediment. This means that the pore
solutions are less important in volume compared with the solids as one goes to depth. It is probable that the equilibria between solution and sediment will tend to increase the
dissolved material and hence, in a volcanogeneic sequence,
silica content will increase. If zeolite composition is a
response to the chemistry of its environment, one would
expect less siliceous forms to appear at the sediment-sea
interface where the concentration of dissolved solids is not
very high. The lower solubility of alumina provokes crystallization of a zeolite whose composition is governed by the
concentration of silica in solution.

As the sediment is buried, more silica enters into
solution and the old low-silica zeolite re-equilibrates to
form clinoptilolite. This zeolite is then subjected to
higher temperatures upon deep burial and begins to readjust
to the physical conditions of its burial which destabilizes
siliceous zeolites progressively. One can present this schematically in a depth-silica content plot (Fig. 59).

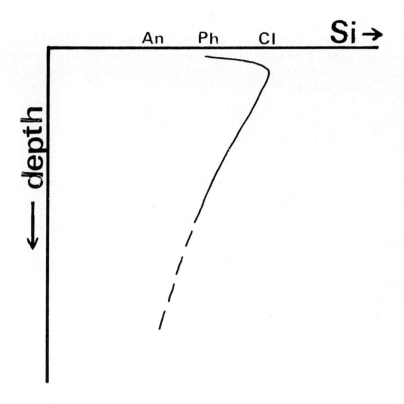

Figure 59 - Depth-silica content plot of alkali zeolites in deep sea sediments. Surface sediments show phillipsite (Ph), near surface layers clinoptilolite (Cl) and deeper sediments show zeolites with decreasing silica content until analcime (An) stage is reached.

It is also quite possible that when a volcanic material recrystallizes, various phases destabilize at different rates which effects differences of silica activity in the accompanying aqueous solutions. These will occur during the period of recrystallization of the volcanic material. A possible result of such an evolutive process would be a sequence of zeolites formed in the same rock but at different times which could only be seen on a microscopic scale (not one of X-ray diffraction). Wise and Tschernich (1976) present detailed microprobe data on zeolites in basalt pore fillings which show that silica activity varied as the phases crystallized. The present author feels strongly that a detailed microprobe study of multi-zeolite phase rocks will show a succession of phases which is caused by varying silica or alkali activity during the total recrystallization process involving different phases in volcano-clastic material.

Conclusions

A consideration of natural occurrence and chemical composition of alkali zeolites allows a certain refinement of the zeolite facies concept previously proposed. The key factor is the grouping of the alkali zeolites into a continuous solid solution series. Other possible coexisting phases of similar composition are sodium and potassium feldspar, natrolite and analcime. The extent of solid solution decreases with temperature, possibly also with pressure. This effect allows the sequential series zeolite-K feldspar, zeolite-analcime-K feldspar, analcime-K feldspar-albite and eventually two feldspars to the exclusion of analcime, the alkali zeolite with the highest stability limits.

The consistent repetition of these assemblages and the large range of apparent stability observed for analcime tend to confirm this conclusion. The actual alkali zeolite which crystallizes in any one given situation may depend more upon happenstance than phase equilibria. Reaction rates, nucleation rates, crystal growth rates and catalysts undoubtedly influence greatly the zeolite crystallization and fluctuation fluid compositions. However, if numerous assemblages are analyzed, a general pattern can be distinguished. The major point to be made is the distinction of three types of phases - feldspars, analcime and natrolite, alkali zeolites - and their gradual suppression as P-T conditions rise upon burial and incipient metamorphism.

7 - Sepiolite - Palygorskite

These two minerals are considered by most authors to be magnesium silicates. It is true that iron is not often found in significant quantities, alkalis and calcium concentrations are less than five weight percent and other elements such as Mn or Ti are extremely rare. However, alumina is almost always present in amounts varying up to a high of 15 weight percent in palygorskite. It is useful to retain the concept that palygorskite and sepiolite are magnesio-aluminum silicates. This idea will be renforced as we investigate the phase relations of these minerals which must reflect their geological environment of formation and the process which produce them.

a - Natural Occurrence

Natural occurrences of these minerals are frequent and varied, however until recently they were little noted, especially when in a clay mineral assemblage, except by french clay mineralogists (Millot and his coworkers), perhaps because they have been known there for 130 years (Cuvier and Brongniart, 1853). Recent work has brought them into prominence through intensive studies on deep-sea samples and through an increased interest in soil clay mineralogy in arid areas (Singer, 1979). They are found in soils especially of the caliche or calcrete type (Rogers et al., 1956 ; Grim, 1968 ; Vanden Heuvel, 1966 ; Paquet, 1970 ; Gardner, 1972 ; Singer and Norrish, 1974 ; Yaalon and Weider, 1976 ; Watts, 1977 ; McLean et al., 1972 ; Hassouba and Shaw, 1980 ; Hay and Wiggins, 1980). One example comes from a temperate climate loess derived soil (Schwaighofer, 1980) which suggests that the chemistry which is important is not solely found in desert regions. Sepiolite has been found to form in a near surface carbonate aquifer (Kautz and Parada, 1976) and in a Quaternary beach ridge complex (Hassouba and Shaw, 1980). Shallow continental or epicontinental rift basins (Evans, 1978) and basin sediments of the sulfate-carbonate type frequently contain sepiolite and palygorskite (Millot, 1964 ; Weaver and Beck, 1977 ; Trauth et al.,

1969 ; Papke, 1972 ; Kübler, 1962 ; Galan and Ferro, 1982 ; Parry and Reeves, 1968 ; Lapparent, 1935 ; Trauth, 1977 ; McLean et al., 1972 ; Latouche, 1971 ; Post, 1978). Lucas et al. (1980) state that palygorskite is very common in phosphatic sediments and sedimentary rocks. Both sepiolite and palygorskite are present in carbonates and salt deposits (Kübler, 1962 ; Bartholomé, 1966b ; Braitsch, 1971 ; Millot, 1964 ; Nathan and Flexer, 1977 ; Trauth, 1977). There appears to be no exclusion of either species from the above environments.

Deep-sea occurrences however seem to be almost exclusively palygorskite-bearing (Bonatti and Joenesu, 1968 ; Hathaway and Sachs, 1965 ; Müller, 1967 ; Chamley et al., 1962 ; Bowles et al., 1971 ; Couture, 1977 ; Timafeev et al., 1977 ; Singer, 1979 and numerous occurrences in deep-sea drilling project initial reports). Fleischer (1972) reports sepiolite forming on diatomite, the only reported case of sepiolite in deep ocean floor sediments. However, this statement does not include Cretaceous continental slope (Africa, U.S. Atlantic coasts) sediments which are probably related to shallow basin occurrences and thus should not be associated with clays formed at the deep ocean-sediment interface (> 2000 meters depth). Veins or hydrothermal alteration of basic rocks produce almost uniquely palygorskite parageneses (Ehlman and Sand, 1962 ; Peters and Von Salis, 1965 ; Gheorghitescu and Medesan, 1972 ; Tien, 1973 ; Furbish and Sando, 1976 ; Haji-Vassiliou and Puffer, 1975 ; Vander Wel, 1972).

Table 5 indicates relative occurrences of sepiolite and palygorskite in the major geological environments.

	Palygorskite	Sepiolite
Vein	X	–
Deep sea	X	0
Soils	X	–
Sediments	X	–

Table 5

X = frequent ; 0 = absent ; – = uncommon

Sepiolite-palygorskite compositions suggest rather special chemical conditions and one can see from the literature that many common clay minerals are absent from sepiolite-palygorskite assemblages. They appear to be stably associated with smectites, both di- and trioctahedral (Trauth, 1977, demonstrates this well) kaolinite, serpentine, alkali zeolites (Couture, 1977), phosphates, carbonates, sulfates, salts and amorphous silica or chert. Iron seems incompatible with their occurrence. Millot (1964) has insisted on the "chemical" nature of their origin, i.e., chemical precipitation of the minerals from solution. It is undeniable that a solution precipitation-mechanism is responsible for their formation. However, it seems apparent that in cases of deep-sea or shallow basin formation, significant amounts of detrital material can be re-incorporated into the minerals of the sepiolite-palygorskite parageneses (Church and Velde, 1979 ; Trauth, 1977).

Although sepiolite-palygorskite occur frequently in closed basin evaporite or lake deposits, these minerals are also known in Tertiary and late Paleozoic deep sea shelf and shallow sea deposits. They have also been reported with persistent frequence by French clay mineralogists in Mesozoic and Tertiary saline and carbonate deposits (Millot, 1964). Despite the claim by Bartholomé (1966b) that the minerals are predominantly Tertiary in age, they do seem to persist in some older, non-metamorphic sediments of Western Europe. Paleozoic sediments are rare there, being almost always involved in an organic cycle. There is no reason to believe, however, that the minerals are unstable in all rocks of this age. However Bigham **et al.** (1980) and Paquet and Millot (1972) demonstrate that they are unstable during weathering, being replaced by smectites.

The absence of sepiolite and palygorskite from sediments and sedimentary rocks in many parts of the world is most likely due to a lack of attention on the part of researchers who have looked at clay mineral suites in the past. This can be explained in part by the similarity of the respective major low-angle peaks which can be confused with montmorillonite (12 Å sepiolite-one water layer montmorillonite) and illite (10.5 Å palygorskite-slightly "expanded" illite). A **priori**, there is no reason why these minerals should be particular to French sedimentary rocks except that workers from this country have been particularly alert to their presence. This opinion is reinforced by the now frequent reports of sepiolite and, to a lesser extent, palygorskite in sea sediments of the Atlantic shelf and ridge, Mediterranean, Red Sea and Pacific deep sea (see JOIDES reports - National Science Foundation Publications) due to an awareness of their potential presence in sediments.

b - Synthesis and Stability

Laboratory synthesis of aluminum-free sepiolite (Siffert, 1962 ; Wollast et al., 1968) at 1 atmosphere, 25°C, demonstrates the inherent stability of this mineral at surface conditions. These experimental studies establish the necessity of an alkaline solution (pH 8) and silica concentration in aqueous solution controlled by the presence of amorphous silica (20-150 ppm) necessary to precipitate sepiolite. Calculations based upon laboratory synthesis data suggest that sepiolite could form in equilibrium with quartz (i.e., 10 ppm in solution) under either very alkaline conditions of high Mg^{2+} concentrations.

High pressure studies using natural sepiolite and palygorskite (Frank-Kamaneckiji and Klockova, 1969 ; Güven and Carney, 1979) indicate that these minerals can contain variable quantities of silica because they exsolve quartz while retaining their basic structural and mineral identity. These experiments also demonstrate that the natural minerals are compositionally intermediate between talc or smectite and quartz. These latter phases are formed upon the thermal breakdown of sepiolite and palygorskite under conditions of 1 and 2 Kbars total pressure. Both sepiolite and palygorskite appear to remain stable in sequences of buried rocks, at least up to the depth where fully expandable dioctahedral smectite disappears (Millot, 1964).

c - Chemical Composition

Since neither mineral is conspicuously alkali-rich, the $M^+R^3-2R^3-3R^2$ plot is not appropriate to represent their bulk compositions. Both sepiolite and palygorskite contain small but variable amounts of Ca, K, Fe^{2+}, Fe^{3+}. Rather constant ionic proportions of Si, Mg and Al are the main variables. As a result, it is useful to consider their compositional variation as a function of Si, R^2, R^3 contents. Figure 60 relates the compositions of 14 natural sepiolites and 12 palygorskites to these coordinates. It is evident from this plot that natural sepiolites and palygorskites form a continuous compositional series, although their structures are different (Preisinger, 1959 ; Christ **et al.**, 1969 ; Nagy and Bradley, 1955). It is important to note their position relative to the Si pole of the diagram. They are the most silica-rich clay minerals stable at low temperatures, and as such could be expected to be the first ones precipitated in sea water or saline solutions saturated with SiO_2. This is born out by laboratory experiments (Wollast **et al.**, 1968 ; Siffert, 1962) and to a certain extent by their natural occurrence.

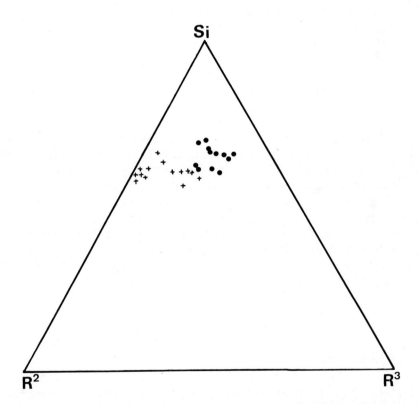

Figure 60 – Composition of natural sepiolites (crosses) and palygorskites (dots) in Si-R^2-Al coordinates. Calcium is excluded from the components.
$$R^2 = Mg, Fe^2 \quad ; \quad R^3 = Al, Fe^3$$

Two points concerning the composition of natural sepiolite and palygorskite should be made. The alkali content, although generally very low can at times become important in palygorskite. Vanden Heuvel (1966) reports 1.03 % K_2O from soil clay mineral sample ; McLean et al. (1972) 1.8 % from a lacustrine lake and Church and Velde (1979) found 3.46 % K_2O for a deep sea sample. This implies some solid solution toward a potassic type for palygorskites, a trend which is not encountered in sepiolite compositions. Echle (1974, 1980) demonstrates the relation between the very rare sodic variety of sepiolite (loughlinite) and the magnesian form. High salt concentration at pH > 7 produces loughlinite from sepiolite. This reaction is observed to be reversed in nature. Natural occurrence of loughlinite is with analcime and dolomite. It appears then that alkali and minor calcium can occur in these minerals and influence their stability. Thus the $Si-R^2-R^3$ representation is not strictly correct. However, appart from loughlinite, it would seem that the alkali content of most natural systems will not provoke the appearance of a form of sepiolite or palygorskite.

The second point is that in the $R^{2+}-R^{3+}-Si$ coordinates, the compositions of sepiolites and palygorskites are quite continuous. The question arises as to whether they represent the same mineral series with two polymorphic forms - in terms of phase boundaries - or whether they represent distinct phases whose compositions will not overlap in multidimensional space. At present there is not enough information available on their behavior as phases in silicate systems to distinguish between the two possibilities. It is certain that the two minerals are structurally different but this is not sufficient to decide upon the chemiographic relations they have with other silicate phases.

It has been suggested by Prost (1975) that sepiolite is a trioctahedral mineral while palygorskite is dioctahedral. Should this be true, it is the only case among clay minerals where the di- trioctahedral sequence is compositionally continuous where only R^2-R^3 ions are concerned. It would seem then that sepiolite-palygorskite compositional trends are more related to those of amphiboles and pyroxenes than sheet structure minerals. Their range in composition does cover most R^2-R^3 ratios as seen in figure 60.

d - Solution Equilibria

Two series of experiments have been conducted which elucidate the stability of pure magnesian sepiolite in aqueous solution, each using a different approach in procedure and each giving concordant and complimentary results. Wollast et al. (1968) have used sea water as a basis for their chemical system where they have controlled the pH and SiO_2 content by addition of NaOH and sodium meta-silicate. This procedure incidentally changes the Na concentration of the system from that of normal sea water, but this does not seem to alter the phase relations. Measurements of Mg^{2+}, H^+ and SiO_2 concentration in solution after precipitation of sepiolite demonstrate the relatively constant pH and Mg^{2+}-SiO_2 concentrations of the supernatant liquid. The result of these experiments is to establish that the precipitation of sepiolite from solution can occur at pH $\geqslant$ 8.2, Mg^{2+} - 56 mmoles, SiO_2 - 0.4 mmoles concentration. Significant in this series of experiments is the fact that Mg^{2+} concentration was high enough to precipitate the added silica without significantly changing its concentration in solution (Mg/Si = 140 in the experiments). Thus the solution always contains Mg^{2+} in approximately constant abundance, which makes it effectively a perfectly mobile component. The same is true for H^+ since pH changes little after precipitation of the sepiolite even though the reaction consumes (OH). The experimental system is then "open" with respect to these two components. A determination of the solubility product constant of a natural iron-calcium-aluminous sepiolite generally confirms the above results (Christ et al., 1973).

The study by Siffert (1962) was conducted using another method resulting in fixed chemical ratios of the components in solution which significantly affects the character of the precipitated product. The molecular ratio of Si/Mg in the initial solution is fixed (values of 1.43 and 0.70 where used) and the initial pH varied for different experiments (Na is introduced into the solutions in varying proportions). Essentially, experiments using either ratio give the same results. Initial SiO_2 concentration (and thus Mg) remains constant, near 150 ppm, until pH 8.5 is reached. At this point (the same pH as that of Wollast et al., 1968) sepiolite begins to precipitate. In experiments maintaining pH at values above 9, smectites and talc were formed. Chemical analyses of the precipitates reveal a greater proportion of magnesium as the pH of the experiment is increased. Recalling the information on amorphous silica solubility, a two-fold increase in solubility of SiO_2 occurs between pH 8 and 10.5 (Krauskopf, 1959) - and thus at higher pH it could be expected that relatively less siliceous phase would precipitate where the masses of Mg and Si are fixed. Final concentrations of Mg-Si in solution were not determined by Siffert and therefore thermodynamic calculations of mineral stabilities cannot be made.

If we consider the stability of sepiolite using the activities of the chemical constituents Mg^{2+}, SiO_2 (in solution) and H^+ as have Wollast et al. (1968), it is apparent that the experiments demonstrate that silica activity higher than necessary for quartz saturation in slightly alkaline sea water provokes the precipitation of sepiolite. Lower values of ionic activity ratio $[Log\ Mg/(H^+)^2]$, (Figure 61) effected principally through a lower concentration of Mg, produce sepiolite at conditions of quartz silica-saturation. These conditions are representative of those in interstitial water of superficial sea sediments or deep sea water (Wollast et al., 1968). The experiments at higher pH indicate that other phases such as phyllosilicates will form from solution under pH conditions likely to occur in saline lakes. It is interesting to note that the magnesian phyllosilicate talc has been reported in sediments formed under such conditions (Braitsch, 1971). One interesting aspect of the Mg-Si-H^+ aqueous system is the existence of a volume where, under conditions frequently realized at the earth's surface, no solid phase exists. If the initial components are considered to be Mg^{2+}, SiO_2 (aqueous), H^+ with water (H_2O) being omnipresent and therefore a component in excess, the system can have three independent variables at atmospheric pressure and 25°C. The existence of the state where all components are in solution, and thus no "phases" are present, denotes the fact that all components are independently variable or mobile. Zones in the diagram where a solid phase appears denotes the fact that one variable $[Mg^{2+}$, H^+, SiO_2 (aq.)] is fixed, reducing the independent variables by one. This is the case for sepiolite stability where pH 8 is necessary for its appearance. As two or more variables become constant two or more phases may coexist, such as the point of silica saturation (≈ 150 ppm) at pH 8 where sepiolite precipitates with the silica.

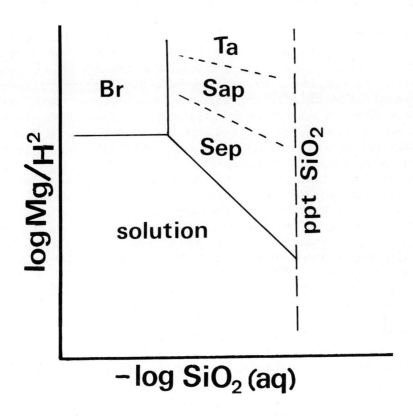

Figure 61 - Representation of the Mg-Si-H$^+$ system in
terms of the Mg/H$^+$ ratio and silica activity
at 25°C and atmospheric pressure.

Solid line boundaries are taken from Wollast et al (1968) ;
dashed lines are approximate boundaries deduced from the
data of Siffert (1962). The appearance of sepiolite is
found only above pH 8 and below 10. Thus, although the
ratio Mg/H$^+$ is a correct measurement, it is a projection
and not applicable to all values of pH. There are no
specified intensive variables in the system (inert
components) and thus a zone of "no phases" exists
which is denoted by solution in the figure.

Br = brucite ; Ta = talc ;
Sap = saponite ; Sep = sepiolite.

Data from Singer and Norrish (1974) and Christ et al. (1973) show that when the minerals considered contain elements other than Mg, Si and H_2O, the phase relations are difficult to determine by experiment. Equilibrium constants derived from solubility experiments do not agree with experiments where a phase was precipitated from solution, as was the case for sepiolite in the Mg-Si system. One reason is that the solid mineral phase does not dissolve integrally in solutions of pH near those where a phase has precipitated in the Mg-Si system. Approach to equilibrium from both "sides" of a reaction equation cannot be easily attained using natural minerals. This is undoubtedly due in part to the low solubility of alumina. Another factor is the oxidation potential of the solution system which must be controlled in such experiments since the natural minerals contain some iron.

As a result we cannot extend the phase diagram of figure 61 into the more complex natural system where Al_2O_3 is present. This excludes most natural occurrences of sepiolite and palygorskite as can be seen from their compositions shown in figure 60. Since talc is alumina-free and saponites generally contain alumina, the fields where they might occur in the simplified Mg/OH v.s. silica system will be necessarily modified when alumina is considered. This would explain why talc is so rare in sediments which almost always contain some alumina. The necessary conditions for its precipitation are almost never realized. The inverse reasoning leads one to believe that alumina combines readily, on a geologic time scale as opposed to the laboratory, with magnesium to form aluminous magnesian silicates. This seems to be substantiated by Trauth (1977) who finds palygorskite-sepiolite and saponite-stevensite to be related in sequences of decreasing alumina content in shallow sedimentary basins. One would have to exhaust all of the alumina from a system in some manner in order to pass from the palygorskite-sepiolite series to form talc.

Experiments by Esquevin (1956, 1960) on Mg-Zn mixtures at 80°C and 1 atmosphere pressure indicate that montmorillonite, not sepiolite, is stable under pH 8, Mg^{2+} and SiO (aq) conditions where sepiolite is precipitated at 25°C. The upper thermal stability of magnesian sepiolite can, therefore, be considered as being below 80°C.

e - Phase Diagram (Mg-Al-Si Variables)

Given the chemical data for natural mineral compositions, it should be possible to construct a phase diagram including those phases which are likely to occur with sepiolite and palygorskite in a system where the mass of the components is an extensive variable of the system (a closed system). Since alkalis enter into the structure of these two minerals in only small quantities, these variables can be ignored in a first approximation. The associations of alkali-rich and alkali-poor systems will be discussed later.

If we consider that the system is "closed", i.e., all components react according to their relative masses, and if we consider that all phases remain stable in the solutions present, R^2-R^3-Si coordinates can be used to describe sepiolite-palygorskite-bearing assemblages (Figure 62). The data for chlorite, saponite and dioctahedral montmorillonite compositional fields have been commented upon previously. Experiments at atmospheric pressure (Estéoule, 1969) demonstrate that the stability of these latter phases extends from metamorphic (300°C, 2 Kbars pressure ; Velde, 1973) to surface conditions. However, the sepiolite-palygorskite phase relations will not be the same under all of these physical conditions. This is principally due to the fact that sepiolite and palygorskite appear at low temperatures, whereas they do not figure in the phase equilibria of the experiments conducted at high pressure and temperature.

Only the pure Mg-Si form of sepiolite has been produced in the laboratory (1 atmosphere, 25°C) ; however, one can suppose that the entire sepiolite-palygorskite series is stable at low temperatures. The extent of solid solution is assumed to be near that represented by the natural minerals in figure 60. This is probably inaccurate to a certain extent since only 23 analyses were used, but underestimation will probably not affect the chemiographic relations of the phases concerned.

We will consider only two parageneses or facies of the system relevant to sepiolite-palygorskite minerals ; that where these minerals are stable and that just above their stability. This is estimated provisionally to be somewhat below 80°C. This temperature is justified through comparison with the observed stability (< 100°C) of natural

236

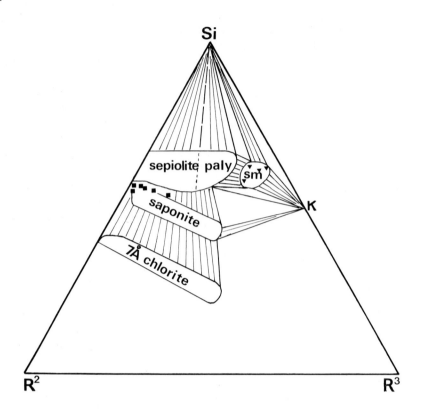

Figure 62 - Phase relations at low temperature (< 80°C) in the system Si-R^2-Al. Sepiolite-palygorskite from figure 60, saponites and smectites from experimental data of Velde (1973) and analyses of natural minerals from Trauth (1977) : squares and triangles. The chlorite field shows 7 Å iron-rich berthierines and a possible aluminous, soil chlorite field as deduced from the chapter on chlorites. Sm = dioctahedral smectite ; K = kaolinite ; paly = palygorskite

aluminous, alkali-bearing smectite, which accompanies sepio-lite-palygorskite in nature, and the fact that experiments at 80°C, 1 atmosphere produce no sepiolite. In the synthetic system R^2-R^3-Si, the aluminous magnesian dioctahedral smec-tite is stable to temperatures well exceeding the supposed stability of sepiolite-palygorskite. As all dioctahedral smectites have been assumed to form a continuous solid solution series, the complete set of tie-lines joining sepiolite and smectites will be situated for the most part out of the R^2-R^3-Si compositional plane.

Data from Trauth (1977) allows us to fix the compositions of the smectites, both di- and trioctahedral, which can coexist with sepiolite and palygorskite. Figure 62 shows the compositions of aluminous dioctahedral smectites and low alumina, magnesian saponites which were found in palygorskite and sepiolite assemblages respectively. The possible compositional limits to the low silica side of the saponite field are based upon compositions deduced from experimental studies at 2 kbars pressure and temperatures above 300°C (Velde, 1973). It is possible that the compositional range is not as extensive as indicated, but for lack of other data it will be left as it is. Also shown in figure 62 are the chlorite compositions, both 7 Å berthierine and those which can be deduced from the fragmentary data on soil chlorites. It might be unwise to suggest these phase relations in that there appears to be a significant difference in the species of R ion present in the minerals. All low temperature (near surface conditions) chlorites concentrate iron in their structure. This is especially true for berthierines which are formed in the sedimentary environment. As we have mentioned, sepiolite-palygorskite are magnesian, most samples reported have $Fe^{2+}/(Fe^{2+}+ Mg) = 0.10$. There is a ferric form of sepiolite, xylotile (Preisinger, 1959) which contains ferric iron but its occurrence seems quite restricted, at least as far as the current literature is concerned. It seems necessary then to entertain the possibility that the $R^2 = Mg + Fe^{2+}$ identity is not correct. It might then be possible to have both chlorite and sepiolite-palygorskite in an assemblage. No reports of significance have yet appeared.

We will restrict our attention to the relations between sepiolite-palygorskite and the following silicates ; kaolinite, dioctahedral smectite, saponite, silica, illite and zeolites – all of which are frequently associated with the magnesian minerals. It should be noted that palygorskite-sepiolite minerals are the most silica rich clay minerals in the Mg-Al-Si system. Thus their occurrence indicates a high silica activity in the solutions from which they formed. This fact and their occurrence at high pH link them chemically to alkali zeolite-forming systems.

One can imagine two types of chemical systems in which sepiolite and palygorskite appear, "closed" and "open" - systems where chemical components are defined by their relative masses (Figure 62) and systems where their chemical potential in solution determines their role in silicate equilibria (Figure 61). Which criteria are necessary to allow the use of one or the other or an intermediate system where there are fewer "inert" components to explain clay mineral assemblages in a given geologic situation ? Let us look more closely at the various environments in which these minerals are found so that we can attempt to establish the chemical system influencing the paragenesis of the clays in each geological environment.

f - Sepiolite-Palygorskite Equilibria in Saline Lakes and Basins

Millot (1964) has gathered the pertinent clay mineral data involving the parageneses of sepiolite and palygorskite in peripheral Tertiary sedimentary basins of north and northwestern Africa. The accumulated information seems to demonstrate the possibility of a direct application of phase analysis to geologic processes involving clay minerals. The mineralogical observations all pertain to equilibria in closed sedimentary basins fed by uplands subjected to tropical weathering which produces laterites. The detrital material was primarily composed of kaolinite, some smectite, chlorite, illite and quartz ; materials which are impoverished in Fe, Ca and alkalis. The streams were therefore considered by Millot to have carried high concentrations of dissolved Mg, Ca, Si and alkalis.

A cross-section of sedimentation in one of these basins would show a decrease in aluminous materials and an increase in magnesian silicates in the sediments as one progresses from the edge to the center of the basin (Figure 63). As the quantity of detrital sediments decreases, the following mineralogical sequence is observed : kaolinite, smectite with minor illite and chlorite ; smectite and palygorskite ; palygorskite and sepiolite ; sepiolite. Chert is a common accompanying phase, forming at times discrete layers in the sedimentary sequence. Of course, this schematic interpretation is not without local contradictions found in the natural assemblages. It seems, however, to be a general rule.

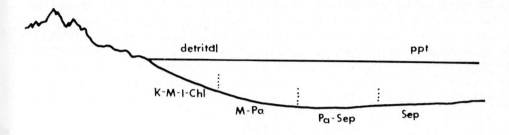

Figure 63 - Schematic sedimentary cross-section of a typical
    northwest African marginal sedimentary basin containing
sepiolite-palygorskite bearing sediments (after the summary
presented by Millot, 1964).
    K = kaolinite ; M = montmorillonite ; I = illite ;
Chl = chlorite ; Pa = palygorskite ; Sep = sepiolite ;
        ppt = zone of silicate precipitation

Comparison of these assemblages with the phase diagram deduced for the system of inert components R^2-R^3-Si, shows the evolution of bulk chemical composition which successive zones have made in the sequence of sedimentation. The initial sedimentation of detrital material is dominated by the aluminous phases kaolinite and smectite (dioctahedral in this case). As the detritus decreases, the phases containing more Mg and Si begin to appear. This indicates an approach to equilibrium between solids and liquid (sea or saline lake water). Eventually the sedimentary assemblage is dominated by phases precipitated from solution in zones where the detritus is absent. By referring to the phase diagram for closed systems at low temperatures (Figure 64), this sequence of assemblages outlined by Millot can be described as a passage through the three-phase areas 1 to 4. Zone 1 (kaolinite-dioctahedral smectite-silica) is assumed by Millot to be purely detrital but it could be also due in part to a reaction between the detrital material and the lake or sea water solution. The presence of 14 Å chlorite indicates a non-equilibrium detrital component. The second phase-field is one containing smectite (dioctahedral) and

amorphous silica. The third field in a traverse from right
to left (R^2 to R^3) contains palygorskite in addition to
smectite (dioctahedral) and silica. The fourth field contains silica-palygorskite and silica-sepiolite. Finally,
Mg-sepiolite is present where only Mg and Si are available
in the solution and a detrital component is almost non-exis-
tent. This is the pure chemical precipitate ; Al^{3+} is in low
concentration in the solution.

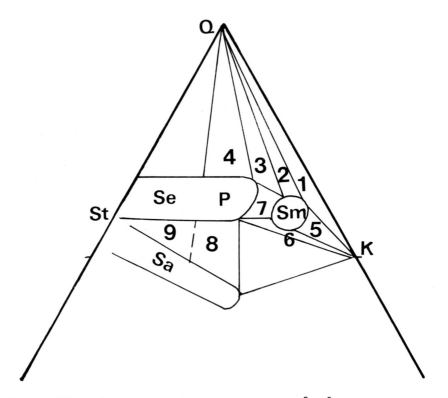

Figure 64 - Phase relations in the $Si-R^2-R^3$ system where Mg
and Al predominate at the R^2 and R^3 poles. Phase fields are
indicated by numbers 1 to 9 where Q = silica phase ;
K = kaolinite ; Sm = dioctahedral smectite ; Sa = saponite
(trioctahedral) ; Se = sepiolite ; P = palygorskite and
St = stevensite the non-aluminous saponite.

A sequence of mineral assemblages similar to those
of the African basins is described by Fontes et al. (1967)
in the Tertiary beds of the Paris basin. The information is

gathered from one geologic section only and therefore the
geographic distribution described in the previous example by
Millot is lacking. However, if we accept a parallelism of
causes of mineral paragenesis, it appears that the Paris
basin section, sepiolite-rich at the bottom and terrigenous
at the top, represents a sequence initially dominated by the
chemical precipitation which becomes more detrital in character at the top. This could be explained by a brusk clos-
ing of the basin and gradual enlarging, or a local regression
of the basin edge giving a transgressional sequence in the
section observed. According to the oxygen and sulfur isotope
studies made on these sediments, their origin is continental
and not marine, thus the basin can be considered as closed
and ionic concentrations would surpass those in normal sea
water.

In the detailed mineralogical determinations made
by Fontes **et al.** (1967) and Galan and Ferro (1982), one fact
is striking. Illite seems to persist until the most sepiolite-rich zones are attained, while kaolinite-chlorite are
found only when neither sepiolite nor palygorskite are present. If we assume that illite remains stable because it is
a potassic mineral (or dominantly so), it will exist as a
phase supplementary to those found in figure 64. The figure
shows that neither chlorite nor kaolinite can coexist with
the highly magnesian phases in the presence of a silica phase, a fact observed in the section described. Thus the mineral assemblages reported by Fontes **et al.** (1967), can also
be explained by the phase diagram presented in figure 64
using the silica-rich assemblages. The common occurrence of
alkali zeolites with palygorskite in ocean sediments can be
explained in the same way.

Trauth (1977) has made a detailed study of some of
the basins described by Millot (1964). It appears that the
general idea of mineral parageneses proposed previously are
confirmed. However, the details of the origin of the material and its exact geological environment are subject to
some questions. From the chemical study of trace elements it
is evident that the material found in the silicate assemblages is of detrital origin. It can be assumed that a dissolution-precipitation process on a very local scale has been
experienced by the sedimentary detritus which incorporates
large amounts of magnesium while releasing alkalis. There is
however a silicate phase which must be largely a precipi-

tate. It is stevensite which has a bulk composition essentially that of non-aluminous sepiolites reported by Trauth. It does contain up to 0.7 percent lithium which might be the component necessary to provoke its crystallization. This mineral typifies the high magnesium sediments which can truely be called chemical precipitates where no solids need be present as a source of an element which has a low solubility in solution.

The use of the "closed" system to describe the assemblages in these closed basins seems justified in that frequently, almost always in fact, the number of clay minerals present in the sediments discussed above is two or more. The presence of amorphous silica or chert raises the total number of phases to three in many instances. In an essentially three-component system, Mg-Si-Al or possibly four if H^+ is considered, there are indications that the chemical components of the minerals are present in relatively fixed quantities in the chemical system which produces the mineral assemblages. None of the first three components is "mobile", i.e., its activity is independent of its relative mass in the solids or crystals present. However, there are sediments which present a monophase assemblage where only one variable need be fixed. Under these conditions sepiolite can be precipitated from solution and pre-existing solid phases need not be involved.

If the characteristic of sepiolite-palygorskite is their range of alumina content, how should one consider their origin - solution chemistry or solid-solution reaction ? It is possibly just an academic question to ask but it should be clarified. There is no evidence that the pre-existing kaolinite or illite structures are ion-substituted to become palygorskite for example. The structures are quite different. If the solubility of one ionic species is quite low, and the activity of other species in the solution is high, one should see that a rapid process of dissolution and precipitation will occur. New clay will grow very near to, or on, an old unstable phase. The process passes through an aqueous stage but the residence time of the low solubility species (alumina in our case) is not at all long. Therefore, it will not be transported any great distance and will appear to be a product of mineral transformation. The control of the activity of the insoluble species in the solution will be almost uniquely at the interface of the old

mineral. There will then be an apparent incongruent dissolution of the mineral. Take illite as an example. The Al-Si
ratio is lower than that of palygorskite. When the illite
dissolves, all Al and Si available will be combined with Mg
and Si already in solution to make palygorskite. The potassium and iron will enter into solution. Thus on a microscopic scale there is an incongruent dissolution : yet, all
species went into solution on a submicroscopic scale. Simply
stated, the low solubility of Al reduces it to an inert component which interacts rapidly with the more soluble elements in solution. There seems to be no way that the activity of Al can be imposed on the sediment from its exterior
since so little is soluble and so much available in the
sediment itself.

Hardie and Eugster (1970) have computed the changes
in water composition as a function of salinity and pH for
evaporating, closed basins which had various initial natural
water compositions. Using a certain number of assumptions as
to the stability and chemistry of the phases encountered,
essentially three sequences are possible :

1 - calcite-sepiolite-gypsum-alkali-salts
2 - calcite-gypsum-alkali-salts
3 - calcite-sepiolite-salts

The initial Ca/Mg ratio of the waters was found to be critical in determining whether or not sepiolite will occur.
However, the authors admit significant imprecisions in the
basic data ; one of the most important is that sepiolite is
not stable below pH 8. This is important because the formation of hydroxylated silicates results in an acidic solution. Further, the sequence sepiolite-montmorillonite accen-
tuates this effect because montmorillonite contains relatively more hydroxyls than sepiolite. Since sepiolite and
palygorskite are known to occur commonly with calcite and
also gypsum, the initial portion of the precipitation sequence proposed (near pH 8) is probably correct. However,
their absence in highly concentrated brine assemblages (those containing alkali salts) would indicate that they become
unstable at high pH, as suggested in Figure 61). As a result
the equilibria calculations should treat the problems of
both sepiolite and montmorillonite stability as they will
affect the pH of solutions from which they precipitate. The
silicates could be a very important control in the evolution
of evaporite deposition.

g - Calcrete-Caliche "Weathering" or Soil Formation

In most instances where sepiolite or palygorskite are present in bed-rock material, they are seen to rapidly disappear during weathering (Millot, 1964 ; Paquet, 1970 ; Bigham et al., 1980). This is equally true of talc or serpentine, the other magnesian silicates with clay mineral-type structures. Since both sepiolite and palygorskite are known to form from highly concentrated aqueous solutions, it is not surprising to find that they are destroyed by weathering. Obviously the low activity of Mg and Si in common weathering solutions will be unfavorable to their persistence.

There are, however, certain soil profiles which indicate that both minerals can be stable in soils and, in fact, are formed in the weathering environment. These examples (Paquet, 1970 ; Vanden Heuvel, 1966) are found in caliche or the carbonate-precipitating soils of arid climates. In all cases the presence of sepiolite and palygorskite is closely related to the formation of the carbonate. This latter mineral is considered to be formed through the evaporation of sub-surface waters which move upward to downward by capillary action under highly evaporite conditions. During the early stage water dissolves salts (and silicates) which are later precipitated when the water content is decreased by evaporation. The pH of these solutions should be 7.8 in order to precipitate calcite (see Garrels and Christ, 1965). We find that sepiolite is found in the carbonate zone, and beyond these zones montmorillonite is present. In some profiles, palygorskite comprises 100 % of the clay-size fraction silicate material (Paquet, 1970).

In figure 65, one can see the assumed trajectory of the rain water in an arid soil profile. Water infiltrates rapidly and easily through dessication cracks to depths below the B and C horizons into the altered rocks. With general evaporation, the water in the lower parts of the profile is brought back up by capillary action and as it evaporates during the movement it becomes more concentrated in dissolved salts which were brought down from the A and B regions of the profile. In the C horizons these elements become active in the sulfate-carbonate-silicate system. The details of the soil profile studied by Vanden Heuvel (1966) show how the magnesio-silicates are associated with the caliche (calcrete) layer, that occurs in the soil profile itself (in the instance studied it covers the upper C horizons). Table 6 shows the clay mineral assemblages identified.

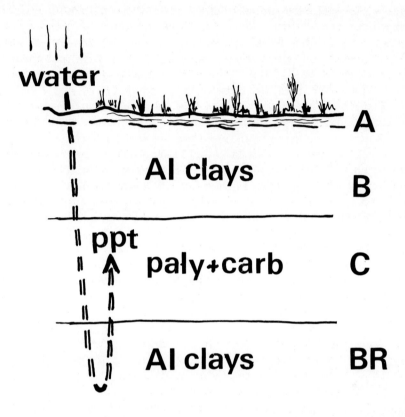

Figure 65 - Sketch of a caliche or calcrete soil profile. Arrow shows path taken by rain water which enters the profile rapidly through dessication cracks and moves back upward by capillary action where solids are precipitated as evaporation become important.
A, B, C indicate soil horizons. Paly + carb = palygorskite plus carbonates ; BR = bed rock ; ppt = zone of precipitation from solution.

It is evident here that sepiolite is associated with calcite deposition. However, palygorskite, although probably related to this process, appears to be less well correlated with carbonate content. If the top and bottom of the profile are assumed to contain equivalent assemblages, it is possible to follow the evolution of the bulk soil silicate chemistry traced as before on the Si-Al-Mg triangular diagram. The silicate phases sepiolite-palygorskite, kaolinite and smectite (Figure 64) are found in the soil sequence. The mineral assemblages listed in Table 6 indicate that the boundaries of the phase fields have been crossed by displacement of the bulk composition toward the R^2-Si edge of the triangle. If kaolinite is associated with palygorskite, a tie-line must join these two phases. This tie-line separates the di- and trioctahedral smectites (Sm_2 and Sa_3 in the figure) and free silica is therefore excluded from these assemblages. The presence of quartz in the soils is not necessarily restrictive because amorphous silica and not quartz will control silica equilibria in low temperature environments. Quartz remains an inert phase. This soil mineral sequence is then distinct from that found in saline lakes where free silica is present and where the assemblage kaolinite-palygorskite is not found. It is probable that the smectite reported by Van den Heuvel was in fact, at certain points in the profile a saponite.

TABLE 6

Horizon	Mont	Mica	Kaol	Sep	Palyg	Carbonate
A	xx	xx	x			
B21	xx	xx	x			
B22	xx	xx	x			
B23	xx	xx	x			
C1a	xx		x		xx	x
C1b	xx		x		xxx	x
C2	x		x		xxxx	x
C3	x		x	xxx	xx	x
C4	x			xxxx	x	x
C5	x			xxxx	x	x
C6	xx		x		xx	
C7	xxx		x		xx	

Mont = expanding mineral ; Kaol = kaolinite ; Sep = sepiolite ; Palyg = palygorskite ; Carbonate = secondary carbonate accumulation in the soil. Table modified from Vanden Heuvel (1966)..

The initial soil clay minerals - kaolinite, illite and dioctahedral smectite - are typically aluminous and alkali-rich. They are characteristic of most sediments and sedimentary rocks as well as soils. The successive elimination of illite, then kaolinite, from the soil mineralogy demonstrates a displacement of bulk chemistry away from the alumina pole of the phase diagram. Such a displacement involving magnesio-aluminous silicates such as palygorskite, indicates that the equilibrium assemblage has been formed by reaction between the silicate solids which contain alumina and elements in solution, mainly silica and magnesium. This mechanism is especially important for palygorskite which contains alumina of low solubility in mildly alkaline waters and magnesium and silica which are highly soluble. The chemical analyses presented by Van den Heuvel for the palygorskite and sepiolite in the soils indicate that both contain considerable Al_2O_3-10.7 and 5.40 weight %, respectively. It is very likely that both phases are the result of silicate-solution equilibria which recrystallize layer silicates into fibrous forms.

Since a soil profile is obviously not a closed system, in the sense that material does enter and leave a given horizon, we cannot consider the bulk chemistry as being totally fixed in its molecular proportions of the constituent elements. On the other hand, the mineralogy of the soils is seen always to be multiphase, usually containing three newly formed phases which can be described by (Mg,Ca)-Al-Si coordinates. It is thus unlikely that the chemical potential of Mg^{2+} or Si^{4+} is totally independent of the silicate present at a given point in a horizon. Mg^{2+} and Si^{4+} should not be considered to be perfectly mobile components. Equilibrium (or a reasonable approach to it) can be assumed to have been established in the different horizons of the soil profile between elements in solution and elements in the solid state. This equilibrium is related to the relative concentrations of the elements, and thus the system is considered as being "closed", i.e., containing mainly inert chemical components. However, some elements do migrate to or from a given soil horizon. Therefore, the major control in the formation of a given mineral assemblage at a given depth depends upon the relative proportions of the elements in the solution and in the solids present. The overall trend in the profile is one of chemical migration (an open system). Thus the assemblage of horizons can be considered "open", but each single horizon produces phase assemblages typical of "closed" systems where local equilibrium is attained.

h - Deep-Sea Sediments

Couture (1977) has made a general survey of palygorskite occurrence reported in the Pacific deep-sea sediments as well as those from the Indian ocean. These two areas present samples from the abyssal depths where terrigenous air-born sepiolite-palygorskite material can be excluded as a major component, and where platform basin or continental margin basins can be excluded. These palygorskites are strictly deep-sea phases. The silicate material is of two origins - wind born continental clays which are illite plus chlorite for the most part and volcanic ash which contains large quantities of glassy material. A certain amount of silica of diatomaceous origin can be found also. Mixed with these sediments one finds layers of basalt.

The conlusion which Couture makes is that one finds the association palygorskite-smectite (dioctahedric)-alkali zeolite (strictly clinoptilolite according to Stonecipher, 1976) to be very common. Varying proportions of the components can be distinguished ; it is frequent that almost monomineral palygorskite layers of tens of centimeters thick can be found. Since the samples are from drill cores, it is possible to know the lateral extent of these layers which would give us a better idea of the type of event which produced them. We can say that there are several elements which are mobile, being transported to form the monomineralic layer. In general, several clay minerals are present together which were produced at ocean bottom conditions. Both the magnesian and alkali minerals are the most silica-rich in their systems.

What then can be the origin of these magnesium-rich alumino-silicates ? It is evident that the detrital material is not of a special character since it is found in most ocean sediments and palygorskite is not all that common. There is no particular evidence of immediate high temperature hydrothermal activity in the sediments such as that which produces sulfide-Fe,Mn oxide deposits (Lonsdale et al.,

1980). Bonatti and Hoenesu (1968) propose reaction of sediments with hydrothermal solutions. Church and Velde (1979) using isotope and trace element measurements show that some of the sources in the palygorskite is derived from terrigenous material, yet the clay is not in isotopic equilibrium with sea water. This suggests a flux of material interacting with the sediments.

Casehetto and Wollast (1979) find that the alumina content of interstitial fluids can increase near the sediment-sea water surface. The concentrations are obviously not controlled by the equilibria determined for the $Al-Si-H_2O$ system. They deduce the existence of a flux of Al from the sediments to the sea-water. Lawrence et al. (1979) found an increase in Mg toward the same interface in sediments underlain by basalts. They conclude that the alteration of these rocks gives rise to the increase in magnesium. Thus the Al and Mg which are necessary to palygorskite synthesis can be available in sediment interstitial fluids.

We will refer to the chapter on basalt alteration in sea water for a more detailed discussion of the processes, but will use the conclusions to begin our explanation of palygorskite genesis on the ocean bottom. The basic process of low-temperature basalt alteration involves increasing potassium and iron content of the rock while Ca, Na, Al and Si are expelled as well as a certain amount of Mg. Normally these elements combine to form alkali zeolites with the excess ions going into solution - notably Mg. If we recall the association cited by Couture, the clinoptilolites are almost always associated with palygorskites in the deep-sea. The excess of magnesium in an alumina-rich solution could be combined to produce palygorskite, should silica be abundant. This requirement is easily fulfilled in diatomaceous or volcanoclastic sediments. It is probable then that one can explain the origin of palygorskite layers in deep-sea sediments as being a by-product of submarine basalt alteration. One should note that hydrothermal high temperature (> 150°C) alteration of basalts produces the opposite chemical effect as that described above, i.e., loss of Ca, Fe K and retention of Mg above all. Palygorskite genesis should then be related to low temperature processes. This follows the conclusions based upon laboratory experiments described earlier in the chapter. In fact, Lonsdale et al. (1980) found iron-rich talc to be the silica-rich, ferro-magnesian phase in high temperature hydrothermal deposits on the ocean bottom. This phase obviously replaces sepiolite-palygorskite in a higher temperature assemblage.

It is proposed here that alumina-rich, but most importantly magnesian, pore solutions carry material towards the sediment-sea water interface. The content of the dissolved ions is controlled by sediment - pore water equilibria which allow concentrations above those in the more dilute sea water solution. At the pelitic sediment - sea water interface the dissolved species concentrations become unstable, or at least become more reactive than when in the pore water state. Here they react with the aluminous material to form palygorskite or palygorskite-zeolite assemblages. A similar process is proposed by Couture (1977). The high alkali (Na principally) and calcium activities form zeolites when the silica activity is very great. One can suppose that the presence of biogenic silica or volcanic glass could supply silica in the necessary form. Magnesium will be incorporated in palygorskite. Both phases are very silica-rich. In this way bi- or mono-mineral layers will be produced. Alumina will be the inert or low solubility component while Mg, Na and Si are the mobile components.

i - Hydrothermal Veins

Sepiolite-palygorskite in veins appears to be most often associated with carbonates in basic or ultrabasic host rocks (Van der Wel, 1972 ; Furbish and Sando, 1976 ; Tien, 1973 ; Gheorghitescu and Medesan, 1972 ; Ehlmann and Sand, 1962). One occurrence in a siltstone host rock has been reported (Haji-Vassiliou and Puffer, 1975). This suggests a strong relation between the availability of magnesium and the exclusion of aluminum from the major phase of low temperature alteration of basic rocks-serpentine. The reaction of hydration alteration of basic rocks at hydrothermal conditions is olivine ± plagioclase ± pyroxene → serpentine + Ca, Mg in solution. Serpentinites are notoriously alumina-poor [see Velde (1973), for a comparison of serpentine and chlorite compositions]. The remaining elements such as Ca, Mg, Al are typically found in veins which are called rhodingites. If this material crystallizes at very low temperatures, it will form sepiolite-palygorskite assemblages if enough silica is present in solution. Since ultrabasic and basic rocks are silica deficient, one would suspect that the solutions carrying the rhodingitic material would need to encounter siliceous rocks in order to mobilize sufficient silica to produce sepiolite-palygorskite which are the most silica-rich Mg-Al-silicates found at low temperatures. The frequent association of these silicates with carbonates is of interest.

SUMMARY

The descriptions of sepiolite and palygorskite-bearing clay mineral assemblages show a strong, if not dominant, tendency for these minerals to form in a chemical system dominated by inert components. This indicates that, although solution equilibria is of utmost importance, the most important factor is the relative masses of several chemical components in solution and solid state. If some elements do act as perfectly mobile components, they must be limited in number. Figure 66 shows the various paragenesis "paths" found in different geological environments where sepiolite and palygorskite are formed.

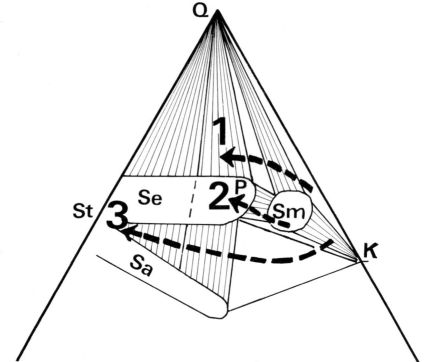

Figure 66 - Chemical paths of different sequences found for the formation of sepiolite and palygorskite. 1 = silica-rich environment ; 2 = median silica values (calcrete-caliche soils and deep sea sediments where alumina activity is high) ; 3 = silica-poor sedimentary basins leading to saponite and stevensite (Sa-St) mineral parageneses.

Path 1 indicates the basins described by Millot (1964) where free silica is apparent and as a result saponite is not found. Path 3 shows closed basins where free silica is not apparent and where one finds the aluminous saponites and stevensites associated with palygorskite and sepiolite. Low silica content is evident in that the last phases are stevensite and not the more silica-rich sepiolite (Trauth, 1977). Path 2 shows a possible soil formation sequence where the palygorskite rich layers are found. When palygorskite and sepiolite occur path 3 is indicated. Deep sea sediments should also be associated with these systems, as far as their chemistry is concerned, in that sepiolite is never found. This indicates neither high silica content nor low alumina content and thus an intermediate path.

An alternative representation of the sepiolite-palygorskite bearing system (R^2-R^3-Si) is one where silica chemical potential replaces silica concentration as a chemical variable. Since most sepiolite-palygorskite rock sequences or sediment sequences contain two phases found strictly in the R^2-R^3-Si chemical space, one can describe them as a series of assemblages governed by Mg-Al ratios where silica chemical potential is imposed on the system from the solution. This potential would be largely governed by the pH of the aqueous solution. Figure 67 shows the types of phase relations one would expect in such a system.

It is possible to sketch the phase relations in an alumina inert, magnesium and silica mobile system. Such a supposition is proposed in figure 68 where chlorite (7 Å), kaolinite, smectite (dioctahedral) saponite and sepiolite-palygorskite phase fields are represented. Exact phase boundary relations are difficult to establish in such a diagram because there is considerable solid solution in the phases which renders it impossible to determine exactly the phase boundaries. However, we can assume that the general spacial relations among the phases is realistic. It should be noted that although this type of a system should be possible, it is rare to find these minerals in nature as a succession of single phase zones, which leads us to believe that natural systems rarely show only one inert component present (alumina in this case).

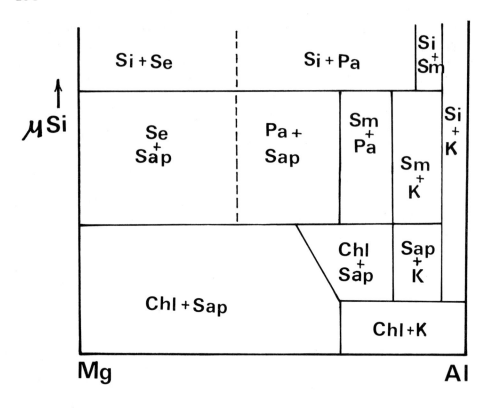

Figure 67 - Possible phase relations in Mg-Al-Si system
where sepiolite and palygorskite are stable phases.
Chemical potential of Si is continuously variable while
the relative concentrations of Mg and Al change.
The phases in the two-phase fields are :
Si = free silica ; Se = sepiolite ; Sap = saponite ;
Chl = chlorite ; Pa = palygorskite ; Sm = smectite ;
K = kaolinite, no pure alumina phase is considered.
Dashed line indicates compositional boundary between
sepiolite and saponite.

      A closing remark might also be made in relation to
the existence of sepiolite in saline basins. It is known that
not all solutions form this mineral. Although silica and
magnesium concentrations are sufficient, other magnesium-
silicate phases are present. This suggests that sepiolite is
not stable and the chemical conditions must exceed the
sepiolite zone in figure 61. The most obvious reason is that
the pH is too high for sepiolite stability, and montmorillo-

nite forms. This corresponds with the experimental results of Siffert (1962) at pH greater than 9. In this instance the phase is suppressed due to its instability as a function of an intensive variable in the system - pH. The other intensive variable which limits sepiolite stability is temperature. It is known to disappear from sediments upon deep burial. Essentially then, sepiolite and palygorskite are low temperature minerals very sensitive to the chemistry of their environment.

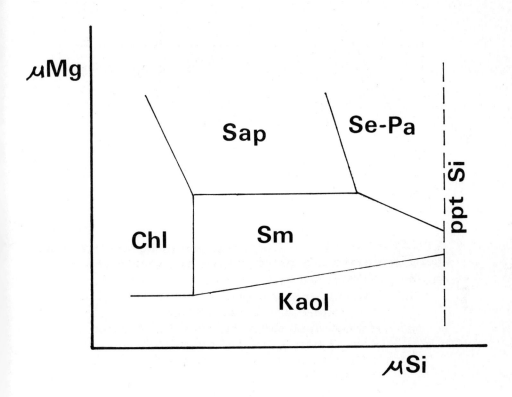

Figure 68 - Possible phase relations of Mg-Al-Si chemical variables where Al is an inert component and both Mg and Si chemical potentials are continuously variable. The phase field boundaries are only tentative in that extensive solid solution occurs in each phase (kaolinite excepted) and thus precise reaction relations cannot be written.
Chl = chlorite ; Sm = smectite ; Kaol = kaolinite ; Sap = saponite ; Se-Pa = sepiolite-palygroskite series.

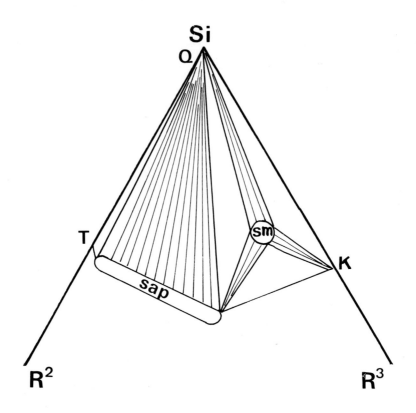

Figure 69 – High temperature assemblages for a portion of
the R^2-R^3-Si system above the stability of a
sepiolite-palygorskites.
Sm = dioctahedral smectite ; Sap = saponite ;
K = kaolinite ; T = talc ; Q = quartz.

        As a parenthesis, Figure 69 shows the system Si-
R^2-R^3 as it appears above the thermal stability limits of
sepiolite and palygorskite. This is based upon the experiments of Velde (1973) in the Mg-Al-Si-H_2O system at 2 Kbars
pressure and temperatures above 200°C, and the experiments
at high pressure of Frank-Kameneckiji and Klockova (1969) on
natural sepiolite. It is important to note that the tie-line
between a dioctahedral and trioctahedral smectite becomes
possible.

III – GENERAL PHASE DIAGRAMS FOR SOME
CLAY MINERAL ASSEMBLAGES

Introduction

Up until this point, clay mineral assemblages have
been described in order to establish their natural occurrence and estimate their stability in nature. An attempt has
been made in the preceding pages to localize chemiographically the position of the principal clay minerals, so that
obvious compatabilities could be deduced in each of the different geologic environments in which they are found. Now
these elements should be used to establish useful graphical
representations of clay mineral parageneses which occur in
various geological environments. Only a few applications for
each diagram are proposed here since the specific use of
each should be apparent in the individual studies of clay
minerals undertaken. Equally, there will be other more appropriate diagrams which could be used to explain clay mineral occurrence in nature. This section is considered at best
as an introduction to the use of a chemiographic analysis of
clay minerals. We will first consider a few cases which can
be deduced from a simplified model for clay assemblages at
atmospheric conditions and then propose more specific formu-
lations for clay mineral assemblages in sediments, and rocks
of specific complex geological environments.

1 - General Systems

a - Alkali and Alumina-Rich Systems at Surface Conditions

Among the eight or nine common chemical components found in clays and clay minerals, several can be taken to form a simplified system which represents a reasonable range of geologic materials. While admitting that the exceptions might outnumber the cases following the rules in such a simple system, we can, as an exercise, use the parameters K-Al-Si-H_2O or H^+-OH^- as the variables which will describe phase relations between aluminous pelitic clay minerals (i.e., those that are dioctahedral) at atmospheric conditions of pressure and temperature. The most well known, both from the standpoint of initial data used to construct the system and from application to geologic problems, is the system using the parameters log activity $(K^+)/(H^+)$ versus log SiO_2 activity in solution with Al_2O_3 considered as an inert component (Hess, 1966 ; or Garrels and Christ, 1965). The phase commonly considered to be present at 25°C, 1 atmosphere are gibbsite, kaolinite, feldspar, potassium mica (dioctahedral). The possibilities of solid solution between Na and K phases are generally ignored as are variations in Si and Al content.

However, before considering such a complex system of four independent variables, which is represented in planar perspective, let us first take the variables as they can be represented in a sequence of change from inert components which, one by one, become "perfectly mobile" or intensive variables of a thermodynamic system. We will first assume that the phases which will be present in some portion of the system are gibbsite, kaolinite, crystalline or amorphous silica, mica, no range of mixed layered illite-smectite but beidellite, K-feldspar (no pure potassium zeolite is present). Initially we will simplify the mineralogy in the following way : G = gibbsite ; Kaol = kaolinite ; Q = amorphous or crystalline SiO_2 ; Mi = potassic mica, Sm = K-beidellite (no mixed layered mica-smectite minerals) ; F = potassium feldspar ; Py = pyrophyllite. This is necessary to simplify portions of the diagrams where our knowledge of phase relations is not sufficient to judge the roles which each individual mineral will play.

The problem of zeolite stability has not been resolved in the present author's mind. There is not really any reason to assume that pH affects the mineral reactions in that H_2O and not OH enters into zeolites. Nevertheless, alkali zeolites are found to be associated with phyllosilicates in situations assumed to be highly alkaline. It is possible that a high alkalinity is necessary to increase silica activity, high enough to destabilize phyllosilicates in favor of zeolites. Hydroxyl ions would therefore be a catalyst to the processes and not an integral part. As was discussed in the zeolite chapter, no reliable data is available which will allow us to decide on the problem. Therefore, zeolites are left out of the simple system for the moment.

1 - Composition diagram

The first representation (Figure 70a) shows a portion of Al-Si-K space where H_2O is present in great abundance and where pH is determined by the phases which are present. The mineral assemblages are determined by the relative proportions of Al, Si and K, which are extensive variables. No intensive variables are considered. The maximum number of phases which can be present in a given composition is three ; three phases will be present in a phase-field.

If we consider the process of recrystallization of the acidic volcanic glass at surface conditions in the soil or sedimentary environment, the assemblage feldspar (plus alkali zeolites in many instances)-smectite-free silica can be deduced from the diagram on the basis of bulk composition. This assemblage is common in such natural materials.

2 - Composition - Chemical potential

If we assume that chemical potential of alkalis varies independently of the masses in the silicate system, the chemical potentials become internal variables of the system where their activity is controlled by potentials or reservoirs outside of the rock observed. Figure 70b represents this situation. Instead of the three-phase fields of figure 70a, we find two-phase assemblages. The vertical lines represent one-phase assemblages - kaolinite, smectite to mica and feldspar.

Such a diagram might be applied to the analysis of the active hydrothermal alteration of a granitic rock where alumina and silica remain immobile, or inert components and alkali potentials are variable. In zones where flow channels are established (where drainage is rapid) alteration bands develop in the rock. At the center of the bands the solutions contain less dissolved material and they would be located at the bottom of the diagram where kaolinite or possibly gibbsite and kaolinite form. Next, when the content of dissolved ionic species due to weathering increases in the fluid, the alkali activity in solution will dictate the formation of an expanding phase and then at high activity of K^+, the stability of mica. Finally, the feldspar-quartz assemblage is stable. This would happen where the solutions migrate slowly enough so that the original minerals are not dissolved and remain stable in the chemical system.

3 - Potential - Potential diagrams

A further step in the "activation" of the chemical species present might result in the active migration of silica in solution. Then a diagram such as that of figure 70c would be applicable. In this system the pH is still controlled by the mineral species present, all of which are stable at some μ-alkali, μ-Si values. A further intensive variable can be conceived as being due to the dissociation of H_2O and considering the activity of the H^+ ion in solution. This is the most commonly used type of representation, as mentioned previously. Here only one-phase fields are present. Field boundaries result in two-phase assemblages and, at the points of intersection of three fields, three-phase assemblages are possible but they are univariant in the intensive parameters. There is only one inert component, Al_2O_3. One point should be noted here. Not all phases will be stable over the range of possible chemical activity. For example, certain minerals will not exist over all pH ranges and, therefore, the simple ratio μ-alkali/μ-H^+ is not valid for all values of the individual H^+ activities.

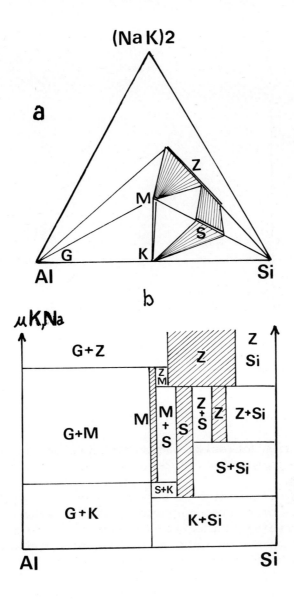

Figure 70 a & b - Phase relations in the system K-Al-Si.
   (a) Three inert, extensive variable systems showing
relations between gibbsite (G), kaolinite (K), mica (M),
smectite (S), zeolite (Z) and a silica phase (Si pole).
   (b) shows the relations as alkalis become intensive
      variables where their chemical potential is the
            determining factor in equilibria.
Shaded areas (diagonal lines) indicate one phase zones due
      to solid solution in Al-Si chemical components.

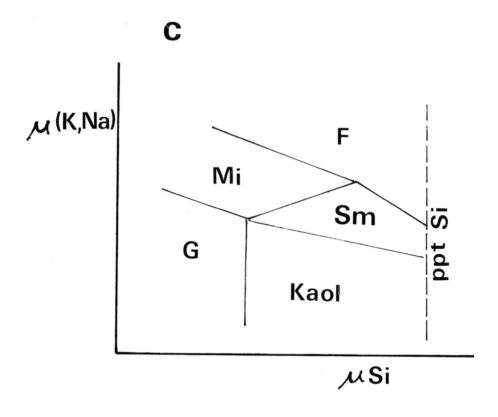

Figure 70 c - Potassium and silica are intensive variables.
Al remains inert or an extensive variable.

In order to construct the activity diagrams in a
rigorous fashion, a certain amount of information must be
available. Some experimental data for the mica-feldspar-
kaolinite-gibbsite-smectite relations are available. Data
for the other minerals are often inferred from measurements
of natural chemical parameters (K^+, SiO_2, H^+ concentrations
in solutions) in situations where the different minerals are
assumed to be stable. The relation between minerals can also
be calculated as a function of K^+, SiO_2 and pH using
thermochemical data for the participating phase (Hess, 1966)
when they are known with precision. Frequently this is not
the case, and one must resort to calculations based upon
thermochemical data of the various oxide components in the
minerals (Helgeson, 1969). Three factors are very important
in considering the results of such studies :

- If solid solution is ignored, Na-K smectite, illite-
  smectite mixed layering and Na-K phillipsite series
  for instance, thermochemical data will be forcibly
  inexact and any calculations made from this information are subject to serious error ;

- Calculations of the free energy of phyllosilicates
  based upon simplified models of mineral chemistry such
  as the simple addition of thermochemical data for the
  component oxides (Helgeson, 1968, 1969 for example),
  cannot be precise enough for detailed analysis due to
  the great lack of knowledge regarding the contribu-
  tions of configurational energy in these complex silicate structures ;

- All stable phases must be included in such diagrams
  just as all unstable phases must be excluded - these
  cannot be arbitrarily decided.

    If we accept the relative accuracy of the thermo-
chemical calculations, let us consider the phases which are
commonly assumed by other authors to be present in representations of the alkali (Na-K), alumina, silica system. Albite
is unlikely to be stable in the temperature range 25-100°C
at high activities or concentrations of H_2O. Experiments as
well as observations on natural minerals show that zeolites
are the stable alkali phases. By contrast, pure potassium
feldspar is stable. Frequently albite and phillipsite are
assumed to be the tectosilicate phases present in a pure
sodium system. As we have seen, albite will be present above
100°C or so but not below this temperature. Most authors
assume that smectite is a strictly sodic phase but both
potassic and sodic beidellite have been formed in the
laboratory. It is necessary to consider the possibility of
total alkali substitution in expanding phases. Further, the
interlayering of mica (mainly potassic below 300°C) and these expanding layers is a common reality in natural mineral
assemblages and the resulting complex structure has a composition which is variable in Na-K-Si-Al space. Since the
expanding phases are interposed between mica, feldspar and
kaolinite in their phase relations, they are quite important
to even a qualitative interpretation of phase equilibria
(Figure 70c).

The most effective representation for which activity-activity diagrams can be used is in geological situations where solutions are in contact with great reservoirs of fluid, such as sea-water for example. The activity of ions in solution will impose phase equilibria on the solids. In these instances, silicate mineralogy will be simple, most likely single-phase. Mono- or bi-mineral zones adjacent to hydrothermal veins can also be effectively represented on activity-activity diagrams.

b - Temperature-Composition Diagrams

1 - The mica-montmorillonite cycle in sedimentation, weathering and diagenesis

An interesting use of phase diagrams can be made in order to explain the apparently paradoxical relationship between dioctahedral mica and montmorillonites in weathering and diagenesis. The observation has been made (Millot, 1964 ; Weaver, 1959 ; Dunoyer de Segonzac et al., 1970 ; among others) that illite and dioctahedral micas are "degraded" or altered to form montmorillonites during weathering. Upon burial and initial diagenesis, the smectite fraction decreases, being replaced apparently by illite. There is an apparent symmetry observed in weathering and diagenetic processes. This observation has led to the idea, or reinforced it, that smectite represents a metastable form of mica which returns to its initial form when exposed to sea water sedimentation and burial ; it becomes reconstituted (Weaver, 1959) upon diagenesis.

Let us consider the first aspect of these statements, the weathering-diagenesis identity. If we use the T-x diagram of the muscovite-pyrophyllite compositional join as an approach to the behavior of the natural smectites associated with illites, both weathering reactions and diagenesis can be portrayed. Figure 71 shows two arrows representing possible paths taken by individual phases during the two processes. Arrow a shows the evolution of the mica component as alkalis, principally potassium, are removed from a rock via weathering processes and as the bulk composition of the system allows the formation of first a mixed layered phase then a smectite. This sequence has been observed in many weathering profiles. The removal of alkalis from the mica is not the only change necessary to produce a smectite. In order to maintain charge balance, the octahedral or tetrahedral ions must become globally more positive in charge, either by ionic substitution (divalent or trivalent ions) or by oxidation of iron in the natural system. As the total alkalis diminish beyond the limit of smectite bearing assemblages, kaolinite becomes apparent in the clays. Should the weathering be rapid, that is, should alkali removal be rapid, kaolinite could appear with only a small amount of the compositionally intermediate smectite phase present in a narrow horizon. However, in slower processes an apparent degradation sequence can be traced on the phase diagram of figure 71 as a function of decreasing alkali content in each horizon of the profile.

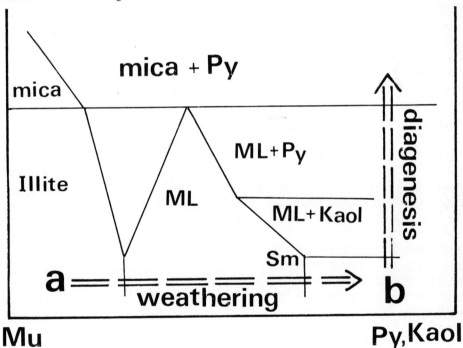

Figure 71 - Representation of a simplified pelitic rock system (compositional poles are muscovite and pyrophyllite or kaolinite plus quartz ;.this system is of course not binary). Chemical evolution due to weathering is indicated by arrow a. Phase assemblage evolution is indicated by arrow b which occurs during burial diagenesis. Phases represented are illite, mica; Py = pyrophyllite; ML = mixed layered smectite-illite; Sm = beidellite smectite; Kaol = kaolinite.

Singer and Stoffers (1980) demonstrate a reverse trend at low temperatures - one of alkali enrichment. Sediments in evaporitic lake deposits were analyzed and it was found that the sequence of smectite → mixed layered → illite was observed in saline deposits where the K/Na values were high. Detrital smectite and kaolinite were destroyed in favor of authigenic illitic-mica. This can be described on the diagram in figure 71 by a displacement in composition to the left hand, alkali-rich side at low temperatures. This change corresponds with the reconstitution of micas proposed by Weaver and Millot in a qualitative way, but we see that the reaction involves more than just smectites in that kaolinite is consumed. Thus a mineral recrystallization is implied and true mineral equilibria are involved. The reason for this last statement is that smectites, even those with high charges, must be more silica-rich than illites or micas. It is not sufficient to put alkali ions into a highly charged structure in order to re-convert it to illite or mica. Studies by Meunier (1980) indicate that weathered muscovite changes its composition beyond one of simple alkali loss. New illitic phases, seen to crystallize during weathering, are more silica-rich than the magmatic micas. Nevertheless, if one regards the X-ray diffraction mineralogy only, it is possible to observe the illitization of expandable phases in the sedimentary environment. But such a process only occurs in very alkali-rich sedimentary basins.

Let us now take a phase of beidellite composition (fully expandable at low temperature) and subject it to an increase in temperature and pressure in an argillaceous system. The following transformations take place ; the initially expandable phase changes composition to become an interlayered mineral with a mica-like component and kaolinite is produced as well as quartz. Higher temperatures effect an apparent reconstitution of the mica-like component which is accompanied by the continued production of kaolinite then pyrophyllite. If one looks only at the smectite-illite part in the assemblage, it takes the reverse course to that observed during weathering. Thus the degradation of a mica due to weathering is in appearance reversed ; illite becomes illite again. However, several other transformations have occurred during the processes. In the first instance alkalis have left the system and the proportion of Al relative to the other elements has been changed from that in the initial 2:1 mica structure. The result is the production of a smectite. In the second transformation, a new non-mica phase was produced as the expandability of the dioctahedral mineral decreased while producing more of the illite-component. By looking only at the alkali-bearing 2:1 mineral in the weathering-diagenesis cycle an apparent sort of circular process might be observed. However, this is accomplished through the removal of material and the subsequent production of new phases in the weathering cycle and crystallization of new phases in the burial metamorphic (diagenetic) cycle. The whole process can be regarded as a normal sequence of phase equilibria attained under varying chemical and physical constraints where minerals recrystallize according to P-T-x variations during geologic processes.

2 - Metabentonites

Using the same diagram (Figure 71), it is possible to explain the formation of metabentonites. These rocks are volcanic ash layers of acidic composition which have undergone a devitrification process which produces an almost uniquely clay mineral assemblage (Weaver, 1956). The composition of different ash layers is frequently variable in the same geologic area (Hoffman and Hower, 1976 ; Velde and Bruzewitz, 1982) and can vary across a single ash bed layer. The edges of the beds can contain more potassium and aluminum than the centers, at least in layers of several meters thickness. It is obvious that a process of elemental migration occurs. The mineralogy of the bed is a highly illitic mixed layer mineral at the edge and a more smectitic phase in the center.

If we assume the composition of the ash bed to be alkali-poor initially, it would lie to the right in figure 71. Infiltration of potassic solution produces a phase towards the mica side of the diagram and as the chemical potential of potassium decreases towards the center of the bed, the clays contain fewer illite layers. The span of mixed layered mineral composition encountered will depend upon the temperature conditions under which the process has taken place. Very low temperatures should allow a fully expandable smectite, whereas higher temperatures will give a mineral of lower expandability plus kaolinite and possibly chlorite. This is probably the case for those samples reported by Pevear et al. (1980) where the temperature of transformation is estimated at 145-160°C, producing an aluminous allevardite and kaolinite.

The above examples indicate that even a simplified phase diagram can be useful to explain various geological processes. What is important to know is if the general chemical environment is open or closed to chemical migration. If the elements vary, the x coordinates must be considered whereas if temperature changes one must look at the T coordinate. One must not forget that both T and x can vary simultaneously which will give a diagonal trajectory across the diagram.

c - Phase Relations in $MR^3-2R^3-3R^2-SiO_2$ Composition Diagrams

Let us use the system $MR^3-2R^3-3R^2-SiO_2$ as the most applicable in the determination of pelitic assemblages in buried systems, and let us accept that such pelitic assemblages present near 0 % porosity and thus will have very low permeability to fluids. We can then consider the evolution of clay mineral assemblages in the framework of this simplified chemical system which is nearly closed to chemical migration and contains no perfectly mobile components. Then $P_{H_2O} = P_{lith}$ or P_{total}, and the assemblages saturate the solution with SiO_2. A second projection toward alkali-poor compositions shows the phases containing predominantly divalent ions.

At lowest temperatures the minerals illite-mixed layered mineral are stable as well as kaolinite and expanding chlorites. Inherited phyllosilicate minerals that cannot be represented in the system described will remain under certain conditions. High oxidation states and low silica activity permit 7 Å chlorite to form. High alkali concentration and silica activity permit zeolites to form and low alkali activity and high pH and silica activity permit sepiolite-palygorskite formation. The conditions permitting 7 Å chlorite, zeolite and palygorskite-sepiolite formation occur at times near the sediment-sea water interface or in shallow burial. These minerals persist upon burial to significant depths once the bulk chemistry of the rock has been modified by their formation.

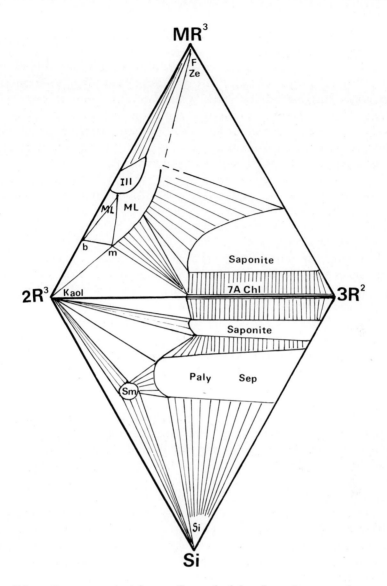

Figure 72 - Representation of probable low temperature phase assemblages in MR^3-$2R^3$-$3R^2$-Si coordinates. The SiO_2 vector commences at about 70 % Si in order to combine the MR^3-$2R^3$-$3R^2$ projection which assumes saturation with SiO_2 with the magnesio-ferrous phases 7 Å chlorites, saponite, sepiolite.
Sm = dioctahedral smectite ; Paly = palygorskite ;
Sep = sepiolite ; ML = either beidellite (b) or
montmorillonite (m) mixed layered mineral series ;
Ill = illite ; Kaol = kaolinite ; Si = amorphous silica ;
F = alkali feldspar ; Ze = alkali zeolite.

If we consider the components $MR^3-2R^3-3R^2-SiO_2$, the phases will be arranged as in figure 72 at conditions of initial burial. The solid solution series are somewhat abbreviated for simplicity. The phase relations in the alkali system are dominated by fully expanding and mixed layered minerals which cover a large portion of the compositional surface. Notably two dioctahedral expandable minerals exist as does a large undefined series of trioctahedral phases which can be designated as vermiculite and saponites.

The lower triangle $2R^3-3R^2-SiO_2$ is not complete for all silica compositions since we wish to use the $MR^3-2R^3-3R^2$ representation where silica is in excess. The lower triangle "starts" at about 70 % silica where chlorite is projected from more silica-poor compositions to join kaolinite on the base line. All this means is that we have eliminated the R^2 and R^3 oxides from consideration. All phases in the upper triangle occur with quartz, except possibly 7 Å berthierine-serpentines. This is necessitated if we consider alkali saponites and non-alkali forms to be in continuous compositional solid solution ; a reasonable assumption. This joins the two saponite fields thus isolating 7 Å chlorites from free silica.

We have, in the low alkali zone, sepiolite and palygorskite which occur in evaporitic environments, either sediments or soils. They indicate coexistence with a solution of high silica activity. Lower dissolved silica contents will give the saponites which one finds in weathered ultrabasic rocks. And then, even lower silica activity gives berthierines which form in microsystems in sediments. This analysis seems correct in that magnesian serpentines appear to be very unstable in weathering processes (Fontanaud, 1982 ; Wildman and Whittig, 1971 ; Ducloux et al., 1976) where a silica loss is apparent.

The second implication of the phase diagram couple is that kaolinite will also be isolated from free silica due to smectite (dioctahedral)-silica tie lines. Again this must be assumed if the interlayer ion in smectites is completely interchangeable at low temperatures. Certainly this seems reasonable in that one finds kaolinite forming in granite weathering when the silica content of the rock begins notably to decline (Meunier and Velde, 1982). The presence of quartz in surface geological environments does not indicate low silica activity of aqueous solutions in that they will not be saturated by quartz alone. Thus kaolinite represents a silica-poor environment, even in the presence of quartz because this latter phase has a low solubility and lower reaction kinetics of crystallization from solution. We can then leave this low temperature facies and move to higher temperatures.

The second facies is marked by the instability of the fully expanding dioctahedral phases and the existence of a kaolinite-illite tie line (Figure 73). In this facies the siliceous alkali zeolites (other than analcime) become unstable ; the compositional range of the trioctahedral and dioctahedral expanding phases is reduced and aluminous corrensite phase becomes stable. The disposition of phases in the $2R^3$-$3R^2$-SiO_2 portion of the figure are greatly simplified. We now have 14 Å chlorite-quartz tie lines which dominate and a 7 Å serpentine of low alumina content appears. Here we are in the stability field of serpentinization phenomena.

Although there is little information available we assume that non-aluminum saponites (stevensite) are not stable, nor are magnesian dioctahedral smectites. All of the expanding minerals occur as mixed layered phases. One should remember that sodium can form the rectorite phase (50 % smectite-50 % paragonite) in aluminous environments.

The existence of rectorite in sedimentary rocks has been discovered recently (Paradis et al., 1983) in a series of lighly metamorphosed black shales. Similar samples have been studied previously by Dunoyer de Segonzac and Heddebaut (1971) where a regular mixed layered mineral was designated as allevardite. The more recent study, benefitting from recent progress in mineral analysis techniques (electron microprobe) indicates that the superstructured mineral in pyrophyllite-bearing black shales is in fact sodic and thus rectorite. Almost no iron or magnesium is present and thus one has a paragonite-sodic beidellite mixed layered mineral phase which is a true rectorite (Brown and Weir, 1963).

Although we can "explain" the clay mineral assemblages in these rocks in an MR^3-$2R^3$-$3R^2$ diagram, one should note that the pyrophyllite-rectorite assemblage is found only in black shales, where all iron was initially in the R^{2+} state. It is probable that this condition needs to be met to permit the formation of such an assemblage.

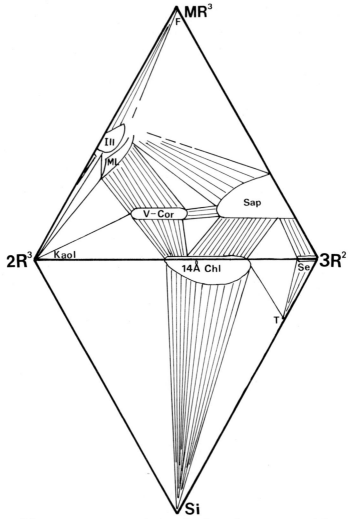

Figure 73 - Representation of the phase assemblages in the MR^3-$2R^3$-$3R^2$-Si system at temperatures above 150°C and below 200°C. The silica vector begins at about 70 % Si so that kaolinite and chlorites fall on the same base line. The appearance of vermiculite-corrensite phases is important (V-corr) however, as discussed previously, the speciation of Mg and Fe^{2+} will allow coexistence of chlorite with corrensite and a mixed layered phase. Sap = saponite ; Chl = chlorite ; T = talc ; Se = serpentine (low alumina content) ; Kaol = kaolinite ; ML = mixed layered mineral ; Ill = illite ; F = alkali feldspar. It should be noted that the effect of temperature is to reduce the number of phases present to a large extent.

One can use the data given by Paradis **et al.** (1983) to establish phase diagrams for the last clay mineral facies to contain expandable dioctahedral phases. The minerals involved are pyrophyllite, chloritoid, 92-97 % potassic smectite-illite-mixed layered phase, rectorite (an ordered sodic, beidellite-paragonite mixed layered mineral with one half of the layers expanding) chlorite, albite and illite. There are two types of aluminum mixed layered minerals present in these rocks ; one with low expandability, the other is 50 % expandable. This can be distinguished by X-ray diffraction as well as by electron microprobe analysis. There is no evidence of an expanding trioctahedral mineral. The chlorites contain 70-90 % iron in the R^2 sites and chloritoid contains about 90 % Fe in R^2 sites. The chlorite present has a high R^3 component. The potassic mixed layered mineral contains little iron and magnesium. However, the analyzed zones are possibly multiphase and therefore care must be taken in their interpretation. It is probable that some pyrophyllite is also present. The highest temperature facies contain a rectorite phase (a sodic mineral). This regular mixed layered phase is accompanied generally by chloritoid in the rocks studied, but this may not necessarily be the case for all samples.

Since the number of samples studied is quite limited one cannot generalize to any great extent. We have information from only one region which probably represents only one metamorphic gradient. It is quite possible that an IMII structure and rectorite will occur in the same rock. The assemblage pyrophyllite-allevardite-type mixed layered phase ± chloritoid reported by Dunoyer de Segonzac and Heddebaut (1971) in several areas in France and in Algeria could very well include a rectorite mineral. However, there is not enough information to establish all of the assemblages occurring in each area. We can nevertheless, establish an approximate temperature limit for these facies. The latest data on pyrophyllite stability (Hemley **et al.**, 1980) suggests that 270°C at 1-2 kbars will be the lower limit of pyrophyllite stability. The IMII assemblages in the presence of pyrophyllite must occur above 270°C. The reaction which produces chloritoid ; chlorite + pyrophyllite = chloritoid, must then occur above the pyrophyllite-chlorite-IMII facies. It is here that one finds the sodic phase rectorite. We do not know if it can occur at lower temperatures. Further, there is no information from the natural mineral assemblages which allows one to deduce the pressures at which the mineral assemblages formed. It might be reasonable to estimate that the upper limit of expandable aluminous phases occurs near 300°C at moderate pressures of 1-2 Kbars. The key minerals will be pyrophyllite-chloritoid. If the rock composition is less aluminous, the illite-chlorite assemblage will occur well below these temperatures. Figure 74 shows the situation where no expanding dioctahedral solid solutions are stable, nor are there any trioctahedral expanding phases.

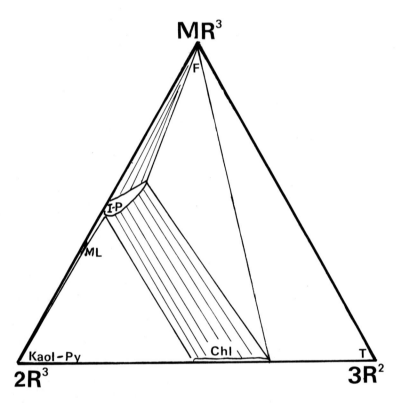

Figure 74 - Phase relations above the stability of rectorite or IMII-type mixed layered phases which shows the illite-chlorite facies. F = feldspar.

These stages in the evolution of buried sediments are only approximate, but they show the probable major phase changes in pelitic rocks as defined by the evolution of the significant stable phyllosilicate assemblages.

It is evident that sediments in the early stages of burial will contain metastable minerals, even phyllosilicates that have not reacted to form the stable assemblage under the prevailing P-T conditions. However, the trend of mineral neo-formation should be to create the groups of minerals outlined.

Two minerals frequently encountered in sediments and sedimentary rocks are not carefully considered in the figures. These are glauconite and iron-rich chlorite, the two major iron bearing phyllosilicates in sediments and sedimentary rocks. Glauconite formation can be explained on the basis of its ferric iron content. When large amounts are present in a system, Fe^{3+} is no longer the chemiographic equivalent of Al^{3+} and a new phase appears at low temperatures. It remains stable upon burial when there is little further chemical migration, and because the quantity of iron present is too great for other possible phases normally present, to absorb. By contrast, chlorite which is frequently initially present in sediments, has been noted to increase in quantity in the presence of illite-kaolinite-mixed layered minerals. In many instances four major neo-formed phyllosilicate phases are apparently stable together. This cannot be represented in the simplified triangular system.

The explanation for the growth of chlorite in the presence of three other phyllosilicates can very well lie in its reputedly high iron content. If chlorite can selectively incorporate iron into its structures, it is possible that its presence is due to the iron (Fe^{2+}) content of the rock. A relation such as that of Figure 75 can lead to two chlorite-bearing assemblages depending upon the iron content of the rock ; either mixed layered magnesian chlorite for magnesian-low potassium compositions, or illite-mixed layered iron chlorite for more iron-rich compositons. Higher potassium content implies the existence of iron chlorite. Thus, under certain circumstances (high K or Fe contents) chlorite can be an additional phase to those normally present in the MR^3-$2R^3$-$3R^2$ system. Chlorite stable in the presence of illite and a mixed layered phase will be iron-rich. When an expanding mineral is no longer stable, the iron content of the chlorite in equilibrium with illite will become more variable (Figure 75). If chlorite is present due to a relatively high Fe/Fe + Mg content of a rock, it can occur with three other aluminous phases such as illite-smectite and kaolinite. Thus the four-phase phyllosilicate assemblage common to argillaceous rocks can be accounted for by dividing the R^2 ions into two types (Mg^{2+} and Fe^{2+}) and by increasing the number of chemical variables necessary to represent the clay mineral assemblages.

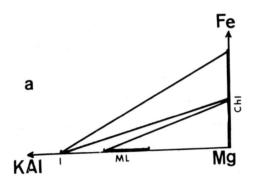

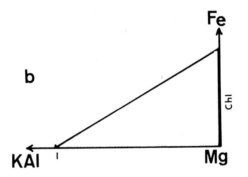

Figure 75 - Possible phase relations in systems with variable Fe^{2+} content. Chl = chlorite ; ML = mixed layered illite-smectite ; I = illite.
a - Smectite and mixed layered phase stable
b - Mixed layered phase unstable.

An interesting possibility arises when this four-phase assemblage does exist in a sedimentary rock. Since the phases which coexist are all members of solid solution series, their specific compositions at a given set of P-T conditions is fixed if they are equal in number to the extensive variables. That is to say, the variations of the compositional parameters will change the relative proportions of each of the phases present, but not their composition. At P_1 and T_1 the chlorite compositions will always be the same in the presence of kaolinite, illite and a mixed layered mineral. But at P_2 and T_2 the chlorite composition will be different, as will that of illite and the mixed layered phase. We know that the substitutional range of Mg = Fe^{2+} is large in chlorite, and it is also known that such a substitution is commonly a function of temperature in other silicates. It is thus reasonable to assume that if the Mg-Fe ratio in a chlorite coming from this four-phase assemblage could be determined, it should be possible to estimate the pressure-temperature conditions under which it formed. Unfortunately, attempts have not yet been entirely successful in establishing a method of Fe/Mg determination for sedimentary or poorly crystallized (clay size grains) chlorites. When a method is developed, it should be a great aid in establishing the physical conditions of formation of clay mineral assemblages.

2 - Weathering

a - Introduction

A number of studies have been carried out at the University of Poitiers (France), in the recent past which have been designed to determine the exact location of mineral growth and to identify the clays found in weathering of coarse grained rocks. The materials were chosen so that mineral separates of the initial magmatic or metamorphic phases, could be made in order to identify the new minerals that they contained by X-ray diffraction. Optical microscopy as well as electron microprobe studies were made on the rock samples so that the exact site of clay mineral formation and the chemical nature of the phases could be determined. The method is outlined in Meunier (1980). On the basis of a dozen or so studies, there are several general trends which are obvious ; however these observations do not seem to have come to the attention of previous workers.

The first point is that weathered rocks are not homogeneously altered, i.e., the horizon concept is only partially valid in what is considered as the saprolite and saprock zones. Most granular rocks, and other types for that matter, are fractured. This mechanical inhomogeneity leads to a chemical one. Water, following the path of least resistance, flows into the cracks and reacts with the silicates in these zones first. This effect is accentuated in areas of good drainage and of course lessened in areas of poor drainage where the water table is near the surface. But let us consider a favorable case, one of good drainage. If one classifies the clay mineral assemblages according to their stage in the process of alteration, i.e., low alkali and alkaline earth as altered, high alkali and ferrous iron-bearing minerals as unaltered, one finds that altered areas are distributed in a pattern such as is outlined in figure 76.

The most evident features on weathered crystalline rocks are the bleached or oxidized zones which are formed in structural fractures. These portions of the rock-water system are to a large extent set apart from the rest of the system. In these zones the fluid content is variable and intermittent ; high flow rate during rainy periods and dry at other times. The mass of the rock remains humid however and as a result chemical reaction between fluid and rock is constant with time ; there is a greater approach to an equilibrium between solids and liquids. In the fractures, the main process is dissolution since the water flows through at a great rate and has little chance to be saturated with the elements present in silicates.

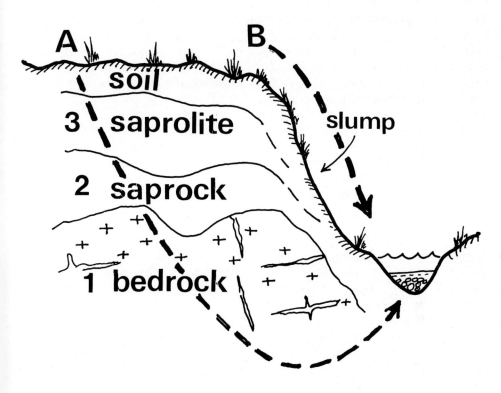

Figure 76 - Diagram of erosion and transport in rock weathering. Solids are moved above all at the soil-air surface (B) however some material moves downwards in the rock. Dissolved material moves essentially in the groudwater via fissures in the altered and altering rock (A). Materials coming from all horizons will be present in the stream-born waters.

A second effect is **elutriation** - the transportation of solids from higher levels in the profile and their deposition along cracks and fissures. Mineralogical observations show that the clays and oxides transported in a weathering profile tend to be of the same species at all levels. In the case of granites one finds kaolinite plus iron oxides. If one samples the free-flowing water in such a system one will find that its composition reflects its contact with kaolinite, yet the major chemical processes which are occurring within the rock are not presented by such a geochemical sample. The clay coating on the walls of pores and fractures is called a cutane by Brewer (1964). The clay minerals present there usually indicate advanced stages of weathering because they are derived from upper horizons in zones of great water flux. Basically the fracture-pore system of a weathering rock should be considered separately from the rest, at least in temperate climates, because it represents a special set of circumstances - those of rapid circulation of unsaturated waters.

The next important observation is that despite these corridors of alteration which can be vertical and horizontal the rest of the section can be classed in a vertical pattern according to the profile-horizon concept of soil chemists. We have in effect blocks of material which are altered more or less as they are found in the vertical sequence from the surface to bed rock. This permits one to assume a horizon classification in the classical manner for the least altered sectors of each layer (Fig. 77).

Now, if we look at samples under the microscope, we can see a repetition of this pattern on a microscale. Grain boundaries show the first signs of alteration, then intra-grain cracks become chemically active and finally each grain becomes destabilized. The result is a division of an altering rock into a number of microsystems which are related to each other by the chemical activity of some of the ions in the altering solutions. In each micro-area certain other elements are related to the composition of the minerals found in their immediate environment. There is short range and long range chemical mobility and therefore chemical potential influences.

The third, and ultimate observation as far as clay mineralogy is concerned is the de-structurization of the rock into a clayey mass dominated by the chemistry of clay minerals. Here the clay minerals formed in microsystems dictated by local chemistry and pre-existing minerals are homo-

genized chemically producing in many instances a new clay
mineral which is typical of the soil horizon as a whole.
This is the B zone or upper C zones of soil chemist [See
Berry and Ruxton (1959), for example] or the upper saprolite
zone.   Subsequent alteration of the clay assemblage will
occur towards the surface, into the various B and A subdivisions. The clay minerals which form in these zones will tend
to be more homogeneous in kind on a horizontal scale than
those in the C zones. Nevertheless, as shown by Ildefonse et
al.   (1979) these new soil minerals, formed in an argillaceous medium, are inhomogeneous in composition from grain to
grain, which reflects some very local chemical controls.

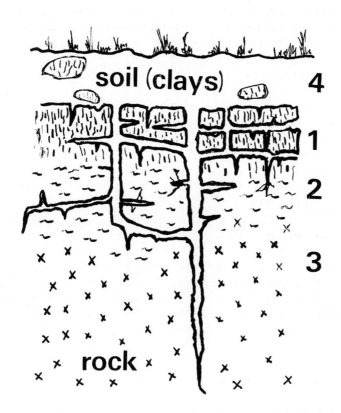

Figure 77 - A schematic diagram of a rock weathering system
where fractures and fissures occur. The alteration horizons
   are rock (3), saprock (2), saprolite (1) and soil (4).
      Fractures and fissures are present in each horizon.
   The clay mineralogy of these zones is the same for all
horizons and equivalent to that of the soil in many cases.

It is obvious that the immediate chemical system active in a given area of a rock or soil will determine the phase which crystallizes and its specific composition : the concentrations of certain elements are controlled over long distances (centimeters), others over short ones (millimeters). It is important to insist upon the aspect of crystallization of new phases in weathering. It has been rarely found that an old mineral is only slightly modified to form a new weathering phase. Optical and microprobe studies show definitively that only a small fraction of high grade minerals are gradually transformed into clay minerals. Recrystallization is the rule rather than the exception. Old phyllosilicates more often form entirely new phases in weathering than they are modified in composition to produce the same phase of a different composition. For example, muscovite does not readily transform into illite even though new illite can form in the altering rock. However, biotite has been seen to be transformed into dioctahedral vermiculite-illite interlayered phase, as much as this can be called a transformation in that the octahedral layer must be completely reorganized from tri- to dioctahedral (Meunier, 1980). In basic rocks, the new phyllosilicate phases have no relation to previous structures and are thus crystallized under weathering conditions. Weathering, at least in its initial stages, is a process of rapid reorganization of silicate material.

If local chemical systems are important in weathering one must not overlook two global aspects of the process ; total loss of material and oxidation. Attempts have been made in past years to establish a mass balance of the material in a weathering sequence (Lelong, 1969 ; Brewer, 1964 ; Millot and Bonifas, 1964). This can be done using as a basis for comparison a highly inert mineral which changes little during weathering. These methods present problems which do not allow great confidence in the resulting calculations. However, one thing is certain ; much material leaves the immediate profile and this includes all elements, even though some tend to be precipitated locally more than others. In a way, observing a weathering profile is like looking at the left overs of a great feast. Loss of material predominates.

Another important aspect of weathering is oxidation. The weathering profiles in which iron remains reduced into the uppermost horizons are rare. Oxidation of iron is not always completed in the initial phase of weathering ; some Fe^{2+} can be incorporated in clays, essentially triocta-hedral phases. However, Fe^{3+} quickly becomes the most important form of iron and when it remains in clays, it produces a dioctahedral mineral. Thus we often find the transition from tri- to dioctahedral minerals when oxidation occurs. Serpentine and saponite are transformed into nontronite or else one finds that nontronite is the first clay to form in basic rocks which do not contain a phyllosilicate. In this last example, the initial rock containing Fe^{2+} produces an Fe^{3+} silicate assemblage.

Reactions between clay minerals due to oxidation have been described by Ducloux et al. (1976) where the reaction chlorite + smectite$_1$ → smectite$_2$ + interstratified mineral and by Eswaran and Sys (1970) where nontronite + gibbsite → kaolinite + iron oxide occurs as the iron leaves the silicate to form an oxide. In these instances, oxidation changes the position of iron from one phase to another provoking reaction between the soil clay minerals to form a new assemblage.

Finally, it is important to remember that vermiculite, either di- or trioctahedral in form, is a very common mineral produced in rock weathering and soil forming processes (Jackson et al., 1952 ; Rich and Obenshain, 1955 ; Rich, 1958 ; Rich and Cook, 1963 ; Johnson, 1964 ; Kerns and Mankin, 1967 ; Tardy and Gac, 1968 ; Seddoh et al., 1969 ; Eroshcher-Shak, 1970 ; Clayton, 1974 ; Proust and Velde, 1978 ; Ildefonse et al., 1979 ; Meunier, 1980 ; Proust, 1982 ; among many others). This mineral does not always form from phyllosilicates. It is frequently not stable in the upper levels of the soil profile. It can belong to either the dioctahedral evolution or the trioctahedral phyllosilicate mineral which produces a dioctahedral vermiculite. As we have seen in the mineral description section, vermiculite has a tendency to have a bulk composition between the di- and tri-octahedral minerals by either having R^{3+} or R^{2+} ions in its interlayer position. Vermiculite seems quite well adapted to its ephemeral role in soil clay mineralogy. It is not often encountered in mature soil profiles nor in sediments and less so in sedimentary rocks. However, it is present in these geological environments (Millot, 1964) in minor but constant quantities. The vermiculite of soils represents the transition between early formed and final clay mineral assemblages in a weathering profile. This role is in fact dictated by the basic shift in bulk composition from R^2 to R^3-dominated assemblages. Vermiculite reflects loss of calcium, loss of magnesium and oxidation of iron. It is crystallized in response to the incorporation of more alumina and Fe^{3+} into the old trioctahedral phases due to leaching of Mg and oxidation of Fe^{2+}. It is crystallized in response to the destabilization of alkali and calcium-rich minerals which show an excess of alumina over silica and alkalis. Since it is so often present in specific chemical environments, forming most often from non-phyllosilicates, it is most likely that vermiculite is a stable phase compared with other phyllosilicates of the same total composition-despite the experimental data of Kittrick (1973) used to label vermiculite as a metastable phase. In any event the regularity of the occurrence of vermiculite on a chemiographic basis will allow us to place it in clay mineral assemblages as a predictable component.

If we summarize the work done at Poitiers by A. Meunier and his co-workers. it is possible to classify weathering into three "geochemical" zones (Figure 77) :

1 - The zone of insipient alteration where the rock is coherent in hand specimen. Here fracture zones and grain boundaries are the most active sites of new mineral formation.

2 - The friable rock zone (saprock) is where individual high temperature mineral grains are distinguishable but where they tend to dissociate easily under moderate mechanical pressure. In these samples internal destabilization of the initial phase is quite evident. The new minerals form a polyphase (generally two phases) assemblage. Grain boundary reactions are of minor importance.

3 - The argillized solifluxed zone (saprolite) is where the clay mineral assemblages formed initially in each magmatic or metamorphic mineral are mixed with one another through mechanical collapse of the initial rock structure. Here the density of the assemblage increases in that conduits or pores within the altering minerals are suppressed. This relation

tends to homogenize the new clay minerals through recrystallization. Vermiculites are produced. This zone and those above it in the soil profile proper, (those influenced by the action of organic materials), can be treated by the horizon method since a large degree of homogeneity has been achieved and local variation is due only to small grains of material which have escaped chemical transformation into a clay mineral species or assemblage. It is possible that fine-grained rocks, sedimentary or low grade metamorphic in nature, will behave chemically as materials in this third zone and one will not see (at least by optical microscope) the grain boundary and internal destabilization episodes of mineral recrystallization even though they exist on a microscopic scale. Thus the soil profile method of reasoning will be directly applicable to these rocks from the beginning to the end.

If the tripartite division is useful for those rocks studied in the West of France, can it be applied to other areas and how ? Most probably it can according to some preliminary observations, and in considering the multitude of descriptions in the literature. The differences which will occur in a given climatic and geomorphologic setting will effect changes in the relative thickness of the middle, disaggregated, saprock zone. In the tropical alteration of crystalline rocks, this zone is centimeters thick whereas the upper clayey zone is decameters thick (G. Pédro, personal communication). Thus the transition between rock and clay is rapid. If we consider ultra-basic rock alteration (Ducloux et al., 1976 ; Fontanaud, 1982) the intermediate zone is reduced even in temperate climates. This is because of the high solubility of the elements composing the minerals in the primary rock, mainly magnesium, which does not participate to any large extent in the formation of soil clay minerals. As we have seen in previous chapters even phyllosilicates, which are predominantly magnesian, such as magnesian saponites, chlorite, sepiolite or palygorskite, are highly unstable during weathering. Thus the initial magnesian minerals are completely destroyed.

If the alteration profile is frequently below the water table, it can behave as the saprolite - soil zone -

where only one mineral occurs per horizontal sector (Proust and Velde, 1978). One would expect that weathering zones of the first and second type (grain edges and internal destabilization) will be relatively thick in climates where the temperature is low, such as in high mountains and northern latitudes. Here we do know that soil zones (those rich in clay materials) are thin.

It should be possible to consider then two aspects of weathering as they affect the relative thickness of the upper two zones of weathering :

1 - Reaction rate governed by the availability of water which causes dissolution into aqueous solution. The factors are rainfall, drainage and temperature.

2 - Reaction rate governed by the chemistry of the altering rocks, i.e., the solubility of the elements Mg and Ca promoting dissolution and Al, Fe, Si promoting precipitation.

The greater the reaction rate, the smaller will be the saprock zone and the larger will be the saprolite-soil argillite zone. The relative influence of the physical and chemical factors mentioned above is summarized in table 7.

Weathering zones	Factors	Influence necessary to decrease zone 2
	Rainfall high	+
4 Soil	Drainage rapid	−
3 Saprolite	Temperature high	+
2 Saprock	Mg,Ca-rich	+
1 Rock	Al,Si,Fe-rich	−
	Rock fractured	−

Table 7

b - Phase Diagrams for Several Weathering Systems

1 - Granites

Weathering mineral assemblages from granites in Western France (Meunier and Velde, 1979 ; Meunier, 1980) show that individual minerals often destabilize into a bimineralic assemblage. If we consider only the acid minerals - feldspar, muscovite and quartz - it is possible to describe most mineral reactions which occur during the different stages of weathering. Figure 78 is based upon the following tie lines which would be found in the fixed composition system K-Al-Si ; smectite-illite, smectite-quartz and smectite-feldspar. This excludes the possibility of a muscovite-quartz tie-line.

The above allows the construction of a system where two variables are relatively inert, Si and Al, and where alkalis (potassium for the most part) have a varying chemical potential in the system. Thus with two chemical components as extensive variables we can have two-phase fields in a phase diagram. The key reactions with increasing alkali (potassium) potential are kaolinite-smectite, smectite-mica, mica-kaolinite, mica-feldspar. We assume that there is no complete solid solution between smectite or expanding phases and the micaceous phase (illite). None has been observed in the studies yet.

In the fracture systems of granite one finds kaolinite plus oxides. However in the lowest sectors of the profiles, gibbsite is a common mineral (Calvert et al., 1980 ; Marcias and Vazquez, 1981). The initial stages of feldspar alteration by water have been described thermodynamically by Helgeson (1969) as giving gibbsite then kaolinite. Such a sequence occurs in the lowest portions of fracture systems in granites. The rest of the rock contains no gibbsite and only small quantities of kaolinite in temperate climates. What then are the reactions in the rock which is unaffected by the fracture system ?

First, the reactions seen in the lowest zone of the saprock are found at grain contacts between mica and orthoclase. A new, siliceous mica (illite) is crystallized in the edges of the feldspar. This reflects a general lowering of the alkali activity which permits a low alkali, silica-rich

mica to form which does so at the expense of the feldspar.
Loss of alkali from a siliceous phase occurs in order to
form the new mica. These grain boundary effects are small
and they do not persist into the overlying saprock zone.

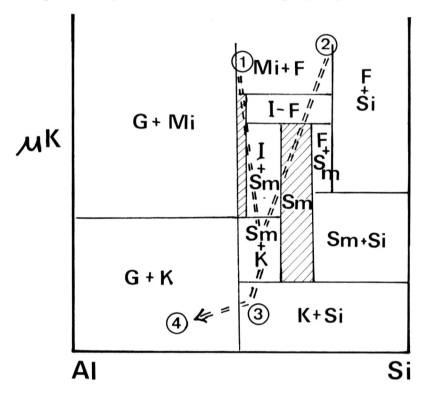

Figure 78 - Phase diagram applicable to the weathering of
granite. Mixed layered minerals do not occur. The more
immobile components are Al and Si, while alkalis and calcium
are mobile. Arrows indicate the path taken by alteration
products of (1) mica and (2) feldspar in successive stages
of weathering. Arrow (3) shows the last, most intense
weathering where silica is evacuated from the system.
This occurs in fractures and fissures in altering rock
or in the upper saprolite horizons of tropical soils.
F = alkali feldspar ; Mi = muscovite ; B = beidellitic
smectite ; Si = silica ; G = gibbsite ; K = kaolinite.
Arrow 1 shows alteration path of mica grains.
Arrow 2 shows alteration path of feldspar grains.
Arrow 3 shows evolution rock in last stages of alteration
in a temperate climate.
Arrow 4 shows evolution in a tropical climate.

Next, the individual mineral grains are seen to destabilize along minute grain fissures in their interior. The following reactions were noted in two different profiles (a and b) :

1. a) muscovite → kaolinite
    b) muscovite → kaolinite + vermiculite (aluminous smectite (arrow 1, figure 78) ;

2. a) orthoclase → smectite + kaolinite
    b) orthoclase → vermiculite (aluminous smectite) + kaolinite (arrow 2, figure 78) ;

3. a & b) plagioclase → kaolinite.

If we assimilate smectite and vermiculite as being functionally the same phase, and if we take into account the fact that quartz grains appear to be totally unaffected and thus inert, we can place the bulk composition of the system between muscovite (calcic plagioclase also) and orthoclase as seen in figure 78. The ratio of Al to Si in the magmatic minerals will be here. The tendency then will be for the silica-rich phase (orthoclase) to de-stabilize to a more aluminous assemblage and for the silica-poor phase (muscovite) to become a more siliceous one (arrow 2, figure 78). The convergence of orthoclase and muscovite assemblages to kaolinite plus smectite (or aluminous vermiculite) then suggests that the altering fluids decrease alkali potential and average the Al-Si relations to those between the initial reacting phases. Plagioclase reacts directly to form kaolinite since all calcium goes into solution and so little alkali is present in the solution that the high Si-Al concentration provokes the crystallization of kaolinite immediately.

There is then, in the first stages of weathering, a tendency to conserve the Si-Al ratio in the system as a whole and to diminish the alkali content. Each magmatic phase reacts to adjust to the new alkali activities.

The fracture zones present a new chemical environment where the chemical potential of alkalis is still lower. Here we descend to the kaolinite-quartz zone. However, there appears to be a decided kinetic barrier to form quartz at low temperatures, but the solutions are never concentrated enough to allow the precipitation of amorphous silica. The result is a systematic elimination of this element. Thus the fracture zones become monomineralic ; silica behaves as a mobile element. The production of kaolinite has a minor effect in the mass of the system ; it does not persist much into the soil horizon and thus the appearance there of this phase will represent an inheritence of lower zone chemical reaction.

When the rock material reaches the saprolite stage, argillization, it appears that a dioctahedral vermiculite is the phase which crystallizes (Meunier, personal communication). The overall weathering of the granite in the saprock zone gives a mixture of clay phases which arrive in the saprolite-soil horizon. They are then transformed into a vermiculitic phase as described by Jackson et al. (1948) in their summary of soil sequences in temperate climate. Kaolinite is formed in the rock-weathering process at many points but this does not mean that the climate was tropical in nature. It means however that in the initial stages of rock transformation certain sectors of the system had chemical activities which dictated the presence of this phase. Kaolinite is often part of a multiphase assemblage and thus must be considered as a stage in the alteration process. It can originate in the fracture or vein system also.

In areas where the rainfall is great and temperatures are sufficiently high to promote rapid chemical reaction ; the process of dissolution will go one step further when the alkalis are exhausted. One arrives in the kaolinite plus quartz zone of figure 78 and the next change is toward an increase in the least soluble element which is aluminum. The change in composition is toward an alumina-rich assemblage by elimination of silica below the concentration which permits the stability of kaolinite. This is the same reaction as that seen in fracture zones in temperate climates. The displacement from the kaolinite composition toward the gibbsite plus kaolinite field (arrow 3, figure 78) shows the ultimate stage in weathering which is seen commonly in tropical soils (Pédro, 1966, 1968). As has been noted by Millot (1964), this stage can be "reversed" by an accumulation of silica in other zones which kaolinitizes gibbsite. In these sequences, there is a significant accumulation of iron oxide along with kaolinite and gibbsite. This is typical of pedologic accumulations of alumina.

In summary, we can say that the weathering of granite produces several different clay minerals which are located in specific sites within the rock mass. They are grain boundaries, internal zones of each magmatic mineral species and fracture zones. Certain of these phases become unstable in the soil horizon as the structure of the rock is lost and old grain boundaries (and hence the limits of each micro-chemical system) are destroyed. This weathering phase can recrystallize to form a new vermiculitic mineral in the lower part of the soil sequence. Subsequent changes which occur as the process of soil formation advances are dependent upon such factors as vegetation, temperature, drainage and so forth. Undoubledly a number of the inherited weathering phases will survive during soil formation to give a polyphase mineralogy in the soil horizons which then contain unstable phases.

Erosion, which does not respect soil horizon sequences, will mix the different products from the stages of weathering and soil formation. The material moved by streams and rivers will reflect all stages of these processes. Thus sediments from granitic terrains should contain clay minerals from all of the different stages of alteration. It will be expected that this mixture of material will be moderately transformed into a new mineralogy upon sedimentation and burial. Such a process is similar to that of the argillization zone where the rock loses its structure and clays from different microsystems are mixed together and react to form a vermiculitic or smectite phase. Thus the general zonation of clay mineralogy in oceanic sediments (especially the detritus dominated Altantic) will reflect a homogenization of the materials found on the continents according to the average weathering regime operative - illite and chlorite in arctic zones, montmorillonite (smectite) in temperate zones and kaolinite in tropical zones (Pédro, 1966 ; Biscaye, 1965). This shows a general decrease in alkali content as weathering reactions become more important and a resulting decrease in the saprock thickness.

2 - Ultrabasic rocks

The two factors which dominate the weathering of ultrabasic rocks are loss of magnesium from the system and oxidation of the iron which might be present. The mineral phases which are initially present which could be called phyllosilicates are serpentines, chlorite and occasionally talc. Differences in these profiles are between clay mineral silicates and oxides (essentially Fe_2O_3) present (Wackerman, 1975 ; Wildman **et al.**, 1968 ; Rimsaite, 1972 ; Eggleton and Boland, 1982 ; Trescases, 1979).

A thesis study by Fontanaud (1982) allows one to see how such a system can change the composition and mineralogy of a rock. In the profile of rock alteration of a serpentinized lherzolite one finds a loss of Ca, Mg and a corresponding concentration of Al, total iron and silica. Iron changes oxidation state and phases as alteration reaches its final stages ; some enters into hydrous ferric oxides while some forms nontronite. The initial peridotite minerals were olivine, orthopyroxene, clinopyroxene and spinel which are replaced during serpentinization by clinopyroxene, talc, serpentine, and spinel with some orthopyroxene relics.

The first weathering reaction shows the destabilization of clinopyroxene into talc and oxides. Some silica will be lost as well as the calcium of the pyroxene. Presumably both are transported in the solutions as we find no apparent trace of them in the clay mineral phases. Talc is a highly siliceous low temperature phase, as would be expected from the reaction clinopyroxene $\rightarrow$ talc + Ca^{2+} + $Si_{(aqueous)}$. Serpentine, forming mostly from olivine, is not formed in the presence of silica as seen in the reaction olivine $\rightarrow$ serpentine + Mg^{2+} . The initial rock assemblage will be considered as serpentine - clinopyroxene - spinel (Figure 79a). The reaction forming talc gives the assemblage serpentine - talc - spinel in the saprock zone.

The second weathering reaction (in the saprolite zone) is that of saponite formation at the expense of other phases. Its composition lies between talc and the oxide (R^3) corner of the system. These minerals contain more alumina than Fe^{3+}. Both talc and serpentine are pseudomorphosed by saponite. The new assemblage shows a bulk composition poorer in R^2 ions than its predecessor. There is a decided tendency to form a single-phase assemblage.

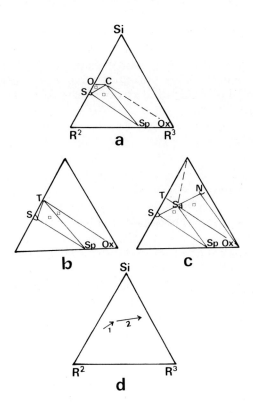

Figure 79 - Phase diagrams of clay mineral paragenesis
during the alteration of an ultrabasic rock (serpentinite).
a - Initial assemblages where $R^2 = Fe^2$,Mg,Ca thus including
clinopyroxene (C), spinel (Sp) and oxide (Ox).
Squares show assemblages encountered.
b - Saprock facies where talc + oxides replace clinopyroxene
c - Saprolite and argillite facies where first saponite (Sa)
occurs, then nontronite (N).
d - Indicates path of bulk chemical composition, 1 for
saprock and 2 for saprolite.
Figure based on data of Fontanaud (1982).

In fissures of the saprock and saprolite, one finds
that saponite is unstable being replaced by nontronite,
which is of course a ferrisilicate. The shift in bulk composition is toward the Si-R^3 side of the system due to a loss
of magnesium and oxidation of iron. The first and second

smectite assemblages are shown in figure 79c. The shift in bulk compositon is indicated by average composition : positions of 1 = saprock, 2 = saprolite stage (Figure 79d). In zones of high water flux (larger fissures and their edges) the nontronite does not form and we have an Si-Mg-Fe "gel" plus iron oxides. This must certainly indicate that the re-crystallization process saponite → nontronite passes through a solution phase when the $Mg-Fe^3-Si$ ions are in a highly concentrated state. One can form the nontronite from this gel. This mechanism has been demonstrated by Harder (1976) for a number of phases believed to crystallize at low tempe-rature. However the gel composition in the ultrabasic rock is more Mg-rich than the nontronite.

The bulk composition of the weathering profile changes as the above mineral assemblages are transformed : there is an increase in alumina content and alkalis, espe-cially K_2O. However both remain low, 6 % and 0,4 % by weight respectively. Concentration of these elements can be found in the smectite which is dominantly iron-rich and thus a nontronite. Some iron (Fe^{3+}) is found in the tetrahedral site. Calcium is notably absent. The gel when it occurs con-tains almost no alumina and no alkalis or calcium. Thus the clay mineralogy is dominated by non-aluminous phases and the phase diagram $Si-R^2-R^3$ could well be $Si-Mg-Fe^{3+}$ at this stage.

Another example of weathering of ultrabasic rocks is a more aluminous serpentinite (16 % by weight) which was studied by Ducloux et al. (1976). Here a chlorite phase was formed in lower parts of the profile. These chlorites con-tain substantial aluminum, 0.9 to 1.4 atoms per $O_{10}(OH)_8$ and they are silica-rich. The general chemistry of the profile is that of loss of Mg, Si, Ca and a relative increase in Fe^{3+}, K and Na. Since the initial alumina content of the profile is relatively important, one sees a chlorite (14 Å) phase as a weathering product. In the example studied by Fontanaud (1982) the alumina content was lower and a saponi-te was formed.

In one horizon (Bg_1) of one of the profiles studi-ed, a new Mg-rich and Al-poor corrensitic phase occurs. This mineral is similar to the saponite of the previous example except for the pre-dominance of Fe^{3+} in the R^3 component. Talc is also present in the clay assemblages but there are no optical and microprobe data which would allow one to establish its coexistence with other phases. The following reaction appears to have occurred between C and B horizons :

Soil chlorite + Si-smectite → corrensite + R^3-smectite

This change in mineral assemblage is most likely due to a decrease in the ferric iron content in the organic-rich B horizon which stabilizes the corrensite to the detriment of the aluminous chlorite phase. In these sequences it is important to know what the Fe^3-Al relations are since they can obviously affect the stability of a phase.

The most striking feature of the soil profiles developed on ultrabasic rocks is the very limited saprock zone. There is a rapid change from rock to clay mineral assemblages. As a result the zone of internal destabilization of minerals such as that found in granites, is not well represented. The rock tends to weather as a whole and not in isolated chemical systems. This promotes reactions between clay mineral species throughout a weathering horizon. For example one has the reaction talc + oxides → saponite or chlorite + $smectite_1$ → corrensite + $smectite_2$. The data of Eswaran and Sys (1970) indicate that the reaction nontronite + gibbsite → goethite + kaolinite occurs in some tropical soils. This situation is less frequent in weathering of other rocks.

Elias **et al.** (1981) indicate that nontronite can destabilize to hematite plus quartz in laterite deposits in western Australia. This seems to be an ultimate step in the weathering process where alumina is removed from the system and silica plus iron oxide remain. Most often one finds that silicates are replaced by iron oxide and alumina when weathering is carried to an extreme case of laterite formation. It is important again to distinguish between the two possible R^3 components Al and Fe^{3+}. The overall tendency is to remove R^{2+} during weathering. Then one should consider the last stages in an Al-Fe^{3+}-Si system to describe the final phase assemblages and chemical changes. This is brought out by the report of Butt and Nickel (1981) who find goethite, kaolinite and at times gibbsite in leached zones of weathered serpentinites.

3 - Basic rocks

The great difference in composition between the primary phases in coarse-grained basic rocks (amphiboles, pyroxenes, plagioclase) leads to an alteration-mechanism quite similar to that of granites. Initial stages show grain contact reactions which continue to be active sites of clay mineral production well into the altered rock (saprock) zone. Internal destabilization is more important however ; overall chemistry of the alteration process of an amphibolite derived from a gabbro in well-drained profile (Ildefonse, 1978) shows a loss of the R^2 ions Ca and Fe^{2+}, with an increase in R^3 ions (Al, Fe^{3+}). Mg and Na are approximately constant as is the Si content. Potassium is concentrated in mid-profile by the crystallization of an alkali zeolite which is lost in the upper argillic horizons.

Petrographic microscope and clay fraction chemical analyses as well as X-ray diffraction studies reveal that the amphiboles and plagioclase grains alter at grain contacts to form a ferric beidellite. Internally, the amphiboles form a nontronite and in intragrain cracks talc is present. Within the plagioclase an aluminous, dioctahedral vermiculite occurs with alkali zeolites. This is the saprock assemblage. As weathering increases in intensity (saprolite) trioctahedral vermiculite appears in the amphibole grains and zeolite is no longer present in the plagioclase grains. In many areas of the saprolite a new vermiculite phase occurs which contains about 2.5 octahedral ions (Ildefonse et al., 1979). This phase forms grains several hundred microns in length. It becomes quite abundant in the upper saprolite horizons. However, in turn it becomes unstable in the lower soil horizons where a ferric beidellite replaces it.

If we consider that silica content variation is not terribly important, which seems to be the case in the whole rock chemical analyses, it is possible to fix R^2 and R^3 ions as inert components and to designate calcium chemical potential as an intensive variable in the system. Chemical analyses show that Ca-content decreases in the clay phases as weathering is more intense. The large grained vermiculite of the saprolite contains less calcium than the nontronite-beidellite assemblage found below it, in the saprock for example.

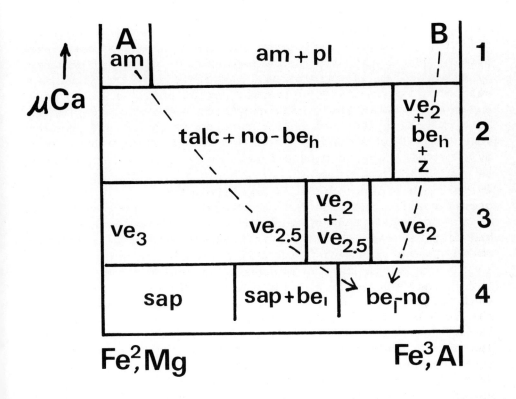

Figure 80 - Amphibolite alteration as a function of the chemical potential of calcium, and relative concentrations of R^2 ions (Fe^2, Mg) and R^3 ions (Fe^3, Al).

The stages of alteration are represented by numbers one through four where :
1 = initial amphibolite containing amphibole (am) and plagioclase (pl) ;
2 = saprock zone with the production of talc, high charge iron-rich smectites, nontronite-ferric beidellite (no-be$_h$), dioctahedral vermiculite (Ve$_2$) and alkali zeolite (z) ;
3 = saprolite zone where trioctahedral vermiculites (octahedral range from 3 to 2.5 ions, Ve$_3$–Ve$_{2.5}$) and dioctahedral vermiculites (Ve$_2$) form.
4 = argillite (soil) zone where saponite (sap) occurs with low charge ferric smectites (be$_l$–no).
Individual mineral grains amphibole (A) and plagioclase (B) evolve giving mineral assemblages along the dashed lines.

Figure 80 shows the phase relations of such a system where two-phase trends occur as the new clay minerals form in the rock. We must treat the rock as two separate systems where certain elements are lost or gained as weathering proceeds. Each mineral, amphibole and plagioclase, maintains its identity during weathering and it thus becomes a separate micro-system. The stages or rock, saprock, saprolite and argillite (soil) are numbered in the figure. Arrows show the chemical "path" taken by each of the reacting systems - amphibole and plagioclase.

In order to produce the aluminous, ferric trioctahedral vermiculite with 2.5 octahedral ions, the composition of the amphibole system must lose some of its R^2 component and possibly gain R^3. Whole rock analyses show a small loss of Mg during weathering and a significant oxidation of iron in the saprolite zone. However, magnesium drops to two-thirds and ferrous iron to 40 % of its initial value in the argillic soil horizon. It is here that a high charge ferric beidellite is the dominant phase. In the more open system where the constituent elements are mixed in the solifluxed zone, the chemistry appears to dictate the presence of a single low charge nontronite clay phase. This suggests that most elements are mobile and that the system is homogeneous. The convergence of the arrows in the figure indicates this effect.

An amphibolite in a poorly drained profile studied by Proust (1976) shows the importance that the migrating, altering fluid configuration will have. In the preceding example, a well drained profile, individual grain contacts and internal grain fractures and cracks were the initial site of alteration. It can be assumed that the altering fluids passed through these channels and thus reaction between fluids and unstable silicate minerals occurred here. The remarkable aspect of the study by Proust is the lack of grain contact reactions. Second, instead of multimineral clay assemblages occurring in each grain system-amphibole and plagioclase, the minerals which form are basically the same phase. In areas within the grains where new phases are found, one sees a vermiculite layer next to the metamorphic mineral. The clay mineral present in the centers of each grain is a beidellite which has a different composition depending upon the type of mineral from which it formed

(Figure 81). It appears that in a "wet" profile the stage of
saprock alteration is more or less skipped over and one is
in the later stages of saprolite alteration as we have described it in figure 77. One jumps from high calcium potential to a much lower one (levels 3 and 4) because the solutions are much more abundant and the reacting silicates cannot produce a high calcium content in them. In this situation the system has many mobile elements which diminish the
number of solid phases present.

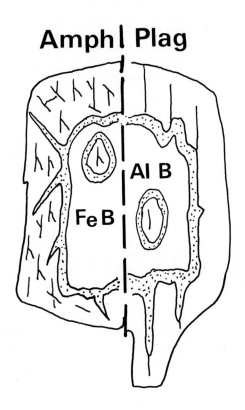

Figure 81 - Schematic view of plagioclase and
amphibole alteration in a system which is
constantly below the water table.
Amph = amphibole ; plag = plagioclase.
High temperature minerals are altered from within the grain.
Innermost zone is a beidellite, either ferric (Fe B)
or aluminoux (Al B). Contact between old grain and
clay is rimmed by a vermiculitic mineral
(stippled zone in figure).

The alteration process seen in detail within a single mineral grain indicates a step-wise recrystallization process between amphibole, plagioclase and beidellite. A thin zone (20-30 µ) occurs between metamorphic mineral and beidellite clay. It contains a vermiculitic phase closer in composition to the altering phase than to the beidellite. This can be considered to be the saprolite stage in figure 77 which occurs in the mineral grain itself. Here then we see the alteration phase relations displayed in a single grain instead of in horizons of a profile. The relative amount of liquid present as alteration occurs appears to be important in determining the phase which will form. The same type of relations are apparent in a fissural area when one attains saprolite facies or soil clay facies even when adjacent saprock zones are present.

Summary

If rock weathering is a matter of hydrology (how much water and for how long a time), this factor is controlled by the physical state of the rock itself. The first reactions occur in fissures and at grain contacts. The reaction products are generally monophase. This indicates that the fluids control the reaction in the measure that the chemical potential of many elements is controlled by sources outside the immediate reaction zone.

The second reactions occur within the grains themselves ; apparently the fluids circulate in micro-fissures. Here the clay mineral products are multiphase. This indicates that the reacting minerals "saturate" the solutions with respect to certain elements (Si, Al and Fe^{3+} in general) and thus the elemental ratios in the reacting phases are found, approximately, in the new clay mineral assemblage. These elements behave as inert components. They can however migrate from their site of origin displacing the bulk composition of the rock slightly.

The third type of reactions characterize the complete saturation of the system by the fluids. This is due to a collapse of the old rock fabric and a large replacement of primary phases by clay minerals. Here the tendency is to form one single chemical system. Under these conditions the clay minerals previously formed react to produce a new assemblage or single phase. The fluids impose a certain mineralogy on the system but the most important reaction is that of homogenization of the different minerals present which puts all parts into the same chemical system. This material can then be described as a horizon where the mineralogy can be classified by layers as they approach the surface.

The different factors of drainage, total rainfall, temperature and organo-biologic activity will determine the chemical potential of elements in solution which will influence the mineralogy of the silicate-oxide portion of the system. Oxidation can become an important factor in soils where certain elements (Fe and Mn principally) enter into the oxide state and thus leave the silicate system. Chesworth (1980) presents a very promising method of phase analysis for soil systems using the activities of Mg, K, H as variables and condisering Si, Al, Fe as immobile components.

There are then two parts of a soil or weathering profile ; that where an essentially high temperature phase assemblage reacts with aqueous solutions and that where clay minerals react with the solutions. Of course, other minerals or aggregates (rock particles or pebbles) can occur in the soil zone but these are gradually integrated into the clay dominated system. In fact one often sees rinds of reaction facies on pebbles or boulders. These rinds repeat the soil-saprolite-saprock-rock sequence found as one descends into the profile. Again, the mineral assemblages respond to the structure and scale of the chemical system.

3 - Hydrothermal alteration

a - Introduction

This geologic phenomenon is difficult to assess initially because it designates conditions which can at times exceed the stability realm of clay minerals and it can at times occur under P-T-x conditions which are associated with other geologic phenomena, such as weathering or burial metamorphism - terms which bring to mind quite different processes. Initially one must define the realm which is to be designated as hydrothermal and then it is possible to describe the processes and attribute geologic observations to them. It will be considered here that hydrothermal alteration indicates water-rock interaction at temperatures above 60 ± 20°C. The temperature chosen is of course arbitrary but might prove to be useful. In general terms the rock involved has crystallized at temperatures well above those of the hydrothermal alteration : this point is possibly the most important in our definition. The solids have attained a crystalline form which is significantly unstable in the presence of water at the temperatures considered.

The solutions concerned are aqueous but contain dissolved solids (Agar, 1981 ; Moore and Nash, 1974) and gaseous or liquid components. Some of these components can be precipitated in the form of carbonates, sulfates, sulfides and oxides. We will consider the silicate-solution relations for the most part here since the subject with which we are dealing is that of clay mineralogy. However, one must always remember the potential of interaction between carbonate and sulfide equilibria with those concerning silicates. For example, an increase in carbonate ion activity could well cause the transfer of iron from silicate to carbonate. Such reactions have been frequently encountered in burial diagenetic settings (Schmidt and Mac Donald, 1979) and they most likely are important in hydrothermal reaction when one considers the frequent reported occurrence of carbonates in altered rocks.

If water-rock reaction is the key association in hydrothermal alteration, the physical configuration of a vein within a rock is the most common geological observation indicating the paleo-existence of a hydrothermal process. The existence of veins suggests flow or transportation of material both in and out of the locally observed system and this then is the most important geochemical consideration in hydrothermal systems. Water-rock interaction with transportation of material along preferential channels is the system which we will study.

Hydrothermal alteration occurs in all rock types as one would expect, and as a result the chemical reaction and phases produced will be directly controlled by rock type. It would be impossible to list the reactions and mineralogies of all possible or known hydrothermal alteration as an example which might serve as a method of study but which will not apply to all cases of hydrothermal alteration found in nature. The system studied is that of porphyry copper type alteration. Studies by the following authors have been used as a basis for generalization : Meyer and Hemley, 1967 ; Fournier, 1965, 1967 ; Steiner, 1968 ; Kelley and Kerr, 1957 ; Keller and Hanson, 1968 ; Lowell and Guilbert, 1970 ; Grim, 1968, p. 499 ; Bundy and Murray, 1959 ; Burnham, 1962 ; Meyer and Hemley, 1959 ; Nielson, 1968 ; Keller, 1963 ; Thompson, 1970 ; Schoen and White, 1965 ; Tomita et al., 1969 ; Bonorino, 1959 ; Patton et al., 1973 ; Sillitoe, 1973 ; Phillips et al., 1974 ; Saegart et al., 1974 ; Moore and Nash, 1974 ; Moore and Czamanske, 1973 ; Camus, 1975 ; Jacobs and Parry, 1976 ; Villas and Norton, 1977 ; Watmuff, 1978 ; Ford, 1978 ; Moore, 1978 ; Lanier et al., 1978 ; Cloke and Kesler, 1979 ; Dowsett, 1980 ; Mac Dowell and Elders, 1980 ; Taylor and Fryer, 1980 ; Agar, 1981 ; Beane, 1974 ; Meunier and Velde, 1982. There are of course other pertinent studies in the literature.

b - Facies Description

Most of the authors describe two types of alteration : pervasive and vein. If we insist that water is introduced into the rock from some exterior source, then even pervasive alteration must have begun as a vein alteration which became infinitely subdivided until the rock was completely altered. The idea of hydrothermal alteration as reported by the authors cited is based upon the fact that the affected rocks are different in mineralogical facies from those which surround them. The altered rocks are frequently of very similar composition and similar mineral facies to the initial igneous material. The major chemical difference now between the rock types is their water content which was induced into the rocks at sometime either late in their cooling history of after their solidification. It is possible that some hydrothermal alteration is due to continued interaction of silicate solids and aqueous solutions upon iso-chemical cooling. However most authors assume that such a system occurs on the scale of an intrusive body but not on the scale of a hand specimen where apparent chemical transport has created the mineral assemblage observed. Figure 82 attempts to illustrate this idea. Figure 82a shows the initial state where silicate magma coexists with aqueous solution ; Figure 82b shows the stage where solidification has occurred giving an igneous mineralogy in the presence of aqueous solution ; Figure 82.c indicates lower temperature reaction between rock and solution which occurs along veins or zones of preferential transport of the solution. Deposition and dissolution occur along these zones. Thus it is possible that whole intrusion be iso-chemical throughout the cooling evolution to hydrothermal alteration but each small sector will show evidence of chemical transport. Of course, one can have hydrothermal fluids transported from sources outside the intrusive body in question.

Our definition of a chemical system will then be restricted to a hand specimen scale and we will leave the problem of larger bodies to geological interpretation.

The utility of such an approach is evident when one realizes that most geologists working with hydrothermal systems must use samples that are obtained by drill coring. Such methods give a linear view of the geology which in fact reduces any observation to a hand specimen scale. The normal two dimensions (surfaces of outcrops) of geological investigation are not available and contiguous successions of change cannot be observed. We will try do deal here with the common material available to geologists.

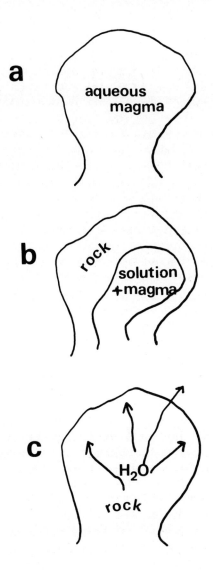

Figure 82 - Stages of acid magma intrusion and cooling in porphyry copper-type systems.
a = intrusion of aqueous magma. b = solidification of aqueous magma. Two sectors are formed, that where rock and solution exist. Reaction between this solution and the rock can occur, giving propylitic-type alterations and potassic alteration. c = hydrothermal alteration due to interaction of aqueous solution and solidified system at lower temperatures. In this stage sericitic and argillic alterations can occur.

For the most part porphyry copper-type alteration occurs in acid intrusive rocks. It can appear in intermediate rocks also but these seem to be infrequent in occurrence. The silicate matrix which we will consider is then composed initially of potassic-feldspar and plagioclase-quartz, muscovite and biotite. The presence of biotite is often important in that certain key minerals are derived from it. Meyer and Hemley (1967) and Lowell and Guilbert (1970) have codified the major mineral facies of porphyry copper alteration, apparently to most authors' satisfaction, and we will use their description in the following discussion.

Four alteration types exist :

1. **Potassic** alteration is characterized by the great abundance of new potassic feldspar and magnesian biotite. This latter phase is more magnesian and aluminous than primary, magmatic biotite in the same or similar rocks (Moore and Czamanske, 1973 ; Beane, 1974 ; Jacobs and Parry, 1976).

2. **Phyllic** alteration is notable by the great abundance of sericite in what often is expressed as a sericite-quartz rock.

3. **Argillic** will be considered here as an alteration which covers a certain span of mineral types - illite is frequently found, as well as mixed layered minerals such as allevardite, an aluminous smectite which might well be potassic which often occurs with kaolinite. Precise descriptions are not common so that one does not know which clay mineral assemblages commonly occur together.

4. **Propylitic** alteration is characterized by the mineral pair chlorite-epidote ; calcite or other carbonates are often associated with this alteration. Calcic zeolites are also frequently found as replacement or vein minerals.

The minerals corrensite and chlorite are probably common in the phyllic and argillic facies and can be found in the potassic facies. These minerals are frequently found to replace biotites in a manner which suggests a low mobility of some of their chemical constituents (Meunier, 1982).

From the descriptions given, it appears that all four alteration facies can be found as pervasive types. All facies can also be found as vein or limited zone alterations.

The most characteristic occurrence in porphyry copper-type alteration is the superposition of one facies upon another - secondary hydrothermal alteration is very common.

According to Lowell and Guilbert (1970), the sequence potassic-phyllic-argillaceous-propylitic suggests lower temperature facies. The association chlorite-epidote found in the Salton Sea drill holes (Mac Dowell and Elders, 1980) occurred at about 220°C whereas smectite-kaolinite is present below 100°C and mixed layered dioctahedral minerals below 200°C. Thus one might suspect that the propylitic facies is higher in temperature than a large portion of the argillaceous facies. The phyllic zone could well overlap the propylitic facies in P-T conditions since sericite is common to both. Here chemistry determines the facies.

c - T-x Relationships

If the types of alteration represent different temperatures and if the superposition of one facies on another is common, what type of mineral distribution is one likely to encounter in hydrothermally altered rocks of the porphyry copper type ? Several examples given by Beaufort (1981) will be used to illustrate the response. Figure 83 shows the configuration of a phyllic vein which alters a potassic alteration facies rock composed of K-feldspar albite phlogopite and sericite. Microprobe analyses of the mica in the vein center are near that of ideal muscovite. This is a deposition phase. Micas found at vein edges are in general illitic with a tendency toward an "overfilled" octahedral layer $[2.05-2.10$ atoms per $O_{10}(OH)_2]$. Micas in the alteration halo which were found to replace plagioclase are decidedly illitic ($K_{0.91-0.85}$) they contain somewhat less Fe-Mg than those minerals at the vein edge and have fewer than two ions in the octahedral sites. Here we see a typical change in mineral composition which can be ascribed to either lower temperatures outward from the vein or lower potassium activity outward from the vein. Since the rock affected by the vein alteration contains K-feldspar, white mica and a phlogopite

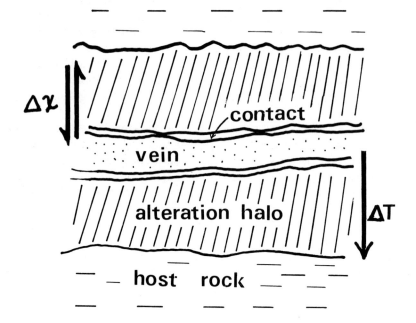

Figure 83 - Diagram of hydrothermal vein alteration. The following zones show specific mineral assemblages : vein = deposition ; contact = earliest solution-rock interaction, alteration ; halo = secondary solution-rock interaction zone. Temperature decreases outward from vein and chemical components can be exchanged between rock and percolating solution. Δx indicates movement of material in solution. ΔT shows temperature decrease outward from vein.

which is transformed to sericite, one can assume that the activity of potassium should initially be relatively high, at least as high as that in the vein itself where mica was deposited. We can therefore ascribe the lowering of K_2O content of the secondary sericitic mica to a lower temperature away from the vein. This means that the vein solutions were introduced into the rock when it had cooled to conditions below that of the phyllic facies and equal to or lower than those of the high temperature argillic conditions. The phyllic solutions then transported material which precipitated as muscovite and which sericitized the wall rock of the vein. A microprobe study of the assemblages produced by this phyllic alteration shows that in the vein muscovite is present, at the vein edge one finds sericite plus aluminous magnesian phlogopite and in the rock the assemblage illite-orthoclase-corrensite is present due to alteration.

Figure 84 indicates these assemblages showing the composition of the phases concerned (data from Beaufort, 1981). The original granitic mineral composition (feldspar + biotite + muscovite) is modified by a relative increase in Al_2O_3 of the biotite and R^2 component in the muscovite. As the aqueous vein material interacts with the rock more and more one goes from **a** to **c** in the diagram. In our $MR^3 - 2R^3 - 3R^2$ plot, we find that the bulk composition of the rock is changed by an increase in alumina as the alteration halo is greater and one finds lower temperature facies - illite, corrensite and orthoclase. This suggests a loss in R^{2+} ions which must be evacuated by the solutions, since they are not found in the system, especially not in the muscovite composition vein material. Globally we see that both temperature and composition variation occur during phyllic alteration of this granitic rock through the interaction of a vein fluid with a granitic rock. If we assume that the same aqueous fluids can continue to flow outward from their center of origin, they must lose thermal energy through contact with the encasing rock, just as they lost it in altering the rock in the halo zone of the vein described above. As a result, these vein alterations will cause clay mineral assemblages of lower and lower temperature facies the further they travel. This results in a general zonation of alteration described by Lowell and Guilbert (1970) on a large scale. The center of alteration at depth shows highest temperatures and as one goes outward and/or upward the temperatures of alteration decrease. Thus the temperature aspect is easy to understand. However, the problem of chemical transfer is not as easily dealt with.

If one considers the different hydrothermal alteration facies it seems that the basic transfer in potassic alteration is a loss of Ca and Fe from the rock and a gain of Mg and K. The importance of potassium transport is possibly exaggerated by the presence of orthoclase and mica. The

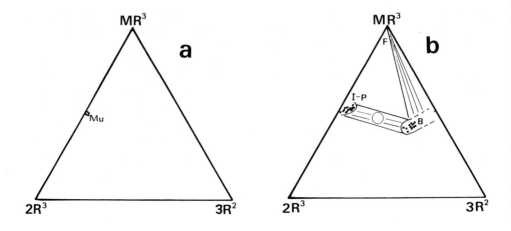

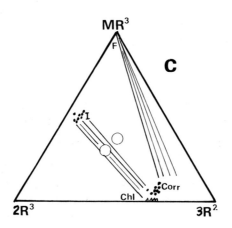

Figure 84 - Representation of phyllic vein alteration
assemblages as they affect a granitic rock which has an
assemblage feldspar, muscovite, biotite.
Figure a shows the vein "assemblage" that of muscovite (Mu).
Figure b shows the vein contact assemblage with aluminous
biotite (B) and illite-phengite (I-P).
Figure c shows the vein halo area with an illite-corrensite
(Corr) orthoclase (F) or illite-chlorite (Chl) facies.
Dots show analyses by Beaufort (1981).
Large circles indicate bulk composition of zone
described as indicated by the phases present.

crystallization of these phases can be explained alternatively as being due to a loss of calcium to the solution or its incorporation into carbonates and a gain in Mg from solution and a consequent incorporation of alumina into a mica ; potassium could remain constant in the process. Potassic alteration facies in more basic rocks shows less orthoclase and muscovite, the final K_2O content seems to be frequently a function of initial rock type (Agar, 1981). There should still be an excess of alumina in the product if plagioclase was abundant initially and if calcium was lost to the solutions through its destruction. Thus potassic alteration might just be largely calcium loss.

If we look at the next lowest temperature facies-phyllic, we see that sericite is the major phase to form. It seems that here alumina has been introduced into the system. It is possible that some of the alumina in the plagioclase destabilized in potassic alteration was transported by the solutions. Potassium is lost from biotites in the lower temperature facies of this alteration and thus these minerals would provide sericite as follows :

$$\text{biotite + aqueous alumina + silica}$$
$$\rightarrow \text{illite (sericite) + chlorite}$$

The argillic alteration can probably be considered to be a lower temperature expression of this same system. It might also be possible that potassium is lost to the solution and transported to still lower temperature zones. One should note that the further one follows the argillic facies, the less potassium is required to form the alteration minerals. In the end an assemblage of potassi-calcic beidellite plus kaolinite or kaolinite alone is found. Both alkalis and magnesium are lost from the silicate-oxide assemblages.

The lowest temperature assemblages of the argillic pervasive alteration pose a problem. In these rocks, most elements have been evacuated to leave only Al-Si, potassium and some alkalis plus minor carbonates. This means that all of the ferromagnesian elements are leached out leaving the pure kaolin that is used in industry. Since these clays form at very low temperatures ($< 100°C$) the hydrothermal system must have more or less run down in its reactivity.

The propylitic assemblages contain epidote and calcic zeolites which indicate temperatures higher than the lower argillic facies which contain beidellite. Thus we cannot evacuate ferromagnesian elements out into a lower temperature propylitic zone, since it forms at higher temperatures. It might be that the lost magnesium found its way into the potassic alteration facies where this element is frequently notably increased through alteration. This means that an up-temperature chemical gradient must be established. This hypothesis must necessarily be impossible in many instances reported where argillic alteration is secondary to potassic and propylitic alterations.

Another possibility for the evacuation of Ca, Na and Mg is through thermal springs. These waters are frequently mineralized as carbonate solutions containing the elements missing from the argillic silicate assemblages. Calcium can always be deposited as a carbonate somewhere along the way but Na and Mg carbonates are rare ; dolomite in low temperature veins is also infrequent. Thus hot spring activity, often associated with granitic terrains could represent the lowest temperature term of the argillic alteration series.

d - Mineralogical Peculiarities

Three studies (Meunier and Velde, 1982 ; Cathelineau, 1981 ; Beaufort, 1981) using electron microprobe techniques have demonstrated that aluminous smectites of the argillic facies are in fact potassic beidellites. Meunier and Velde (1982) have shown that the normal treatment procedures for clay minerals (air drying, glycolation and potassium saturation) will not necessarily indicate that potassium is the major interlayer cation. The mineral behaves as a calcic montmorillonite. It is, however, not completely saturated by alkali or alkaline earth cations since potassium saturation in a chloride solution effects collapse to 12.5 Å at room conditions. There is a decrease in the pH of the saturating solution which suggests the presence of interlayer hydronium ions. These clays are not stable in the sedimentary environment in that they appear to change to a calcic montmorillonite when present in sediments. It appears then that potassic beidellite could be used as an index mineral to identify hydrothermal activity at low temperatures.

Biotites found in the potassic zone, as mentioned above, are more magnesian than those in the host rock. Another feature of their composition is their aluminum content. Data from Beaufort (1981) show that as one goes to lower temperature alteration facies the alumina content of biotites increases. There is also a slight tendency to decrease the potassium content. The same tendency is seen in the ferromagnesian phases which replace biotite : vermiculite-chlorite and corrensite. Each alteration zone brings a more aluminous phase as temperatures decrease. The data on phengite-illites reported by Meunier and Velde (1982) and Beaufort (1981) show the same trend. Each zone shows lower magnesium and iron content as temperatures decrease. The succeeding clay facies containing mixed layered minerals and beidellite continue this trend. The tendency to low Fe-Mg contents distinguishes the hydrothermal clays from those found in sedimentary rocks. It appears that potassic beidellites are typical of hydrothermal origin.

e - Phase Diagrams for Porphyry Copper Alteration

The porphyry copper alterations are rather easily condensed into the $MR^3-2R^3-3R^2$ coordinates. One precaution must be taken concerning the MR^3 pole. In the initial plutonic facies, calcium is an important constituent of the silicate phases. Two feldspars are present denoting the non-equivalence of Ca and K,Na in the phase assemblages. The role of calcium continues to be important into the alteration zones either in silicates such as epidote or in carbonates. Thus we cannot really assimilate Ca to alkalis but must add a new phase to those represented in the triangle of $MR^3-2R^3-3R^2$. Giggenback (1981) has emphasized that high carbonate ion activity destabilizes the plagioclase which liberates alumina to the system thus providing the raw material for the different hydrothermal alteration facies.

Figure 85 shows the various major mineral assemblages frequent in the potassic, propylitic, phyllic and argillic alteration facies. The plutonic facies is composed of feldspars and biotite plus or minus a phengitic muscovite (Figure 84). The potassic facies is composed of a sericite closer to muscovite composition, an aluminous biotite and potassium feldspar. Calcic plagioclase is not stable and most of the calcium seems to have been removed from the

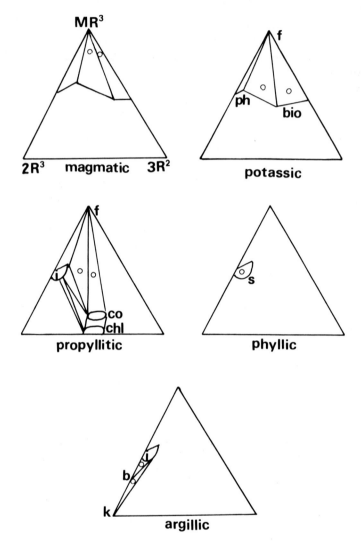

Figure 85 - Mineral parageneses found in hydrothermal
alteration. Initial rock assemblage (magmatic) contains
phengitic mica (ph), biotite (bio) and feldspar (f). Potassic alteration contains the same minerals but bulk composition shifts to lower alkali content in MR³-2R³-3R² coordinates through loss of Na and Ca. Biotite is more aluminous as
is the white mica. Propylitic alteration is characterized by
the presence of chlorite (chl) and corrensite (co). Phyllic
alteration has a dominant sericite (s) component. Argillic
alteration is typified by the presence of illite, mixed
layered minerals, beidellite (b, usually potassic) and kaolinite (k). Circles indicate possible rock bulk compositions.

local system. Therefore the bulk rock composition is less rich in the MR^3 component as indicated by the circles in figure 85. The next facies always encountered in porphyry copper deposits in the propylitic zone where calcium is in great evidence forming epidote in the rock and calcite in the rock or in veins. Ferromagnesian minerals are now chlorite or corrensite and the sericite is definitely illitic in composition with a strong Mg-Fe component. These two facies – potassic and propylitic – are always present ; the potassic representing the inner zone of the deposit and the propylitic the outer zone. The bulk composition of the two is different in their Ca-K ratios but other element abundances are similar. The reaction muscovite + biotite = chlorite + feldspar is evident from the diagrams. This reaction going from left to right indicates a lower temperature (see Velde, 1965). This is concordant with the observations of many authors that the potassic zone is the deeper, hotter area of alteration. It is probable that the two zones are also related by the chemical exchange K $\rightleftarrows$ Ca where the propylitic zone is calcium-rich.

The next two alteration zones are characterized by low Ca-content and decreasing alkali **and** magnesium contents. These are the phyllic (sericite) zone where a muscovitic mica is deposited, and the argillic zone where illite, beidellite and kaolinite are present. The end term of the argillic alteration can be almost pure kaolinite rock. The trends in MR^3-2R^3-3R^2 coordinates are shown in figure 85. We see a strong evolution toward the 2R^3 pole of the diagram.

Now, how can we represent those facies in T-μx space ? The variable of potassium chemical potential seems to be very important, according to most authors, although we must also not forget that of calcium. If we indicate the relative activity of potassium and temperature we can show the various alteration facies (Figure 86). The initial plutonic rock assemblage is separated into two facies – potassic and propylitic. Most authors have noted an apparent rapid change in facies indicating that there is no transition zone between them in T-μx space. However, this point should be more closely examined. We will indicate by a dashed arrow in the figure the possibility of various intermediate compositions at different temperatures. It could be that the mineral reaction muscovite + biotite $\rightarrow$ chlorite +

feldspar masks the gradual change in bulk composition of the rock so that most authors have divided the rocks by mineralogy, not considering the possibility of gradual chemical change.

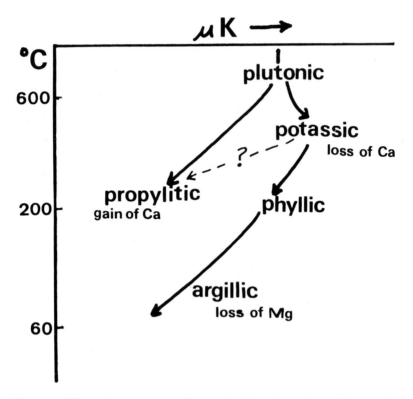

Figure 86 - Representation of the chemical "paths" of hydrothermal alteration of acidic rocks during the formation of porphyry copper-type deposits.
The variables are temperature and the relative-chemical potential of potassium in each system. There is a possible relation between the calcium-poor potassic facies and the calcium-rich propylitic facies.
It is assumed that calcium is found in carbonate phases which do not figure in the previous diagrams.

The phyllic-argillic sequence is one of lower temperatures at lower potassium and magnesium content in a context of low calcium in the silicates (we are not considering the carbonate chemistry in this analysis). Probably the phyllic alteration occurs at higher temperatures than the propylitic. This is deduced from mica-illite compositions (Beaufort, 1981). The sequence of argillic phase assemblages is formed at decreasing temperatures at lower and lower alkali and magnesium ion activities.

It is frequently found that a vein alters a previously altered rock in porphyry copper deposits. Figure 86 can be used to predict what will be the mineralogical effects of solutions responsible for each facies as they are introduced into an altered rock. Take for example a potassic facies rock where an argillic vein is found. In going from vein center to edge and into the rock one will find phase assemblages richer in alkalis and an apparent increase in temperature through mineral analyses, i.e., illites in the center, sericites and muscovite at the edges and phengitic micas in the rock. A phyllic vein which cuts a propylitic zone will show a decrease in alkalis away from the vein and an apparent slightly lower temperature regime and so forth. Thus one should be able to interpret the sequence of events and the relative temperatures which occurred during the alteration phases by using the information in Figure 85.

It is evident that different rock types will respond differently to the alteration process described above. However, the mechanism of alteration appears to be simple - aqueous solutions containing carbonate ions, and of course sulfide ions, etc... - will react with the silicate mineral assemblages. Depending upon the minerals present, some ions will leave the system and others will be concentrated. The result will be a hydrous mineral assemblage formed at temperatures below those of magmatic crystallization.

318

Summary

The nature of hydrothermal alteration is that of chemical transfer in aqueous solution. This occurs over a range of pressures and temperatures. In a single rock specimen, one can find evidence of P-T-x variation. Essentially the vein environment concerns T-μx variation over millimetric to metric distances. It seems that one characteristic of hydrothermal deposits is the superposition of different regimes of T-μx variation. Often one finds pervasively altered rocks altered in their turn by fluids following fractures which form vein wall-rock type alteration. One must understand the significance of chemical variation in a mineral series in order to understand the parameters which formed a given assemblage of minerals. At present we have just the initial parts of the data base necessary to understand the origins of clays in hydrothermal deposits. Probably the only way to advance our understanding is to have systematic microprobe studies performed on hydrothermally altered rocks using X-ray diffraction identification whenever possible. It would be necessary to analyse sericite veins from deep level potassic alteration and those having formed at higher levels in order to see the effect that pressure will have on the mica compositions. The same is true for phyllic and argillic alterations as well as propylitic types.

The low temperature hydrothermal alteration should resemble weathering alteration systems in that the physical arrangement and chemical potentials are guided by the same factors - the relative influence of water on silicates. The question which must be answered is "which material influences the chemistry of the phases the most - rock composition or chemical activity of the species in solution ?". If the rock saturates the solution rapidly, the phases will be determined by its bulk composition, the temperature of the solution and the evacuation of a soluble element, calcium or sodium for example. These two elements are not easily fixed in a stable phyllosilicate at high temperatures where micas tend to form. They seem to be more easily transported and fixed in smectite or mixed layered minerals, in that the phases are frequently observed to be potassic. We know that temperature increases potassium selectivity on montmorillonites (see smectite chapter) and this tendency might well be accentuated for the beidellites found in hydrothermal deposits. The loss of Ca and Na from the silicate system is very important in considering the phase relations of these systems. Of course, one of the greatest unknowns is the composition of the fluids which provoke the alteration and the effect which they will have on mineral equilibria. At present, it does not seem possible to generalize concerning fluid compositions and there is even less data concerning the influence that these solutions will have on the clays. It does seem apparent though that carbonate ion activity is important in the destabilization of silicates (Giggenbach, 1981).

One can say then that the general parameters of hydrothermal alteration of silicate rocks are known. We need to have more information on natural systems in order to form a coherent ensemble of geochemical reasoning.

4 - Deep Sea Basalt Alteration

a - Introduction

For some time it has been known that basic lavas found on deep ocean floors tend to be altered and to have compositions other than basalts. These changes are in large part due to a hydration of the rock which is expressed for the most part by the formation of clay minerals. Intensive research has been carried out recently on deep ocean basalts through the Deep Sea Drilling Program. Many sediment surface drag samples have been studied and now several deep drill holes through the surface layers of basalt have been carried out. The results of petrographic, microprobe and X-ray diffraction studies on this material have been reported in the D.S.D.P. Initial Reports as well as those in many of the leading journals give us quite a bit of information to use in describing the interaction of basalts with waters at different temperatures.

The most striking conclusion, reached almost unanimously by the authors of these studies, is that the basalts behave as open systems when put in contact with aqueous solutions. Loss of some elements and gain of others by the basalt is almost a universal observation. However, the result is rarely a monomineral assemblage, usually three or more new phases are found to form in the samples. Among them are dioctahedral smectites, zeolites, saponites and oxides. An apparently amorphous phase (palagonite) occurs as a result of the alteration of glass when it is present at the edges of the lava blocks. These observations suggest that we are dealing with an open system where several elements remain as inert components. Chemical constituents enter or leave the system, i.e., the basalt rock, and new phases are formed replacing the old, high temperature mineral assemblage.

As a summary of these studies, one can classify the types of alteration into three groups :

1. Deep sea weathering such as that considered by Hart (1970) and Staudigel and Hart (1983).

2. Hydrothermal alteration where characteristically one finds amygdule filling, vein filling and hyaloclastic breccias (Juteau et al., 1978 ; Melson, 1973 ; Schneidegger and Stakes, 1977 ; Novak, 1980 ; Pritchard, 1979 ; Mevel, 1979 ; Mills, 1980 ; Schneidegger and Stakes, 1979 ; Andrews, 1980 ; Humphries and Marriner, 1979 ; Lawrence et al., 1978 ; among others).

3. So called deuteric alteration where all minerals are transformed leaving the serpentine-chlorite mineralogy of serpentinization (Thompson and Melson, 1970 ; Miyashiro et al., 1969a & b, 1970). Samples which contain the typical greenschist facies epidote-chlorite-actinolite assemblage will of course not be considered here. However, they probably represent the closed system equivalent of the serpentinized rocks which means temperatures above about 220°C (Mac Dowell and Elders, 1980) where actinolite and epidote are present.

The two end terms of the classification are relatively easy to define and explain, that of deep sea weathering and that of serpentinization. However, the hydrothermal-hyaloclastic samples present a great variety of minerals and of specific sites of crystallization : it is these samples which have provided the material for the most detailed petrographic studies of deep sea basalts. A summary of the petrographic observations will be given in order to better understand the different types of alteration.

b - Weathering

Hart and Nowalk (1970), Hart and Erlank (1974), Hart (1970), Staudigel et al. (1981) and Murray (1970) show that weathering of the glassy portion of basalts generally occurs in two zones of mineral facies. The outer rim of the samples shows an apparently amorphous, opacified zone where obvious chemical transfer has occurred without apparent crystallization of new phase. There is a loss of calcium, magnesium and silica and there appears to be a gain of potassium and iron in the glassy areas of the basalt. The sample becomes more hydrous. Beyond this zone, which is called palagonite in subaerially altered basalts, one finds that the glass is replaced by a potassic nontronite and possibly other smectite species (Melson and Thompson, 1973). The overall chemical change in the smectite zone is similar to that of the palagonite zone except that there are differences in the amount of chemical change and possibly alkali contents are different. In general, the volcanic mineralogy is unaffected. In fact, a sample studied by the present author showed that magmatic biotite, surrounded by smectite, retained its composition integrally. Plagioclase and pyroxenes are not altered either. Olivine is frequently altered.

The net result is that submarine weathering is not extensive in a geologic sense since it involves just the glassy portion at the edge of exposed basalts. Hart (1970) showed that six million years could be necessary for the exchange process to effect significant chemical transfer. Staudigel et al. (1981) indicate a period of 3 million years. The new clay mineral which is formed is an iron-rich smectite where potassium usually occupies the interlayer site along with some calcium (Melson and Thompson, 1973). This process occurs certainly at ocean water temperatures $(20°C > T > 4°C)$.

A word might be added here concerning the material palagonite. Studies by Furnes and El-Anbaawy (1980), Furnes (1978), Summers (1976), Honnorez (1972), Liou (1974) for example, indicate that this material is found at the chilled edge of basalts formed and transformed in various environments. The point in common, generally, is the absence of response to X-ray crystallographic methods of identification. One assumes that palagonite is amorphous. Yet one finds a striking similarity in composition to the smectite alteration of glassy basalt, i.e., increase in Fe^{3+} and K contents while other elements are lost. It might very well be that palagonite contains microcrystalline clays which are less well developed, in crystal size, than those in more slowly cooled glassy portions of basaltic rocks. Studies of experimentally derived altered basalts (Crovisier et al., 1983) indicate that this is the case.

c - Hydrothermal Alteration

This system is complex and one must be careful in considering the site at which the new phases occur. If we wish to deal with the basalt transformation, we should ignore momentarily the amygdule and vein filling phases. This material has been transported into the sample. When this material is excluded, two facies can be defined ; low temperature nontronite-alkali zeolite and a higher temperature celadonite-Ca zeolite-Al smectite, analcime facies. If we refer to the zeolite chapter, we see that alkali zeolites are low temperature phases whereas the assemblage calcic zeolite plus analcime (strictly sodic) are of high temperature origin. In fact, Mevel (1979) found that the analcime was of low silica content (Si = $\simeq$ 2 Al) which corroborates the higher temperature origin deduction.

1 - Low temperature hydrothermal facies

The most important chemical character of these clay mineral facies is that all olivine crystals are altered, which distinguishes them from the sea water-sediment interface weathering facies. The alteration product of olivine is variable, as is the case for eruptive rocks which contain abundant volatile phases (D. Velde, 1971). The palagonite layer is still apparent at the edge of the rock while the major clay mineral formed as a replacement of volcanic phases in the interior is a nontronite (ferric dioctahedral smectite). The abundance of this phase, which contains oxidized iron, is due to a general oxidation of the rock which has been noted by many authors. The assumed chemical balance is that of Mg, Ca, Na, Si loss and a gain of ferric iron and potassium although Ailin-Pyzik and Sommer (1981) show that iron is immobile and only potassium is gained. The alumina balance is either not well known, or is variable depending upon the rock studied. The bulk chemistry of the original basalt is pushed toward an R^{3+} assemblage with loss of M^+ and R^2 ions if we refer the process to MR^3-$2R^3$-$3R^2$ coordinates. Alkali zeolites are common. They appear at the edges of rock fragments or in vacuoles. For the moment they will be considered to be part of the rock system when they are closely associated with the original basalt.

2 - Medium temperature hydrothermal facies

In these rocks, one finds that the feldspars are altered to zeolite plus clay assemblages, a rare occurrence in the low temperature facies. Ferromagnesian minerals are less altered but when they are, $Al-Fe^{3+}$ potassic smectites are found. Clinopyroxene is especially resistant to alteration (Mevel, 1979). Glass is often altered to palagonite or iron smectite but it does persist in the more interior (away from amygdules and veins) parts of the rocks. The smectites range from aluminous to ferric in composition with many intermediate terms. One suspects the presence of both di- and trioctahedral forms. A new phase occurs in the replacements of magmatic minerals, which is potassic proto-celadonite. This is a mixed layered phase similar to glauconite except for a higher Mg and Al content (see the section concerning these minerals).

Overall, there seems to be a loss of magnesium, sodium and possibly calcium from the rocks. However, this is difficult to ascertain due to a large quantity of secondary minerals which have been deposited in vugs and veins. The general chemical balance can best be inferred from the compositions of the new phases produced.

Ca-K zeolites and analcime have been reported (Mevel, 1979 ; Bohlke et al., 1980 ; Paparassiliou and Cosgrove, 1981 ; Scheidegger and Stakes, 1979). These minerals are the result of higher temperatures than those experienced by the low temperature facies described above.

3 - Deuteric alteration

This phenomenon is well known under the name of serpentinization : the transformation of a basic or ultrabasic rock into a serpentine mono-mineral rock which contains minor oxides and sulfides. In the deep sea, these rocks have only been found at the sediment-sea surface in drag samples (Miyashiro et al., 1969, 1979 ; Thompson and Melson, 1970). The deep drill holes have apparently not attained this type of rock. The most striking character of such rocks is the mobility of the elements which are not found in serpentine, i.e., Ca, Al, Fe, Na, Ti, K. Chlorite, an aluminous phase, has been reported in deep sea rocks (Mevel, 1979 ; Miyashiro et al., 1969) which indicates a retention of this element in the solid phase. Thus the deuteric phase of alteration concentrates R^2 ions and releases some R^3 and all M^+ ions. These facies can be generally considered to be of high temperature compared with clay facies.

4 - Vugs and veins

We can describe the basalt alterations from low to high temperatures as those which cover the range of clay mineral facies. We must nevertheless consider the vein-vug deposits which are especially apparent in the middle temperature range-hydrothermal alteration. There are essentially two kinds of void fillings - those with smectite-celadonite outer rims and saponite inner layers and those with celadonite outer and zeolite inner layers. It appears that the first type is associated with rocks altered at lower temperatures and the latter with rocks altered at higher temperatures as outlined above. However, veins contain other phases such as saponite-calcite (Lawrence et al., 1978), zeolite-calcite (Juteau et al., 1978 ; Mills, 1980) and one can find chlorite in vesicles (Lawrence et al., 1978). Oxides are frequently present. It appears that the elements which have left the basalts as they were altered, can be found as vein and vug vesicle fillings, i.e., Si, Al, Ca and Mg. The clay minerals celadonite-nontronite have been found in deposits at the sediment-sea water interface (Hoffert et al., 1978.a ; Honnorez et al., 1981 ; Schrader et al., 1980 ; Müller and Forstner, 1976 ; Bischoff, 1969). Talc has also been reported in these hydrothermal vent deposits (Lonsdale et al., 1980). This is the extreme expression of the transportation of material in solution.

5 - Hyaloclastites

Hyaloclastites show segregation of the initial basaltic material into Mg, Fe-clay zones in rock fragments and celadonite-zeolite zones deposited on the surfaces of the fragments (Juteau et al., 1978). Similar segregations have been observed in hydrothermally altered volcano-clastic sediments at the ocean bottom (Hoffert et al., 1978b). In these rocks one has saponites, Fe-Al smectites and celadonites plus zeolites as newly formed phases either replacing old volcanic minerals or growing on the rock fragment surface. There is apparently a conservation of most elements through a local dissolution-migration event which results in new mineral growth at short distances from the source material, usually a matter of millimeters or centimeters.

6 - Phase diagrams

What chemical framework can be used to represent such a complex system where all of the major elements are mobile at one time or another ? Since we don't know what element or elements can be considered to be mobile, chemical potential coordinates could be used, but we are in difficulty in chosing any two combinations of elements since certain ions migrate under circumstances and not in others. Some seem critical in the production of new phase at one time and not at another.

It might be useful to look at the major elements Al, Fe^{2+}, Fe^{3+} and Mg where K, Na and Ca are not considered as being critical to form a phase. We assume that they will be found in great enough quantity to fill interlayer sites in micas and smectites or in the zeolite lattices. Their presence will be dictated by the silicate lattice itself. This is a great simplification but one must start somewhere in such a complex geologic system.

We will group Fe^{2+} and Mg at one pole of a triangle and assign Fe^{3+} and Al to the other poles. We will assume further that silica activity is always sufficiently high to produce the most silica-rich phase possible. Thus the Al pole will represent Al-smectite and/or zeolites, the Fe^{3+} pole will represent nontronite or celadonite and the Fe^{2+}-Mg pole will represent saponite or serpentine compositions. Figure 87 shows the compositions of the major phases found in altered basalts excluding amygdule and vein deposition.

In the initial stages of weathering the solutions carry the Fe^2,Mg and Al components outside the system and possibly Fe^3 is added to the system to form nontronite. In low temperature hydrothermal alteration the solutions evacuate Fe^2, Mg and the Fe^3-Al components are fixed in the smectite and zeolite phases. High temperature hydrothermal alteration shows the same disposition of solids and solu-

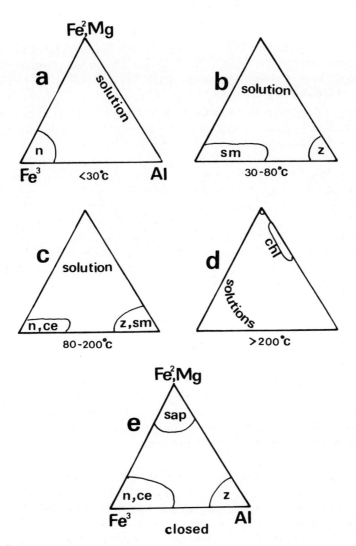

Figure 87 — Chemiographic disposition of new clay mineral
and zeolite phases formed in deep ocean basalts.
a represents the "weathering" assemblage at the ocean
bottom ; solids are potassic nontronite (n) and solutions
contain R^2 and Al. b low temperature hydrothermal alteration
where (Fe^{3+}, Al) calcic dioctahedral smectite (sm) and
zeolites (z) occur. c high temperature hydrothermal
alteration where nontronite celadonite (ce), zeolite and
calcic aluminous smectite are formed. d serpentinization
(S). Chlorite and serpentine are present. e closed system
forming hyaloclastites, saponite (sap), nontronite,
celadonite and zeolite occur.

tion-born material yet two new phases are found - celadonite or mixed layered nontronite-celadonite and aluminous
smectite. It seems that the range of Fe^3-Al substitution in
the smectite shifts toward each pole to a certain extent
(Mevel, 1979). This change in composition of the layer lattice is reflected by a dominance of K in the interlayer site
for the Fe^{3+} phase and Ca in the interlayer site for the
more Al-rich phase.

The deuteric phase, serpentinization, shows a complete reversal of the lowest temperature alteration in that
the solids are now found at the Fe^{2+}, Mg pole while the elements going into solution are Fe^{3+} and Al (Figure 87d). In
fact the field of solids is very reduced in the diagram.
This means that basalts altered at high temperatures will
provide much material which can be deposited under lower
temperature conditions.

The hyaloclastite assemblages are found at all poles of the diagram. There is little evidence that any of the
components are displaced from the rock-breccia matrix complex. To a certain extent one can consider the hydration
reactions as occurring in a closed system composed of rock
plus open fractures. Exchange between basalt and solution
does occur, but the solute is precipitated directly as it
reaches the free-flowing aqueous solution in the fissures
and amygdules. It is possible that some material is brought
in by the solutions, in that many fractures are filled by
clays and calcite at the end of alteration. However, even
this assemblage could be explained by precipitation of carbonate, whose calcium came from the basalt and CO_2 from the
in-flowing solution.

Now let us consider these alteration facies in a
temperature-depth sequence where thermal energy comes from
depth. Five diagrams (Figure 87) are necessary to represent
essentially three geologic types of altered basalt and related material. Figure 88a shows the typical altered basalt
pillow with its weathering rim, fracture fillings and amygdule deposits. In such a sample one has two processes represented which have been operative - weathering and precipitation from a solution which is moving slowly toward the
surface. If these rocks are buried under other lava flows,
the altering fluids will have a higher temperature ; the rock
will be more thoroughly "reacted" with the solutions and the

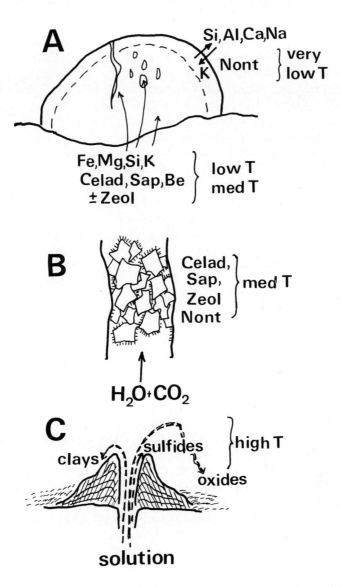

Figure 88 - Representation of deep-sea basalt alteration and resultant production of clay minerals. A = Weathering facies producing potassic nontronite from glass. Hydrothermal alteration by deposition in veins and vugs or vacuoles, low temperature and alteration of glass and plagioclase, medium temperature. B = Hyaloclastic alteration at medium temperature in a system closed to all but volatiles. C = Vent-type deposition at temperatures near 300°C where mineralized solutions precipitate oxides, sulfides and clays and reach the sea-water interface.

hydrothermal burial facies will appear. Deposition in fissures and vugs will occur as at higher levels in the volcanic pile. Tectonic movements or adjustments due to retraction on cooling of the lavas will produce fractures and brecciated material. Here reaction between fluids and solids will be rapid due to a high surface area of the rocks. The solution will become more rapidly calcium, Fe, Al and silica-rich. The aqueous solutions move upward by thermal convection carrying the dissolved species into cooler regions. The stable minerals of the alteration facies become Fe^{3+}-Al rich. The solutions will lose their material dissolved at depth as zeolites and smectites and will pick up the material now stable in solution which is Fe^{2+}, Mg-rich. Lower temperature will cause this material to precipitate as saponite if the system becomes more confined and interaction between altering basalt and solutions becomes more intense. This is the hyaloclastite facies where solutions become saturated will R^3 and R^2 elements forming saponite from the R^2 component which is largely magnesium. Hoffert (personal communication) has stated that vacuoles are almost always lined first with saponite followed by other phases, either celadonite or zeolite. It then appears that the magnesian components are less soluble at these temperatures than those of the alkali-alumino silicate series.

Stakes and O'Neil (1982) have demonstrated the temperature relationships of the different alteration types using oxygen isotope methods. In extracting the clay fractions from different rocks, one necessarily mixes phases of different temperature regimes (for example vacuole and vein fillings versus glass alterations) yet a general pattern is developed when one considers the dominant alteration type. The temperatures range from 200-350°C for chlorite-epidote rocks, as one would expect, to 130-170°C for saponite-rich rocks (vein fillings) with a value near 35°C for nontronites and celadonite vesicle fillings. Certainly more detailed work could be done ; however, the temperature intervals are certainly defined in an adequate manner in this paper.

7 - Sea water-sediment interface deposition

If the basalts at depth are hydrothermally leached in certain sectors, how does this material get re-deposited ? We know that celadonite and zeolite material occurs as vacuole and vein filling in intermediate rocks. A possible source for this material could well be the high temperature hydrothermal solutions. There is another mode of deposition which is more spectacular - that of the black smokers where solutions of 350°C enter into the sea water at the ocean bottom (Mac Donald **et al.**, 1980). The minerals which attract the most attention are the transition metal sulfides which are deposited massively as well as a large quantity of Mn-Fe oxides. However, other minerals have been formed - celadonite, nontronite and talc (Lonsdale **et al.**, 1980 ; Hein **et al.**, 1979 ; Schrader **et al.**, 1980 ; Honnorez **et al.**, 1981 ; Bischoff, 1969 ; Hoffert **et al.**, 1978.a). Remarkable among these minerals is a lack of an aluminum-bearing phase. It appears that iron and silica are easily transported by these solutions but aluminum and magnesium less so. Hein **et al.** (1979) and Muller and Forstner (1976) indicate that iron-rich montmorillonite (smectite) is commonly associated with manganese nodules in general and this silicate material has an origin at the ocean bottom. Figure 88c shows the general disposition of the precipitates in relation to the vent of introduction into the sea-water environment. McMurtry **et al.** (1983) find formation temperatures of 30-50°C for nontronites.

In general, the black smoker vent deposits show that transition metals and sulfur are transported easily to the surface, while alumina and alkalis seem to have been lost on the way up from the zone of high temperature hydrothermal alteration. Figure 88c shows these different processes in a schematic way. They are saturated with dissolved species and eventually, if flow rate is restricted, a type of closed system occurs which is the hyaloclastite facies (Figure 88b).

Now, how does this explanation based upon geological-petrographic observation compare to laboratory experiments ? Hajash (1975), Motte and Holland (1978), Seyfried and Bishop (1979 & 1981), Crovisier **et al.** (1983) among others have used hydrothermal experimentation (70-500°C, several hundred bars pressure) to simulate interaction of aqueous solutions (often sea water is used) and basalts. In the experiments above 200°C, magnesium is concentrated in the basalt while most other elements are lost in various proportions depending upon the experiments. At low temperatures the process is too slow to have formed a crystalline phase - the result is similar to palagonitization. There is a loss of Mg, Na and K and a gain of Ca and Si in the solution. The magnesian deuteric alteration phase occurs in natural sea floor basalts at 200°C-350°C as an upper limit. Since the hydrothermal vent fluid temperatures have been measured to be 350°C, the experiments applicable to this temperature range are of course subject to problems of reaction kinetics because their duration was never much more than a month. The experiments, generally performed using glassy basalt and sea water solutions, indicate that the solids gain in magnesium content and lose most other elements to the aqueous solution. This is compatible with the mineralogical observation on serpentinites which contain mostly Mg-Si bearing phases. The hydrothermal fluids effect a major transfer of material from buried basalt rocks to the sediment-sea water interface, depositing Fe,Mn oxides and iron-rich smectites and celadonite. Thus the experiments reinforce our conclusion based upon observations of natural basalt alteration parageneses.

Up to this point no mention has been made of oxidation during the hydrolysis of basalts by hydrothermal fluids. Most authors remark on the change in color and general aspect of the altered basalt as a function in the intensity of alteration and approach to the sea-water interface. It seems that one of the basic functions of the reaction is to change Fe^2 to Fe^3. Most of the authors cited who have worked on deep sea drill cores have remarked on the oxidation of some rocks, and the studies on deep-sea weathering have shown a relation between Fe^{3+} and H_2O content of altered basalts. This effect is very important in the alteration process. Ferromagnesian minerals become rapidly unstable the more iron they contain. Since the stable phase at lowest temperatures is ferric smectite and one of the phases at medium temperature is celadonite, also a ferric phase, it is evident that much of the iron remains in the silicate system and is not "lost" in an oxide phase. The low temperature oxidation process seems to have a global effect of releasing the other R^2 component into solution Mg as well as Ca and Na. In fact, this is quite analogous to continental weathering reactions except that the ferric ion tends to form an oxide phase. This is undoubtedly due to a higher oxidation potential of the atmospheric environment. It is probably the case that oxidation of the submarine basalts will tend to form the low temperature clay mineral facies.

Summary

On the basis of experimental, mineralogic and petrographic observations we can classify basalt alteration at the ocean bottom and below it into four major clay mineralogical facies where open systems pertain - low temperature weathering where nontronite and palagonite are the major phases ; hydrothermal of low temperature where Fe-Al nontronite and minor celadonite form ; higher temperature hydrothermal where nontronite-celadonite, zeolite and Al-smectite form and finally the serpentine facies of deuteric alteration. Clay minerals precipitated from circulating fluids which bear elements dissolved from basalts during alteration are the following - talc, saponite at higher temperatures, celadonite-nontronite at lower temperatures.

Zeolites are precipitated during short distance transportation at rock edges in hyaloclastic rocks in the medium temperature hydrothermal alteration facies conditions, where the basalt interacts with the fluids in an apparently closed system.

5 - Mixed Layered Minerals in Sequences of
Buried Rocks (P-T Space)

a - Introduction

It has been known for some time (Burst, 1959) that argillaceous rocks frequently present a continuous sequence of clay mineral assemblages as depth of burial increases. Weaver (1959) attempted to duplicate these transformations by applying high pressure to natural montmorillonites at room temperature. Since these studies were made a number of investigations of deeply buried sediments have been completed ; all show similar parageneses (Dunoyer de Segonzac, 1970 ; Mitsui, 1975). The most valuable information gathered in such studies is that of mineralogical variation as a function of both depth and temperature. With such data one can corrolate the mineral facies observed in the context of a geothermal gradient and ultimately delimit the existence of critical assemblages as a function of pressure and temperature. Eventually a grid of diagenetic facies can be produced for argillaceous rocks.

The most important prerequisite in selecting information of this sort is that there be no major unconformity in the sequence of sediments and sedimentary rocks studied and that they be recent in age. A disconformity is even worse but more difficult to detect in drill hole cuttings. It is absolutely necessary that the depositional sequence has experienced only the geothermal gradient which is at present imposed on the silicate mineral assemblages. If the sediments experienced a previous cycle of burial and subsequent uplift, creating an unconformity, the mineral assemblages below this surface cannot be treated with those above. This is simply normal geological reasoning since it is well known that rocks tend to maintain the silicate assemblages formed at the highest physical conditions. Retro-metamorphism is a slow process at low temperatures.

Basically, the available information is of two kinds : that from sequences of rocks in sedimentary basins

and geothermal areas where the gradient is much higher
($\simeq$ 130°C/km). The very close correspondence of mineral
transformations under both gradients leads one to believe
that the parageneses observed are both a function of depth
(pressure) and of temperature. It should be noted that in
areas of high geothermal gradient, rapidly circulating
fluids frequently increase the temperature locally, and most
notably, produce hot springs at the surface. In these cases
a hydrothermal gradient is superposed locally upon the geothermal gradient. Schoen and White (1965) and Steiner (1968)
have observed that in alteration zones around rock fissures
a new mineral assemblage is produced adjacent to the site of
circulating fluids. However, the general mineralogy of the
rock series appears to conform to a general trend which is
dependent upon the geothermal gradient for the area.

It is important to distinguish between the different observed types of interlayering which derive from the
regularity of the repetition of the types of layer units in
mixed layered minerals. We can distinguish four types among
the X-ray diffractograms published. This classification is
based upon the considerations of Reynolds and Hower (1970)
and those found in Brindley and Brown (1980). First one must
consider a situation where no ordering or sequential repetition of mica and smectite layer will occur. This gives the
disordered structure which has a slightly less than 10 Å
reflection upon glycollation and 18 Å upon glycollation.
Short range ordering - sequences of mica-smectite repeated - can give a 27 Å reflection, sometimes called a superstructure reflection. The type mineral allevardite presents
this structure. It is composed of equal numbers of mica and
expandable layers. It is possible to have an ordering reflection with other proportions of mica and smectite. Presence of a 27 Å reflection with variable percent smectite
layers in the structure distinguishes what is called here an
allevardite-like mineral. This is distinct from the currently accepted rectorite mineral which is 50 % smectite only. A
fourth type of ordering would give an ordering peak approximately of 47 Å due to a four layer ordering unit (10 + 17 +
10 + 10 Å). This structure gives a 10 Å reflection and one
near 11.2 Å when glycollated ; this is the IMII or four
layer ordering which can occur in minerals with less than
15 % expanding layers (see Reynolds in Brindley and Brown,
1980).

It is also important to consider that identification of fully expandable smectite are difficult to make. The range of mixed layering between 100 and 70 % expandable layers gives very similar X-ray diffraction patterns (see Sròdon, 1981) if one considers only the reflections near 17 Å. It is probably necessary to assume that phases reported as fully expandable could range in composition from 100 to 70 % smectite.

b - Natural Mineral Sequences

In a general way unordered interlayered minerals are succeeded by ordered ones as physical conditions become more intense. Browne and Ellis (1970), Muffler and White (1969), Steiner (1968), Schoen and White (1965), Eslinger and Savin (1973a & b), Mac Dowell and Elders (1980) and Sigvaladson and White (1961) report the following clay minerals in rocks of varying origin - volcanic tuffs to normal terrigenous sediments - which are found in "hydrothermal" areas where the geothermal gradient is high (above 230°C at one kilometer depth) :

1. Montmorillonite exists up to a temperature of 100°C at 100 meters depth. Calcic montmorillonites may persist to 150°C or so at more shallow depths.

2. Mixed layered clays, most often ordered but not showing a superstructure reflection, are present up to temperatures near 200°C at depths of 300 to 1500 meters. The minerals form in two distinct zones. At shallow depths (between 100 and 200°C) mixed layering is between 90 and 0 % smectite. Above 200°C or so one occasionally finds allevardite-type interlayering showing the superstructure reflection near 27 Å when glycollated. Possible IMII-structured material has also been found (Steiner, 1968).

3. Depending on the depth, at temperatures above 200-220°C only illite or sericite is found, usually with chlorite. No dioctahedral, mixed layered phase is present. This is the "illite-chlorite" zone.

Mixed layered minerals with lower expandability are frequently encountered near veins or fissures (Steiner,

1968 ; Browne and Ellis, 1970). The occurrence of kaolinite is generally erratic but in the terrigenous sediments (Muffler and White, 1969) it can apparently react with dolomite to form the assemblage calcite + chlorite between 120-180°C. Expandable chlorite was noted in shear zones, and iron-rich chlorite is common in most of the rocks becoming more evident at greater depths. In the terrigenous rocks observed, the alumina content of chlorite decreases with depth. Alkali zeolites have been observed at temperatures up to 100°C in deeply buried rocks. Above this, one finds albite in tuffs and also in sandstones (Boles, 1981).

Iijima (1970), Perry and Hower (1970, 1972), Lahann (1980), Schmidt (1973), Dunoyer de Segonzac (1969), van Moort (1971), Weaver and Beck (1971), Hower **et al.** (1976), Yeh and Savin (1977), Boles and Franks (1979) and Aoyagi and Kazama (1980) have studied the sequences of clay minerals found in deeply buried sediments, both terrigenous and tuffaceous. Their data are similar to that obtained from "hydrothermal" areas ; however, more complex types of mixed layered minerals are found :

1. Smectite or near smectite.

2. Ordered expandable minerals between 60 and 40 % smectite in composition.

3. Allevardite-type minerals with 40-20 % smectite layers.

4. IMII-type structures with less than 10 % smectite. This phase is not always present in the samples studied, mainly Gulf Coast of the U.S.A. However, it appears from the present author's experience that it is common in North Sea sediments.

The upper limit of highly expandable dioctahedral smectites appears to be slightly variable at different depths but it is generally below 100°C and above 60°C. The range of mixed layering between 60 and 30% smectite is restricted to temperatures between 80°C and about 120°C, depending upon the depth and precision of the temperature observations. The allevardite-type mineral which has 40-20% expandable layers is present over a much larger temperature range. In fact, it exists up to the greatest depths in the rocks studied. A

last and ill-defined field is that of the IMMI-type ordering
where 10-5% smectite is present. This represents the highest
temperature range of mixed-layered dioctahedral minerals
and, by consequence, the lowest amount of expandable mineral
layers present. Kaolinite seems to be stable to the greatest
depths in some cases. Chlorite is commonly present but no
expandable trioctahedral minerals have been reported. Zeolites are found in tuffaceous rocks (Iijima, 1970) presenting
the three assemblages : alkali zeolite, analcime, and analcime-albite as a function of increasing depth.

It is important to note that in all cases where the
bulk composition of the argillaceous samples was determined
no major systematic bulk compositional variation was observed as a function of depth (Perry and Hower, 1970 ; Weaver
and Beck, 1971 ; Dunoyer de Segonzac, 1969 ; van Moort,
1971 ; Hower et al., 1976 ; Heling, 1978). This is especially true for potassium. Thus the occurrence of illite or mica
in shales is apparently not a function of bulk composition
but one of pressure-temperature conditions. A second important observation, made by van Moort, is that the sequence of
mineral changes does not appear to be related to the age of
rocks older than Tertiary age, i.e., younger rocks do not
appear to be richer in montmorillonite than older rocks for
given P-T conditions and fully expandable minerals can be
found in pre-Cambrian shales. In the deep drill hole studies
of more recent sediments (Tertiary) the ages of the rocks
vary enough so that it is obvious that physical conditions
are the predominant factors in forming the mineral assemblages, but there seems to be a kinetic factor involved at
temperatures below 100°C.

Figure 89 compiles the available information on a
temperature-depth plot. The smectite ("fully expandable phase" 100-70% smectite), mixed layered between 70 and 50%
smectite and the ordered (allevardite type) 30-40% expandable minerals have definite zones of occurrence. However,
information is not abundant for the IMII-illite boundary at
great depths and low geothermal gradient, i.e., the zone
where no partially expandable dioctahedral phase can exist
in a pelitic mineral assemblage. It has been suggested by
Hower et al. (1976) that this limit is nearer to 200°C at
greater than six kilometer depths. Boles and Franks (1979)
observed the IMII-phase at 210°C, 4 km and Steiner (1968)
found it at 220°C, < 1 km depth. Notable in this diagram is

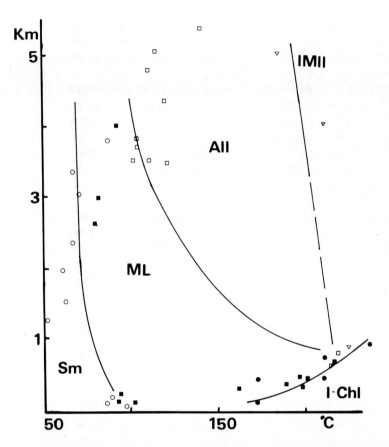

Figure 89 - Depth temperature plot of available data from
deep drill holes and drill holes in hydrothermal areas.
Sm = 100-70% smectite, unordered (Yeh and Savin, 1977; Boles
    and Franks, 1979; Hower et al., 1979; Zahann, 1980 ;
Steiner, 1968; Schmidt, 1973; Perry and Hower, 1970, 1972)
    indicated by circles. ML = ordered mixed layered 60-40%
expandable (Perry and Hower, 1970, 1972 ; Weaver and Beck,
    1971; Schoen and White, 1965; Browne and Ellis, 1970;
Mac Dowell and Elders, 1980; Boles and Franks, 1979;
    Yeh and Savin, 1977; Schmidt, 1973; Hower et al.,
1976) shown by solid squares. All = allevardite-type,
superstructure phase (Yeh and Savin, 1977; Weaver and
Beck, 1971; Steiner, 1968; Perry and Hower, 1970, 1972;
Hower et al., 1976; Boles and Franks, 1979; Lahann, 1980)
    shown as squares. IMII = less than 10% smectite ordered
    phase (Boles and Franks, 1979; Hower et al., 1976).
I-Chl = illite-chlorite facies (Mac Dowell and Elders, 1980;
    Steiner, 1968; Muffler and White, 1969) shown as dots.

the enlarged field for allevardite at great depth. This
suggests that the initial stage of mixed layering, 70-30 %
expandable, will be greatly reduced at great depths and low
temperatures. Such an effect has been observed by Weaver and
Beck (1971). There is an obvious influence of pressure on
the appearance of the super-structure ordering reflection.

c - Experimental Studies

It is instructive to compare the natural mineral
assemblages with those in the simplified system which has
been studied experimentally. The system muscovite-pyrophyllite is useful because it contains phases analogous to natural minerals. The system is dominated by two factors :

1. The stability of the expandable phase (potassic beidellite) either alone or as a mixed layered phase ;

2. The stability of kaolinite in the presence of quartz.

It appears from the data presented by Velde (1969) that the
temperature of transformation from mixed-layered to an ordered superstructure 30% smectite mixed layered phase (allevardite-type) is controlled by the stability of kaolinite
plus quartz. The slope of the reaction kaolinite + quartz =
pyrophyllite is considered to be slightly positive between 1
and 2 Kbars near 300°C (Velde and Kornprobst, 1969). This
temperature is much higher than those where natural superstructure minerals are found to occur. Further, the slope of
the transformation in natural minerals is negative as is
that for the stability of smectite in the synthetic system.
The major phase fields and their disposition as a function
of composition in the muscovite-pyrophyllite system seem to
correspond with the information obtained from the natural
mineral assemblages. In the synthetic system, muscovite is
the end member of a field of low charge, silicic, potassium-
deficient mica - a phase assimilable to illite. At low temperatures complete solid solution in the form of mixed
layering between illite and beidellite is possible. Under
higher temperature conditions, there is a gap in solid solu-

tion between illite and mixed layered minerals. Also, the
maximum extent of mixed layering with an expandable phase
decreases rapidly as temperature increases. Above 300°C, the
mixed layering becomes approximately constant ($\simeq$ 30 % smectite) and ordering is more apparent. This situation is maintained until the expandable phase becomes unstable. The
ultimate stability of beidellite-mica (illite) solid solution is dependent upon pressure as well as temperature, the
maximum thermal stability decreasing as pressure is greater.
However, in the synthetic aluminous system, the upper stability is much higher (300-400°C) than that observed in clay
mineral assemblages from argillaceous rocks at low pressures
($\simeq$ 200°C). The relations between phases are very similar and
the sequence of charges is identical in nature and synthetic
systems.

Velde (1977) has performed a number of experiments
on natural materials which have various types of interlayering and various non-expandable phases present such as illite, kaolinite and quartz. The starting materials were chosen in order to determine the effect of composition as well
as physical conditions upon the transformation of expandable
minerals. This expands the information from the synthetic
system described above by adding the chemical variables Mg
and Fe to those of Si, Al and K.

Briefly, the samples chosen verified the construction of the phase relations proposed in the simple system.
The only difference between what can be surmised from the
data on natural minerals and the experimental results is the
production of a corrensite-like ordered trioctahedral mixed
layered mineral at conditions approaching those which produce ordering in the dioctahedral mixed layered minerals. We
will discuss these results here only as they affect the
sequence of ordered minerals found as P-T conditions increase. Figure 90 summarizes the experimental results as a type
of phase diagram where P-T conditions effect different
arrangements in the mica-expanding minerals present between
a muscovite and a chlorite composition. We see that the lowest temperatures would give disordered interlayer minerals.
The second step with metamorphism is a reduction in the
expanding layers present in the structure and an ordering of
the units.

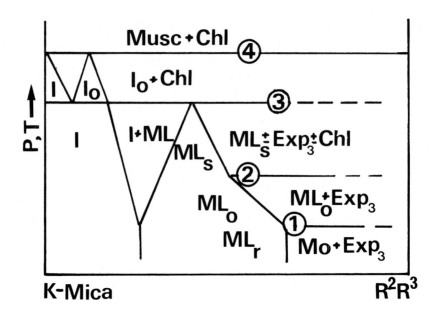

Figure 90 - P,T-x plot of general phase relations between
   potassic, aluminous mica and non-alkali compositions.
   Mo = smectite ; Exp_3 = trioctahedral expanding phase ;
   Chl = chlorite ; ML_r = random mixed layered mineral ;
ML_0 = ordered mixed layered phase without superstructure
reflection ; ML_s = allevardite-type superstructure phase ;
   I = illite ; I_0 = IMII phase ; Musc = muscovitic mica ;
   Circled numbers show key reactions which can easily
               be seen in pelitic rocks.

        Since most sedimentary rocks contain several clay
minerals at the same time, the phase relations that they
reflect are those of the phase fields to the right of the
figure. If a rock contained a dioctahedral mixed layered
mineral only, it would be represented by the central portion
of the diagram, the ML zone. Such rocks do exist, they are
called metabentonites. In some instances, there is a variation in chemistry of the rocks between the edge and center
of a metabentonite bed (J. Hower, A-M. Bystrom-Bruzewitz,
personal communications). One can see what the effect of
chemical variations has on the system at constant P-T conditions. This is especially important for the types of interlayering as they are affected by the bulk composition of the

phase. It appears that the low potassium content mixed layered phases are randomly interstratified from 100 to about 50 % expanding layers. One finds ordered minerals and then minerals with a superstructure reflection in the 30-20 % expanding layer compositions. In the experiments, the type of ordering produced is a function of the physical conditions employed which change the proportions of phases present by changing the composition of the mixed layered phase. Only ordered phases were encountered near the 30 % expandable phase region. However, this is not true for all natural mineral assemblages. In the less than 15 % expanding phase samples, ordering is of the type IMII, designated as I_0 in the figure. Such minerals are found at high temperatures in the experiments and in the later stages of diagenesis in rocks. In most assemblages of clay minerals in pelitic rocks, the degree or ordering and composition of the mixed layered phase will be dependent upon the physical conditions of crystallization.

Now let us consider the mica-like component in the system. In looking again at the phase diagram for the aluminous system the compositional field of the mica-like phase (an aluminous illite) is seen to decrease as temperature increases. Although the experimental data are imprecise, it can be expected that some 10 % "chlorite" component is lost between 300 and 400°C. Interestingly, a similar effect has been observed in sequences of deeply buried sediments and sedimentary rocks (Dunoyer de Segonzac, 1969 ; Dunoyer de Segonzac et al., 1968). Using a crystallinity index or sharpness ratio proposed by Weaver and redefined by Kübler (1968), these authors have observed that the shape of the illite reflection becomes sharper and narrow-based as depth and temperature increase. It can be assumed that better crystallinity can be assimilated to a more micaceous composition of the mica-like phase, that is, one with + 1.0 charge satisfied by an alkali ion in the interlayer position [per $O_{10}(OH)_2$]. This would correspond to the narrowing of the compositional range for the micaceous phase in the synthetic system. Thus, as depth and temperature increase, the illitic and mixed layered phases become clearly defined, ordered and better crystallized ; the association illite (possibly of the $2M_1$ polymorph) and allevardite-type mixed layered structure is the stable assemblage. The illite will contain more potassium and less silica, iron and magnesium than at low temperatures.

Thus the sharpening of the basal reflection is probably due to the increasing K_2O content of the phase, as suggested by Dunoyer de Segonzac (1969) and Weaver and Beck (1971), which permits a more ordered structure, i.e., a more ideal mica form. It is known that illite is usually of the lMd polymorph, where there is disorder in the stacking sequence in the c sin ß crystallographic direction. This would be expected where less than ideal occupancy of the interlayer ion site would inhibit orderly arrangement of the layering sequence producing stacking faults. It is also possible that some of the low total structural charge could be due to a small admixture of expanding low charge smectite layers which broaden the basal reflection to low angles (Reynolds and Hower, 1970). A greater frequency of $2M_1$ polymorphs, as noted by Dunoyer de Segonzac (1969), in the illites with a sharpened peak is most likely the result of mica compositional minerals which can become ordered in the stable polymorph near the muscovite composition (Velde, 1965a).

Considering the compositions of the mixed layered minerals found in sedimentary rocks, it is obvious that magnesium-iron expandable dioctahedral minerals will be in equilibrium not uniquely with kaolinite but also in many instances with a magnesium-iron phase, either chlorite or an expanding trioctahedral mineral. In such a situation the slope in P-T space of the reaction mixed layered → allevardite + phyllosilicate will be controlled not by the aluminum silicate phases, as in the muscovite-pyrophyllite system, but by the production of chlorite or another trioctahedral phase. The reaction most likely to occur in the range of conditions concerned is the transition between a trioctahedral expandable phase and 14 Å chlorite + quartz. In the experimental system $MgO-Al_2O_3-SiO_2-H_2O$ investigated by Velde (1973), this transition has been observed to maintain a negative slope in P-T space. Of course, the temperatures at which this phase change occurs in the synthetic system are well above those found in the natural system, due mainly to the presence of iron in nature ; but the implication remains that such a reaction "fits" the slope defined by the data for natural assemblages. If the parallel between aluminous and magnesio-aluminum systems can be assumed, kaolinite stability and that of expandable chlorite can be considered analogous in their influence upon the amount of interlayering present in the illite-smectite structures present. If we look back to the experimental studies on natural expandable minerals at high pressures, it can be recalled that the production of a chlorite phase occurred when interlayering in the natural dioctahedral mineral had reached about 30 % interlayering. It is possible that below this transition only expandable phases are present for most magnesium-iron compositions ; one is dioctahedral, the other would be tri-octahedral. Thus, at temperatures below the transition to an ordered allevardite-type phase, dioctahedral mixed layered minerals will coexist with expandable chlorites or metamor-phic vermiculites as well as kaolinite. The distinction between these two phases is very difficult because both respond in about the same manner when glycollated. There can also be interlayering in both di- and trioctahedral mine-rals. The temperature of mineral transition to non-expanding minerals will be a function of the $Mg-Fe^{2+}$ content in the system as a whole. It follows that magnesian 14 $\overset{o}{A}$ chlo-rite in sediments will be in dis-equilibrium until allevar-dite is stable. It can be suggested that most of the 14 $\overset{o}{A}$ chlorite in sediments is of detrital origin. The data of van Moort (1971), Perry and Hower (1970) and Hower **et al.** (1976) suggest such a conclusion in that chlorite content appears to decrease until the allevardite zone is reached where chlorite content begins to increase.

d - Superstructure Minerals

Let us now consider more closely the conditions under which allevardite and IMII-superstructure expandable dioctahedral phases disappear from sedimentary rocks. There are several key assemblages which have been reported that distinctly limit the possible physical conditions for this transition. Most notable is the assemblage allevardite-type mineral-pyrophyllite, reported by Dunoyer de Segonzac (1969) in a series of shales found in the French pre-Alps as well as in shales of a Paleozoic basin in northern Africa by Esquevin (personal communication), by Frey (1970, 1974) in Mesozoic sediments of the Swiss Alps, for Paleozoic rocks in northern France and by Dunoyer de Segonzac and Heddaut (1971) for Paleozoic rocks of the French Pyrénées. The mine-ral pair has also been reported in supposed hydrothermally altered shales in Utah (Ehlmann and Sand, 1959). The stabi-lity of pyrophyllite relative to kaolinite + quartz has been determined to be near 270°C, at 1 and 2 Kbars pressure (Hem-

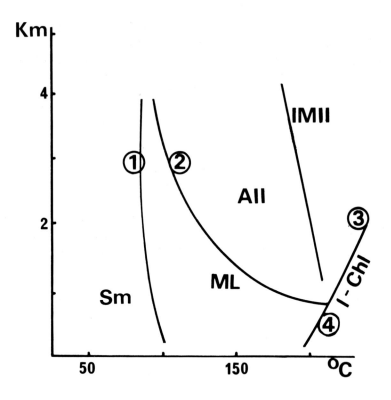

Figure 91 - Depth-temperature plot of mixed layered
minerals showing the maximum solid solution of
smectite component for a given temperature and pressure.
Numbers refer to reaction boundaries in P,T-x diagram
of figure 90 ; phase symbols as in figure 90.

ley et al., 1980). As we have seen earlier, the IMII structure seems to disappear in pyrophyllite-bearing rocks and
one can find rectorite in some instances (Paradis, 1981). It
is quite possible that the instances of ordered mixed layered mineral plus pyrophyllite, reported by several authors,
could well include a rectorite (Na) phase instead of an
IMII (potassic) phase. In hydrothermal alteration one does
not seem to find an IMII structure although allevardite-
types are known (Meunier, personal communication). Since
hydrothermal deposits are assumed in most instances to have
occurred at only several kilometers depth, it is possible
that the IMII is a higher pressure phase which explains its
frequent absence from geothermal and hydrothermal alteration
zones. For this reason the All-IMII field boundary is found

to intersect the illite-chlorite zone at several kilometers depth in figure 91. This figure shows the phase boundaries of figure 90, which are most easily discerned in X-ray diffraction studies of argillaceous sediments and sedimentary rocks. The boundary mentioned is number three. Four shows the transition between clay mineral facies and metamorphic rocks. It must intersect the pyrophyllite lower stability limit just above 270°C in order to permit the associations observed by Paradis et al. (1983) but we do not know the depth (pressure) at which this occurs.

If one considers the boundaries 4, 3, 2 and 1 which are figured as horizontal in the diagram P,T-x (Figure 90) as they are placed in depth temperature space, it is evident that the effect of depth is to increase the temperature range of the ordered mixed layered mineral facies ; that which is largely eliminated is the ML ordered non-superstructure type. Disordered high expandability smectite is not greatly affected.

e – Recrystallization Kinetics

There are, as we have said, two ways of looking at clay mineral assemblages and the reactions which took place to form them. One is to say that most assemblages or different constituents in an assemblage under given geologic conditions are not the stable forms. This supposes that reaction rates are too slow, at a given temperature, for the true equilibrium assemblage to form from the materials initially present. If a range of temperatures occurs in a sequence of rocks, different approaches to the equilibrium assemblages will be observed depending upon the length of time which the temperature persisted and the rate of the reaction at a given temperature. This point of view is held by Eberl and Hower (1976) whose laboratory experiments were used to demonstrate that aluminous smectite (beidellite) is unstable under geologic conditions. It will be replaced by an assemblage of mica + hydrous alumino-silicate when either sodium or potassium ions are available. Thus aluminous smectites found in deeply buried rocks should be considered to be metastable according to these authors. Similar experiments were performed by the present author (Velde, 1969) from which he concluded that smectite is stable at low temperatures but the amount of smectite which can exist in a mixed layered structure (solid solution between smectite and mica) will diminish as temperature increases. Both series of experiments were performed at temperatures above those at which a fully expandable smectite would be stable according to the thermal conditions in natural rock series where smectite occurs in pelitic sediments. The conclusions of Velde (1969) are that aluminous smectites in argillaceous rocks can represent an approach toward equilibrium.

Here we are confronted by a classical problem : what do the laboratory experiments mean compared with the observations made upon geological materials ? It is probable that both sets of experiments [Eberl and Hower (1976) and Velde (1967)] can be interpreted in two ways since the results are similar using similar materials. However, if we turn to natural materials as the final referee, we are still confronted, to a certain extent, by a time-temperature problem (kinetic). This is possibly due to a basic geologic configuration and a lack of geological information. If we consider the source of information used to construct depth-temperature-facies plots (Figure 89), it appears that in recent basins, those which are deepest (i.e., have the thickest series or sediments) are those with the lowest geothermal gradients. Those with lower sedimentation rates have higher geothermal gradients. Thus for a given depth, the rocks will be hotter and older in shallow basins than those in deep basins. It seems that there is a general pressure (depth)-temperature-time surface for sedimentary basins. This relation creates a problem in distinguishing between time, temperature and pressure effects as independent variables. The problem is compounded when one considers the measurements in deep bore holes reported by Boles and Franks (1979) on the difference between logged well temperatures and the temperatures of producing fluids. At 100°C the difference can be up to 50°C but it diminishes rapidly towards 200°C. One hopes that the data given in the various studies cited here represents a systematic deviation from true values in all cases.

How then can one go about sorting out the importance of each factor concerning the stability of mixed layered phases in sedimentary rocks ? At the moment there is probably no decisive argument since we do not know how long a geothermal gradient is maintained during a period of an orogenic cycle. How then should one proceed in interpreting clay mineral assemblages ? If we consider the simple depth-temperature plot of the mixed layered mineral facies (Figure 89), we see that the limit for high expandability mixed layered minerals (100-80 % smectite) seems to be somewhat independent of depth, and one can assume it lies at 70°C ± 20°C. There is a possibility that this limit decreases in temperature as depth increases. This limit does not appear to depend on the age of the sediments. The data of Perry and Hower (1972) are possibly the best supporting evidence for this.

      The next facies limit, that where about 30 % expandable layers are present in a superlattice structure (allevardite-type interlayering) seems to be more variable in time-temperature-depth space. Here, the reaction is not the same as that of a simple reduction of smectite layers which are transformed into illite layers. The alternation of illite-smectite must be respected in allevardite which suggests a selective organization of ions in the tetrahedral and octahedral sites in each layer. The kinetics of this reaction should be different from those of a simple, random change of smectite to illite layers as the material recrystallizes (i.e., the first facies boundary), and as a result one would expect different relations on the time-temperature plane. Since the reaction involves a relatively large release of water (see Perry and Hower, 1972), it is likely that pressure, and hence depth, will become an important variable in the kinetics of the reaction. In low geothermal gradient sedimentary basins, this change appears to occur between 100-140°C. In areas of high geothermal gradient, this reaction occurs at temperatures above 200°C, but we do not know how long these high temperatures have persisted in the areas investigated (New Zealand and California). If one considers the laboratory experiments, the transformation of smectite to low expandability (< 20 % smectite) mixed layered minerals occurs at 250°C in several months time. If illite plus kaolinite (or chlorite) were the stable phases (Eberl and Hower, 1976), they would surely have already formed in the hydrothermally altered rocks. As a result, we can tentatively place an upper limit for the reaction to form allevardite in time-temperature space at low pressure, as being somewhat above 200°C, in fact at 220°C in New Zealand (Steiner, 1968). In hydrothermal areas, it appears that the illite-chlorite facies (i.e., no interlayered aluminous minerals are present in pelitic rocks) follows closely after the allevardite-bearing rocks. At lower pressures, less than 0.5 km depth, the allevardite minerals are not present and one passes from low expandability non-superstructure minerals to illite-chlorite assemblages. Again according to the kinetic studies of Eberl and Hower (1976) which were performed in this temperature range, the reaction times for this reaction are short, in geological terms, and one would expect that the clays present in these rocks would represent an approach to equilibrium.

In this way, we can put outer limits on the mixed layer mineral facies between 90°C and 200°C at shallow depths. There remains now the more normal geothermal gradients which occur in most sedimentary basins. Here, the problem of reaction kinetics will undoubtedly be important in determining the precise clay mineral assemblage in a shale. The data of Boles and Franks (1979) indicate that Eocene Gulf Coast sedimentary rocks attain lower smectite content assemblages at temperatures below those of Oligocene and Miocene rocks (Perry and Hower, 1972 ; Hower et al., 1976). It appears that, if present-day geothermal gradients had been maintained throughout the history of the Gulf Coast basin, 20 to 40 million years could produce a difference of 20°C in the apparent temperature for the appearance of alle-vardite-type mixed layered minerals of 30-20 % expandable layers at 3-5 km depths. There is significant overlap in transition temperatures for series of different ages, which might suggest that some assumptions of constant temperature over the time period, or possibly differences in reaction rates due to differences in starting materials results in a variance of the observed assemblages.

Even though there is a significant difference in the apparent temperature of transition to the allevardite facies from one drill-hole to another, isotope data do suggest that the clays adjust relatively rapidly to geothermal gradients. Aronson and Hower (1976) show that mixed layered clays formed during diagenesis have nearly the same radiogenic age for a stratigraphic age span of 5×10^6 years. The radiogenic age is about 3×10^3 years older than the oldest sediments in the section studied. If we assume that the geothermal gradient has remained nearly the same since the last sediments were laid down, the reaction time can be considered to be 3 x 10^6 years for these sediments buried between 3 and 5 kilometers depth at temperatures around 110°C. If this study can be considered to be a general case, it would seem that reaction rate should not be the major factor in the dispersion of data on the depth-temperature plots for the transition into the allevardite facies. The major factor then remains unknown in the 80-140°C range and one must conclude that the lower limit of the allevardite facies cannot be determined with precision at present for deeply buried rocks. One might interject here the observation that the reaction kinetics which allow the transformation of hydrous cristobalite to quartz are greatly increased near 100°C (see silica chapter). If quartz is the stable phase, all phyllosilicates which crystallize in the presence of amorphous silica or cristobalite will be metastable and they will be transformed as quartz becomes stable. This could explain our difficulties near 100°C.

The last stage in the evolution of mixed layered minerals is the IMII interlayered form which is perhaps easier to interpret but we have less depth temperature data as to its occurrence. Steiner (1968) reports it occurring at 220°C, 0.7 km depth and Hower (personal communication) has identified the phase at 5 km depth in rocks having experienced temperatures of 180°C. Boles and Franks (1979) report its occurrence in samples at 210°C at 4 km. Since it has been reported in rocks containing pyrophyllite and chloritoid, suggesting temperatures near 280°C, the IMII-type interlayering must exist over a large range of temperatures.

It would seem that reaction kinetics are not the dominant factor at high temperatures (> 140°C) in determination of a given type of mixed-layered mineral in a sedimentary rock, at least in the range of 3 x 10^6 years residence time. It seems difficult to imagine another factor in argillaceous rocks which are generally considered as chemically closed systems. There remains the initial data which seems weak as concerns the temperature determinations made in deep bore holes. Boles and Franks (1979) demonstrate that above 150°C, the log temperatures are close to being correct whereas those below 100°C can be up to 50°C from correct values. It is most likely that when correct temperature information (or at least consistent data) is available the differences in reaction temperatures will be lessened.

f - The Effect of Bulk Composition

There is a possible effect of bulk composition on the clay mineral paragenesis in sedimentary rocks. Hoffman and Hower (1979), Hein and Scholl (1978), Reynolds and Nadeau (1981), Boles and Franks (1979), Howard (1981), among others, have remarked that the clay mineralogy of rocks of different lithologies is frequently different from that of detrital argillaceous rocks. Boles and Franks suggest that the smectites in sandstones are more beidellitic than those in shales. If we recall the discussion in the section on smectites, we should assume that beidellite and montmorillonite mixed layered mineral series are not quite equivalent and, due to differences in their chemistry, they will show parallel evolutions which will not occur at the same temperatures. It might well be important to use only argillaceous, detrital rocks as a basis for mineralogical comparison in depth-temperature sequences. The same is true in comparing volcanic ash metabentonite beds. Hoffman and Hower (1979) indicate a systematic difference between the expandability of mixed layered minerals in shales and metabentonite beds. This is due to a difference in the chemical system forming the mixed layered minerals. Shales, as we have said appear to behave as a closed system concerning potassium and aluminum. Thus the phases which form will be controlled in their compositional range by coexisting minerals. However in the metabentonites, it is evident that significant migration of elements, especially potassium and probably aluminum occurs as the ash becomes a mixed layered mineral (Velde and Bruzewitz, 1982). In this way the illite content of the mixed layered mineral can increase at constant temperature while that in the shale remains constant.

A second possible effect of composition can be seen in the data presented by Hower et al. (1976). In their exhaustive study of the mineralogical changes occurring during burial metamorphism in the gulf coast sediments of the United States they indicate great changes in mineralogy in a short range of temperature. The major reaction invoked by the authors in montmorillonite + K^+ $\rightarrow$ illite + chlorite. This is effected gradually **via** a reduction of the expanding layers in the mixed layered mineral through a loss of mica as an individual phase and feldspar. However, they also note that there is a great loss of kaolinite when the

increase in illite layers occurs. We also know that the character of the organic matter changes also with a concurrent
decrease in the Fe^{3+} content of the rock.

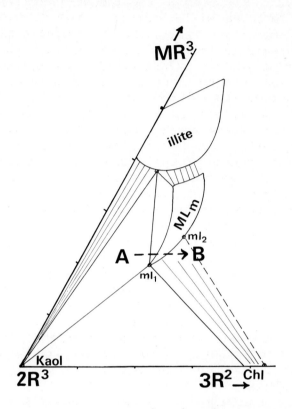

Figure 92 - Portion of MR^3-$2R^3$-$3R^2$ plot concerning the
phases illite-kaolinite-mixed layered mineral and chlorite.
Point A shows initial rock composition with a kaolinite
(Kaol)-illite-mixed layered illite-montmorillonite
mineral of composition ml_1. Change in oxidation
state of iron, R^2 to R^3, shifts the bulk composition
of the system such that B represents the new phase
assemblage of chlorite (Chl) and another mixed layered
phase composition, ml_2, which has fewer expandable layers
than that of the assemblage at composition A.

If we consider the phase diagrams in systems using
synthetic minerals, or those using natural minerals, it is
evident that an increase in temperature increases the amount
of illite present. This is observed as a general fact in the

depth-temperature plot. However, if we look at the details of $MR^3-2R^3-3R^2$ plot concerning illite and mixed layered minerals (Figure 92) we can see what happens as we increase the Fe^2 content ($3R^2$) through the reduction of iron oxide. The Fe^{2+} (R^2) species will enter into the silicate system and the bulk composition will shift from point A to point B. Initially we are in a three-phase field where illite, kaolinite and a mixed layered illite-montmorillonite mineral of composition A (ml_1) occur together. If we shift to composition B through reduction of Fe^{3+} we are in a two-phase field where a mixed layered mineral and chlorite coexist. However, the composition of the mixed layered mineral in assemblage B is one with a greater amount of illite layers than that in the assemblage A (ml_2). The reaction observed is illite + kaolinite + mixed layered mineral (1) + Fe^{2+} → chlorite + mixed layered mineral (2). At constant temperature we can thus observe an increase in the illite component of mixed layering through a change in oxidation state of iron.

It is highly probable that the reaction as proposed by Hower **et al.** (1976) does take place as temperature increases. The loss of potassium feldspar from the coarse-grained fraction of the rock most probably enters into the reaction described by these authors. However, the loss of kaolin from the average mineral assemblages in the rocks studied and the corresponding increase in chlorite suggest that a more complex reaction occurs where the mixed layered mineral has changed composition, due in part to a displacement in rock bulk composition ; at least that concerning the silicates. We can then propose two parallel reactions :

    1. mixed layered mineral + K^+ (from feldspar)
       → illite (in mixed layers)

and

    2. kaolinite + illite + mixed layered mineral A + Fe^{2+}
      → chlorite + mixed layered mineral B

It is possible that this type of coupled reaction can account for some of the scatter on the depth-temperature plot concerning the appearance of allevardite type ordering, as mentioned previously.

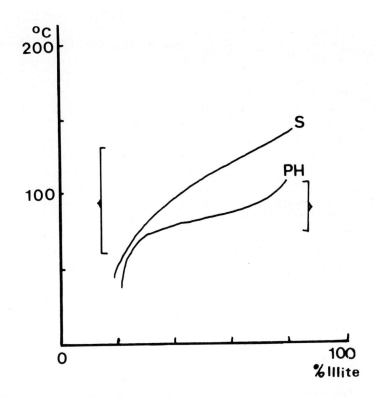

Figure 93 - Temperature-composition plot of mixed layered
minerals in two Gulf Coast wells.
Data from Schmidt (1973) = S and Perry and Hower (1972) = PH.
The wells show sediments of 30 and 38 million years at
greatest depth respectively.The brackets show a 70 and
30°C interval for 20-80 % illite in the wells. This
indicates that conversion in the PH well was twice
as fast as that in the S well. It is possible that
such differences reflect two different types
of chemical reactions responsible for
the smectite → illite "conversion".

        In pursuing this line of thought further it is
instructive to look at the depth - % illite plots used
currently by many authors to describe the effects of burial
diagenesis on the clay mineral fraction ; such plots have
been used to construct figure 89. If we consider two of
these plots, one given by Schmidt (1973) and the other by

Perry and Hower (1972) (Figure 93), it can be seen that the span of temperature over which the essential part of the smectite to illite conversion occurs, is quite different. In one case it takes place over a range of 30°C, in the other 70°C. Both sequences studied have nearly the same ages, 30 and 38 m.y. at well bottom, so that the problem of reaction kinetics cannot be directly involked as a cause of differences in reaction. The absolute temperature at which the reactions occur is also the same, so we can assume that the kinetics will occur at the same rate if the reaction is the same in both cases. It then seems reasonable to assume two different reactions cause the mineral transformation observed, as proposed above. Since there is a large difference in the temperature span over which these reactions occur, we might propose that the type observed by Schmidt, is thermally dependent reaction (1), while that observed by Perry and Hower is in fact reaction (2), one that is more isothermal in character. This last statement will only be partially true in natural .situation because the rate of reduction of ferric to ferrous ion will be dependent upon the reactions occurring in the organic matter (the reducing agent) which will occur at various temperatures.

In conclusion, one should look carefully at the depth-mineralogy profile in a sequence of buried sediments in order to determine how the clays evolve (mixed layered minerals) even when one has been careful enough to select samples having the same lithology. It is quite evident that the reactions governing the transformation of mixed layered clay minerals are complex ; several will occur simultaneously influencing the temperature at which a given percent illite interstratified mineral will occur in a diagenetic burial sequence.

Summary

The most important aspect of the information on buried sediments is the apparent similar sequence of mineral assemblages found in deep and shallow series. High and low geothermal gradients, pelitic or acidic volcanic materials, zeolite-bearing or calcareous, all rocks containing a predominantly dioctahedral phyllosilicate mineral assemblage are found to have concordant mineral assemblages. Further, there is no evidence that the bulk rock composition changes significantly during these transformations and the elements most likely to vary (alkalis) remain more or less constant at depth increases, although minor changes certainly occur (Leikine, 1981). The sequence of mineral stabilities - smectite, mixed layered, allevardite-type, IMII, and uniquely illite - can be used as an index to the pressure-temperature conditions which a rock has undergone. This gives a useful facies grid for a large range of physical conditions which englobe most sequences of deeply buried rocks. It should be remembered that the assemblages containing kaolinite should indicate the composition of mixed layered minerals with the maximum amount of expandable layers stable at given P-T conditions. Another very important observation to be made is whether or not a high spacing ordering peak is present, indicating the stability of the allevardite-type phase. With such information available, a reasonable assessment of mineral facies can be made.

CONCLUSIONS

Basically, it is best to let the summary of each chapter presented here speak for itself. A general summary of the clay mineral analyses presented is not really useful. Certainly, many more things could be said and one hopes that they will be, when one considers the immense amount of information available concerning clay minerals. The approach presented here has been less encyclopedic and more an attempt at understanding the fundamental relations between minerals and chemical potentials. Using this as a basis for conjecture, several general statements can be made. First, the major processes concerning clays and acid or pelitic rocks turn around the chemical potential of alkalis in the system considered. It seems that in many cases the alkalis even determine in a certain manner the silica chemical potential. It is possible that the coincidence of high pH and alkali content work toward siliceous zeolite phases, and that as alkalis decrease so does pH in most natural situations. The end result is that one can trace clay mineral assemblages as a function of the importance of Na and K in solutions when alumina is present in considerable quantities.

A second important concept is that the only micas are potassic ones and that expanding phases although sodi-calcic begin to release these elements in early stages of diagenesis (increase of temperature for the most part). Potassium is fixed in either aluminous (illite) or ferric (celadonite-glauconite) minerals at very low temperatures, while sodium seems to remain in the ocean repository and calcium finds its way into carbonates. A third principle to keep in mind is the importance of the R^2-R^3 shift as oxidation affects more basic rocks and minerals. Although divalent clay minerals can form, they are short lived in most geologic cycles. When clays occur and persist, they are generally trivalent. This is true for both di- and triocta-hedral minerals. As temperature increases, the R^2 component can reside in a phyllosilicate more easily - chlorites occur. The shift to an R^3 mineralogy means loss of R^2 (Ca, Mg) to solution or oxidation. A fourth important concept is the

reversibility of clay mineral reactions. One can see this
either in chemical variable space or P-T space. Examples are
the glauconite system and the weathering-diagenesis cycle
for pelitic and acidic rocks. One must always be careful
that the chemical system is the same or that not a great
amount of material has been selectivity transported out of
the system. A fifth and last comment rests upon the absolute
necessity to establish all of the clay phases forming or
stable together in a given environment. If two or more are
present, several elements must be considered as being intensive variables of the system and one can normally best
represent the system in x-μx or simply composition coordinates. In the end, presentation is not the basic problem but
comprehension.

Clay minerals are the major solid phases present
during the immense chemical transfer processes which occur
at or near the earth's surface. In clay environments, one
finds the most extreme chemical segregation known in geological cycles. If we wish to interpret the past events (geology) we must understand the reasons for the appearance of
clays which remain. This will allow us to understand the
other half of the problem - chemical transfer in solution.

REFERENCES

ADAMS W.A., EVANS L.J. and ABDULLA H.H., 1971 - Quantitative pedological studies on soils derived from Silurian mudstones. **Journ. Soil Sci.**, **22**, 158-65.

AGAR R.A., 1981 - Copper mineralization and magmatic hydrothermal brines in the Rio Pisco section of the Peruvian coastal Batholith. **Econ. Geol.**, **76**, 677-693.

AIELLO R., COLELLA C. and SERSALE R., 1970 - Zeolite formation from synthetic and natural glasses. **Amer. Chem. Soc.**, **2nd Int. Zeolite Conf.**, 48-58.

AILIN-PYZIK I.B. and SOMMER S.E., 1981 - Microscale chemical effects of low temperature alteration of DSDP basaltic glasses. **Journ. Geophys. Res.**, **86**, 9503-9510.

ALMON W.R. and DAVIES D.K., 1979 - Regional diagenetic trends in the lower Cretaceous muddy sandstone, Powder River Basin. **S.E.P.M. Spec. Publ.**, **26**, 379-400.

ALMON W.R., FULLERTON L.R. and DAVIES D.K., 1976 - Pore space reduction in cretaceous sandstones through chemical precipitation of clay minerals. **Journ. Sed. Petr.**, **46**, 89-96.

ALIETTI A. and ALIETTI L., 1962 - Su due diversi tipi di montmorillonite riconosciuti nella bentonite di gemmano (Forli). **Periodo Min.**, **31**, 261-286.

AMES L.L. and SAND L.N., 1958 - Factors effecting maximum hydrothermal stability in montmorillonites. **Amer. Min.**, **43**, 641-648.

ANDERSON D.M. and REYNOLDS R.C., 1966 - Umiat bentonite : an unusual montmorillonite from Umiat, Alaska. **Amer. Min.**, **51**, 1443-1456.

ANDREWS A.J., 1980 - Saponite and celadonite in layer 2 basalts, DSDP Leg. 37. **Contr. Min. Petr.**, **73**, 323-340.

AOYAGI K. and KAZAMA T., 1980 - Transformational changes of clay minerals. Zeolites and silica minerals during diagenesis. **Sedimentology**, **27**, 179-188.

APRIL R.H., 1980 - Regularly interstratified chlorite/vermiculite in contact metamorphosed red beds, Newark group, Connecticut valley. **Clays Clay Min.**, **28**, 1-10.

ARIMA M. and EDGAR A.D., 1980 - Importance of time and H_2O contents on the analcime - H_2O system at 465°C and 1 kbar P H_2O. **N. Jb. Miner. Mh.**, **12**, 543-554.

ARONSON J.L. and HOWER J., 1976 - Mechanism of burial metamorphism of argillaceous sediments. 2 : Radiogenic argon evidence. **Bull. G.S.A.**, **87**, 738-744.

ATAMAN G. and BAYSAL O., 1978 - Clay mineralogy of turkish borate deposits. **Chem. Geol.**, **22**, 233-247.

ATAMAN G. and S.L. GOKSEN, 1975 - Determination of source and paleoclimate from the comparison of grain and clay fractions in sandstones : a case study. **Sed. Geol.**, **13**, 81-107.

BAILEY R.J. and ATHERTON M.P., 1970 - The petrology of a glauconitic sandy chalk. **Journ. Sed. Petr.**, **40**, 1420-1431.

BAILEY S.W., 1969 - Polytypism of trioctahedral 1:1 layer silicates. **Clays Clay Min.**, **17**, 355-371.

BAILEY S.W. and BROWN B.E., 1962 - Chlorite polytypism : Regular and semi-random one-layer structures. **Amer. Min.**, **47**, 819-850.

BAILEY S.W., HENLEY P.M. FAIRBAIRN H.W. and PINSON Jr W.H., 1962 - K-Ar dating of sedimentary illite polytypes. **Bull. Geol. Soc. Amer.**, **73**, 1167-1170.

BAIN D.C., 1977 - The weathering of ferruginous chlorite in a podzol from Argyllshire, Scotland. **Geoderma**, **17**, 193-208.

362

BALGORD W.D. and ROY R., 1970 - Crystal chemical relationships in the analcite family. **Amer. Chem. Soc., 2nd
Int. Zeolite Conf.**, 321-327.

BALL D.F., 1968 - Interstratified illitic clay in Ordovician
ash from Conway, North Wales. **Clay Min.**, 7, 363-366.

BARONNET A., AMOURIC M. and CHABOT B., 1976 - Mécanismes de
croissance, polytypisme et polymorphisme de la muscovite hydroxylée synthétique. **J. Cryst. Growth**, 32, 37-52.

BARSHAD I. and KISHK F.M., 1970 - Factors affecting potassium fixation and cation exchange of soil vermiculite
clays. **Clays Clay Min.**, 18, 127-137.

BARTHOLOME P., 1966.a - Corroded quartz grains in sedimentary ores of iron and manganese. **Econ. Geol.**, 61, 886-
896.

BARTHOLOME P., 1966.b - Sur l'abondance de la dolomite et de
la sépiolite dans les séries sédimentaires. **Chem.
Geol.**, 1, 33-48.

BASS M.N., 1971 - Montmorillonite and serpentine in Orgueil
meteorite. **Geochim. Acta**, 35, 138-139.

BASSET W.A., 1963 - The geology of vermiculite occurrences.
Clays Clay Min., 12, 61-69.

BATES T.F. and STRAHL E.O., 1957 - Mineralogy, petrography
and radioactivity of representative samples of Chatta-
nooga shale. **Bull. Geol. Soc. Amer.**, 68, 1305-1314.

BATTACHARYYA D.P., 1983 - Origin of berthierine in ironstones. **Clays Clay Min.**, 31, 173-182.

BAYLISS P. and LOUGHNAN F.C., 1963 - Mineralogical evidence
for the penecontemporaneous laterization of the basalts
from New England, NSW. **Amer. Min.**, 48, 410-414.

BEANE R.E., 1974 - Biotite stability in the porphyry copper
environment. **Econ. Geol.**, 69, 241-256.

BEAUFORT D., 1981 - Etude pétrographique des altérations
hydrothermales superposées dans le porphyre cuprifère

de Sibert (Rhône). **Thesis 3ème cycle,** Univ. Poitiers, 147 p.

BECHER A., 1965 - Eine Tonmineralfolge vom Beckenrand zum Beckeninnern im Buntsandstein Nordost-Bayerns. **Beiträge Min. Petr., 11,** 586-613.

BELL D.L. and GOODELL H.G., 1967 - A comparative study of glauconite and the associated clay fraction in modern marine sediments. **Sediment., 9,** 169-202.

BENTOR Y.K. and KASTNER M., 1965 - Notes on the mineralogy and origin of glauconite. Journ. **Sed. Petr., 35,** 155-166.

BERNAT M., BIERI R.H., KOIDE M., GRIFFIN J.J. and GOLDBERT E.D., 1970 - Uranium, thorium, potassium and argon in marine phillipsites. **Geochim. Acta, 34,** 1053-71.

BERRY L. and RUXTON B.P., 1959 - Notes on weathering zones and soils on granitic rocks in two tropical regions. Journ. **Soil. Sci., 10,** 54-63.

BERRY R.W. and JOHNS W.D., 1966 - Mineralogy of the clay-sized fractions of some North Atlantic-Arctic ocean bottom sediments. **Bull. Geol. Soc. Amer., 77,** 183-196.

BESSE D., DESPRAIRIES A., JEHANNO C. and KOLLA V., 1981 - Les paragenèses de smectites et de zéolites dans une série pyroclastique d'âge éocène moyen de l'Océan Indien (DSDP Leg 26, site 253). **Bull. Min., 104,** 56-63.

BIGHAN J.M., JAYNES W.F. and AILEN B.L., 1980 - Pedogenic degradation of sepiolite and palygorskite on the Texas High Plains. **Soil Sci. Amer. Journ., 44,** 159-169.

BIRCH G.F., WILLIS J.P. and RICKARD R.S., 1976 - An electron microprobe study of glauconite from the continental margin of the west coast of South Africa. **Marine Geol., 22,** 271-283.

BISCAYE P.E., 1965 - Mineralogy and sedimentation of recent deep-sea clay in the Atlantic and adjacent seas and oceans. **Bull. Geol. Soc. Amer., 76,** 803-832.

BISCHOFF J.L., 1969 - Red Sea geothermal brine deposits : their mineralogy, chemistry and genesis. Hot Brines and Recent Heavy metal deposites in the Red Sea ; E.T. DEGENS, D.A. ROSS ed., Springer Verlag, 368-406.

BISCHOFF J.L., 1972 - A ferroan nontronite from the Red Sea geothermal system. **Clays Clay Min.**, **20**, 217-223.

BISCHOFF J.L. and KU T.L., 1971 - Pore fluids of recent marine sediments : II - anoxic sediments of 35°-645°N Gibralter to mid-Atlantic ridge. **Journ. Sed. Petr.**, **41**, 1008-1017.

BISCHOFF J.L., RADTKE A.S. and ROSENBAUER R.K., 1981 - Hydrothermal alteration of graywacke by brine and sea-water : Roles of alteration and chlorite complexing on metal solubilization at 200°C and 350°C. **Econ. Geol.**, **76**, 659-676.

BISCHOFF J.L. and TEH-LUNK KU, 1970 - Pore fluids of recent marine sediments : I - Oxydizing sediments of 20°N, continental rise to mid-Atlantic ridge. **Journ. Sed. Petr.**, **40**, 960-972.

BLACK P.M., 1975 - Mineralogy of New Caledonian metamorphic rocks. IV. Sheet silicates from Onégoa district. **Contrib. Min. Petr.**, **49**, 269-284.

BLADEL van R., GAVIRIA G. and LAUDELOUT H., 1972 - A comparison of the thermodynamic double layer theory and empirical studies in Na-Ca exchange equilibria in clay water systems. **Proceed. int. Clay Conf.**, 385-398.

BLANC-VERNET L. and CHAMLEY H., 1971 - Sédimentation à attapulgite et **globigerinoides tribolus f. dehiscens** dans une carotte profonde de Méditerranée orientale. **Deep Sea Res.**, **18**, 631-637.

BLATTER C.L., ROBERSON H.E. and THOMPSON G.R., 1973 - Regularly interstratified chlorite-dioctahedral smectite in dike intruded shales. **Clays Clay Min.**, **21**, 207-212.

BOETTCHER A.L., 1966 - Vermiculite, hydrobiotite and biotite in the Rainy Creek igneous complex near Libby, Montana. **Clay Min.**, **6**, 283-296.

BOHLKE J.K., HONNOREZ J. and HONNOREZ-GUERSTEIN B.M., 1980 - Alteration of basalts from site 396B, DSDP ; Petrographic and mineralogic studies. **Contrib. Min. Petr.**, **73**, 341-364.

BOLES J.R., 1971 - Synthesis of analcime from natural heulandite and clinoptilolite. **Amer. Min.**, **56**, 1724-1734.

BOLES J.R., 1972 - Composition, optical properties, cell dimensions and thermal stability of some heulandite group minerals. **Amer. Min.**, **57**, 1463-1493.

BOLES J.R., 1981 - Active albitization of plagioclase, Gulf coast Tertiary. **Amer. Journ. Sci.**, **282**, 165-180.

BOLES J.R. and COMBS D.S., 1975 - Mineral reactions in zeolitic Triassic tuff, Hokonui Hills, New Zealand. **Bull. Geol. Soc. Amer.**, **86**, 163-173.

BOLES J.R. and FRANKS S.G., 1979 - Clay diagenesis in Wilcox sandstones of Southwest Texas: implications of smectite diagenesis on sandstone cementation. **Journ. Sed. Petr.**, **49**, 55-70.

BONATTI E., 1963 - Zeolites in Pacific pelagic sediments. **Trans. N.Y. Acad. Sci.**, **25**, 938-948.

BONATTI E. and JOENESU O., 1968 - Palygorskite from Atlantic deep sea sediments. **Amer. Min.**, **53**, 925-983.

BONORINO F.G., 1959 - Hydrothermal alteration in the Front Range mineral belt, Colorado. **Bull. Geol. Soc. Amer.**, **70**, 53-90.

BOWLES F.G., ANGINO E.A., HOSTERMAN J.W. and GALLES O.K., 1971 - Precipitation of deep-sea palygorskite and sepiolite. **Earth Planet. Sci. Lett.**, **11**, 324-334.

BRAITSCH O., 1971 - Salt Deposits. Their origin and Composition. Springer-Verlag, Berlin, ed., 291 p.

BRECK D.W., 1970 - Recent advances in zeolite science. **Amer. Chem. Soc.**, **2nd Int.** Zeolite Conf., 1-18.

BREDEHOEFT J.D. and HANSHAW B.B., 1968 - On the maintenance of anomalous fluid pressures. I - Thick sedimentary sequences. **Bull. Geol. Soc. Amer.**, **79**, 1097-1106.

BREWER R., 1964 - Fabric and Mineral analysis of soils. John Wiley Sons, New-York ed., 470 p.

BRINDLEY G.W., 1982 - Chemical compositions of berthierines : a review. **Clays and Clay Min.**, 30, 153-155.

BRINDLEY G.W. and BROWN G., 1980 - Crystal structures of clay minerals and their identification. **Min. Soc. Monograph**, 495 p.

BROOKS R.R., PRESLEY B.J. and KAPLAN I.R., 1968 - Trace elements in the interstital waters of marine sediments. **Geochim. Acta**, 32, 397-414.

BROWN E.H., 1967 - The greenschist facies in part of Eastern Otago, New Zealand. **Contr. Min. Petr.**, 14, 259-292.

BROWN G. ed., 1961 - The X-ray Identification and Crystal Structure of Clay Minerals. Mineralogical Society, London, 479 p.

BROWN G., CATT J.A. and WEIR A.H., 1969 - Zeolites of the clinoptilolite-heulandite type in sediments of south-east England. **Min. Mag.**, 288, 480-488.

BROWN G. and WEIR A.H., 1963 - The identity of rectorite and allevardite. 1st Int. **Clay Conf. Proceed.**, 27-36.

BROWNE D.R.L. and ELLIS A.J., 1970 - The Ohaki-Broadlands hydrothermal area, New Zealand : mineralogy and related geochemistry. **Amer. Journ. Sci.**, 269, 97-131.

BRYDON J.E. and KODAMA H., 1966 - The nature or aluminum hydroxide-montmorillonite complexes. **Amer. Min.**, 51, 875-889.

BUCKE D.P. and MANKIN C.J., 1971 - Clay-mineral diagenesis within interlaminated shales and sandstones. **Journ. Sed. Petr.**, 41, 971-981.

BUCKLEY H.A., BEVAN J.C., BROWN K.M., JOHNSON L.R. and FARMER V.C., 1978 - Glauconite and celadonite, two separate mineral species. **Min. Mag.**, 42, 373-382.

BUNDY W.M. and MURRAY H.H., 1959 - Argillization in the Cochiti mining district, N. Mexico. **Clays Clay Min.**, 6, 342-368.

BURNHAM C.W., 1962 - Facies and types of hydrothermal alteration. Econ. Geol., 57, 768-784.

BURST J.F., 1958 - Mineral heterogeneity in "glauconite" pellets. Amer. Min., 43, 481-497.

BURST J.F., 1959 - Postdiagenetic clay mineral environmental relationships in the Gulf Coast Eocene. Clays Clay Min., 6, 327-341.

BURST J.F., 1969 - Diagenesis of Gulf Coast clayey sediments and its possible relation to petroleum migration. Bull. Amer. Assoc. Pet. Geol., 53, 73-93.

BUSENBERG E., 1978 - The products of the interaction of feldspars with aqueous solutions at 25°C. Geochim., 42, 1679-1686.

BUTT C.R.M. and NICKEL G.H., 1981 - Mineralogy and geochemistry of the weathering of disseminated nickel sulfide deposit at Mt. Keith, Western Australia. Econ. Geol., 76, 1736-1751.

CAHOON H.P., 1954 - Saponite near Milford, Utah. Amer. Min., 39, 222-230.

CAILLERE S. and GIRESSE P., 1966 - Etude minéralogique de diverses "glauconies" actuelles. Nouvelle contribution à la genèse des minéraux de fer sédimentaire. C.R. Acad. Sci., Paris, 263, 1804-1807.

CAILLERE S., HENIN S. and ESQUEVIN J., 1957 - Synthèse des minéraux argileux. Bull. Groupe Fr. Argiles, IX, 67-76.

CAILLERE S. and LAMBOY M., 1970 - Etude minéralogique de la glauconite du plateau continental au Nord-Ouest de l'Espagne. C.R. Acad. Sci., Paris, 270, 2057-2060.

CAILLERE S., MATHIEU-SICAUD and HENIN S., 1950 - Nouvel essai d'identification du minéral de La Table près Allevard, l'allevardite. Bull. Soc. Fr. Crist. Min., 73, 193-201.

CALLEGARI E. and JOBSTRIBITZER P.G., 1964 - Sulla presenza di analcime nella "pietra verde" degli strati di Livinallongo della lacalitàtipo (alta Valle del Cordevole-Dolomite). **Rend. Soc. Miner. Italiana,** 20, 21-82.

CALVERT S.E., 1971 - Nature of silica phases in deep sea cherts of the North Atlantic. **Nature (Phys. Sci.),** 234, 133-134.

CALVERT C.S., BUOL S.W. and WEED J.B., 1980 - Mineralogical characteristics and transformation of a vertical rock-saprolite-soil sequence. **Soil Sci. Amer. Journ.,** 44, 1056-1103.

CAMPBELL A.D. and FYFE W.S., 1965 - Analcime-albite equilibria. **Amer. Journ. Sci.,** 263, 807-816.

CAMUS F., 1975 - Geology of the El Teniente orebody with emphasis on wall-rock alteration. **Econ. Geol.,** 70, 1341-1372.

CARR R.M. and FYFE W.S., 1958 - Some observations on the crystallization of amorphous silica. **Amer. Min.,** 908-916.

CARROLL D., 1969 - Chlorite in central north Pacific ocean sediments. **Proc. 1st Int. Clay Conf.,** 1, 355-358.

CARROLL D. and STARKEY H.C., 1960 - Effect of sea water on clay minerals. **Clays Clay Min.,** 7, 327-341.

CASCHETTO S. and WOLLAST R., 1979 - Dissolved aluminium in interstitial waters of recent marine sediments. **Geochim.,** 43, 425-428.

CATHELINEAU M., 1982 - Les gisements d'uranium liés spatialement aux leucogranites sud-armoricains et à leur encaissant métamorphique. **Sciences de la Terre,** mém. 42, 375 p.

CHAMLEY H., PAQUET H. and MILLOT G., 1962 - Minéraux argileux de vases méditerranéennes. **Bull. Serv. Carte Géol. Als.-Lorr.,** 15, 161-169.

CHATTERJEE N.D., 1968 - Phasenpetrologie der aplidisch-metamorphosierten Gesteine in den italienischen Westalpen nebst Untersuchungen zur Stabilität des Paragonites. **Habilitationschrift Ruhr Univ. Bochum,** 162.

CHEN P.Y. and BRINDLEY G., 1976 - Beidellite clay from Chary-Yuan Taiwan : geology and mineralogy. **Clays Clay Min.**, **11**, 221-234.

CHESWORTH W., 1980 - The haplosoil system. **Amer. Journ. Sci.**, **280**, 969-985.

CHRIST C.L., HATHAWAY J.C., HOSTETLER P.B. and SHEPARD A.O., 1969 - Palygorskite, new X-ray data. **Amer. Min.**, **54**, 198-205.

CHRIST C.L., HOSTETLER P.B. and SIEBERT R.M., 1973 - Studies in the system $MgO-SiO_2-CO_2H_2O$: III - The activity-product constant of sepiolite. **Amer. Journ. Sci.**, **273**, 65-83.

CHURCH T.M. and VELDE B., 1979 - Geochemistry and origin of a deep-sea Pacific palygorskite deposit. **Chem. Geol.**, **25**, 31-39.

CHURCHMAN G.J., 1980 - Clay minerals formed from micas and chlorites in some New Zealand soils. **Clay Min.**, **15**, 59-76.

CLARK Jr S.P., ed., 1966 - Handbook of Physical Constants. **Geol. Soc. Amer. Mem.**, **97**.

CLAYTON J.L., 1974 - Clay mineralogy in soils of the Idaho Batholith. **Bull. Geol. Soc. Amer.**, **85**, 229-232.

CLAYTON R.N., MUFFLER L.J.P. and WHITE D.E., 1968 - Oxygen isotope study of calcite and silicates of the River Ranch No. 1 well, Salten Sea Geothermal field, Calif. **Amer. Journ. Sci.**, **266**, 968-987.

CLOKE P.L. and KESLER S.E., 1979 - The halite trend in hydrothermal solutions. **Econ. Geol.**, **74**, 1823-1831.

COLE W.F., 1966 - A study of a long-spacing mica-like mineral. **Clay Min.**, **6**, 261-281.

COOMBS D.S., 1970 - Present status of the zeolite facies. **Amer. Chem. Soc.**, **2nd. Int. Zeolite Conf.**, 556-566.

370

COOMBS D.S., ELLIS A.J., FYFE W.S. and TAYLOR A.M., 1959 - The zeolite facies, with comments on the interpretation of hydrothermal syntheses. Geochim. Acta, 17, 53-107.

COOMBS D.S. and WHETTEN J.T., 1967 - Composition of analcime from sedimentary and burial metamorphic rocks. Bull. Geol. Soc. Amer., 78, 269-282.

COPELAND R.A., FREY F.A. and WONES D.R., 1971 - Origin of clay minerals in a Mid-Atlantic Ridge sediment. Earth Planet. Sci. Lett., 10, 186-191.

COULTER B.S. and TAILBURDEEN O., 1968 - Calcium : aluminum exchange equilibria in clay minerals and acid soils. Journ. Soil Sci., 19, 237-250.

COULTER B.S., 1969 - The equilibria of K:Al exchange in clay minerals and acid soils. Journ. Soil Sci., 20, 72-83.

COURBE C., VELDE B. and MEUNIER A., 1981 - Weathering of glauconites : reversal of the glauconitization process in a soil profile in Western France. Clay Min., 16, 231-243.

COUTURE R., 1977 - Composition and origin of palygorskite-rich and montmorillonite-rich zeolite-containing. Chem. Geol., 19, 113-130.

CROVISIER J.L., THOMASSIN J.H., JUTEAU T., EBERHARD J.P., TOURAY J.C. and BAILLIF P., 1983 - Experimental sea-water-basaltic glass interaction at 50°C : Study of early developed phases by electron microscopy and X-ray photoelectron spectrometry. Geochim. Cosmochim. Acta, 47, 377-387.

CUVIER G. and BRONGNIART A., 1853 - Description géologique des environs de Paris. 3ème ed., d'Ocagne, Paris.

DAPPLES E.C., 1959 - The behavior of silica in diagenesis. Soc. Econ. Pal. Min., 36-51.

DAPPLES E.C., 1962 - Stages of diagenesis in the development of sandstones. Bull. Geol. Soc. Amer., 73, 913-934.

DAPPLES E.C., 1967.a - Diagenesis of sandstones. In LARSEN G. and CHILINGAR C.V., 91-125.

DAPPLES E.C., 1967.b - Silica as an agent of diagenesis. **In** LARSEN G. and CHILINGAR C.V., 323-342.

DAVIES D.K., ALMON W.R., BONIS S.B. and HUNTER B.E., 1979 - Deposition and diagenesis of Tertiary-Holocene volcano-clastics Guatamala. **S.E.P.M. Spec. Pub.**, 26, 281-306.

DAVIS S.N., 1964 - Silica in streams and ground water. **Amer. Journ. Sci.**, 262, 870-891.

DECARREAU A., 1980 - Cristallogenèse expérimentale des smectites magnésiennes : hectorite, stevensite. **Bull. Min.**, 103, 579-590.

DECARREAU A., 1982 - Etude expérimentale de la cristallogenèse des smectites. Thèse Doct. Etat, Univ. Orsay (France).

DEER W.A., HOWIE R.A. and ZUSSMAN J., 1962 - Rock-forming Minerals. Longmans, London ed., vol. 3, 270 p.

DEGENS E.T. and CHILINGAR G.V., 1967 - Diagenesis of subsurface waters. **In** LARSEN G. and CHILINGAR G.V., 477-502.

DEIST J. and TAILBURDEEN O., 1967 - Ion exchange in soils from the ion pairs K-Ca, K-Rb and Na-K. **Journ. Soil Sci.**, 18, 124-137.

DICKINSON W.A., 1962 - Petrology and diagenesis of Jurassic andesitic strata in Central Oregon. **Amer. Journ. Sci.**, 260, 281-500.

DOWSETT F.R., 1980 - Hydrothermal alteration of the Johns peak stock, Routt County, Colorado. **Econ. Geol.**, 75, 30-44.

DREIZLER I., 1962 - Mineralogische Untersuchungen in zwei Gipsvorkommen der Werraserie (Zechstein). **Beitr. Min. Petr.**, 8, 323-338.

DRIBLE W.E. and TILLER W.A., 1981 - Kinetic model of zeolite paragenesis in tuffaceous sediments. **Clays Clay Min.**, 29, 323-330.

DUNOYER de SEGONZAC G., 1968 - The birth and development of the concept of diagenesis. **Earth Sci. Rev.**, **4**, 153-201.

DUNOYER de SEGONZAC G., 1969 - Les minéraux argileux dans la diagenèse. Passage au métamorphisme. **Mém. Serv. Carte Géol. Als.-Lorr.**, **29**, 320 p.

DUNOYER de SEGONZAC G., 1970 - The transformation of clay minerals during diagenesis and low-grade metamorphism. A review. **Sediment.**, **15**, 281-346.

DUNOYER de SEGONZAC G., FERRERO J. and KUBLER B., 1968 - Sur la cristallinité de l'illite dans la diagenèse et l'anchimétamorphisme. **Sediment.**, **10**, 137-143.

DUNOYER de SEGONZAC G. and HEDDEBAUT C., 1971 - Paléozoïque anchimétamorphisme à illite, chlorite, pyrophyllite, allevardite et paragonite dans les Pyrénées basques. **Bull. Carte Géol. Als.-Lorr.**, **24**, 277-290.

DUNOYER de SEGONZAC G., TARDY Y. and MILLOT G., 1970 - Evolution symétrique des édifices micacés au cours de l'altération superficielle et de la diagenèse profonde. **Bull. Gr. Fr. Arg.**, **22**, 51-68.

DUCLOUX J., MEUNIER A. and VELDE B., 1976 - Smectite, chlorite and a regular interlayered chlorite-vermiculite in soils developed on a small serpentinite body, Massif Central, France. **Clay Min.**, **11**, 121-135.

DZOTSENDIDZE G.S. and SKHIRTLADZE N.I., 1964 - Paragenesis of the analcime and halloysite in the Bathonian sediments of Georgia. **Amer. Chem. Soc., 2nd Int. Zeolite Conf.**, 197-201.

EARLEY J.W., OSTHAUS B.B. and MILNE I.H., 1953 - Purification and properties of montmorillonite. **Amer. Min.**, **38**, 707-724.

EBERL D.D., 1971 - Experimental diagenetic reactions involving clay minerals. **Thesis, Case Western Reserve University, Cleveland, Ohio, U.S.A.**

EBERL D.D., 1978 - The reaction of montmorillonite to mixed-layered clay : the effect of interlayer alkali and alkaline earth cations. **Geochim.**, **43**, 1-8.

EBERL D.D., 1980 - Alkali cation selectivity and fixation by clay minerals. **Clays Clay Min.**, 28, 161-172.

EBERL D.D. and HOWER J., 1976 - Kinetics of illite formation. **Bull. Geol. Soc. Amer.**, 87, 1326-1330.

EBERL D.D., JONES B.F. and KHOURY H.N., 1982 - Mixed-layered kerolite/stevensite from the Amargosa desert, Nevada. **Clays Clay Min.**, 30, 321-326.

EBERL D.D., WHITNEY G., KODA E.J., 1978 - Hydrothermal reactivity of smectite. **Amer. Min.**, 63, 401-409.

ECHLE W., 1961 - Mineralogische Untersuchungen an Sedimenten des Steinmergelkenpers und der Roten Wand aus der Umgebung von Göttingen. **Beiträge Min. Petr.**, 8, 28-59.

ECHLE W., 1974 - Zur Mineralogie und Petrogenese jungtertiärer tuffitischer Sedimente im Neogen-Becken nördlich Mihaliggik (Westanatolien, Türkei). **N. Jb. Miner. Abh.**, 121, 43-84.

ECHLE W., 1980 - The transformations sepiolite = loughlinite : experiments and field observations tuffaceous neogene clays (Turkey). **N. Jb. Miner. Abh.**, 133, 303-321.

EGGLETON R.A., 1977 - Nontronite : chemistry and X-ray diffraction. **Clay Min.**, 12, 181-194.

EGGLETON R.A. and BOLAND J.N., 1982 - Weathering of enstatite to talc through a sequence of transitional phases. **Clays Clay Min.**, 30, 11-20.

EHLMANN A.J., HULINGS N.C. and GLOVER E.D., 1963 - Stages of glauconite formation in modern foraminiferal sediments. **Journ. Petr.**, 33, 87-96.

EHLMANN A.J. and SAND L.B., 1959 - Occurrences of shales partially altered to pyrophyllite. **Clays Clay Min.**, 6, 368-391.

EHLMANN A.J., SAND L.B. and REGIS A.J., 1962 - Occurrence of sepiolite in Utah and Nevada. **Econ. Geol.**, 57, 1085-1094.

374

ELIAS M., DONALDSON M.J. and GIORGETTA N., 1981 - Geology, mineralogy and chemistry of laterite nickel-cobalt deposits near Kalgoolie, Western Australia. **Econ. Geol.**, **76**, 1775-1783.

ELLIS A.J., 1968 - Natural hydrothermal systems and experimental hot water/rock interaction : reactions with NaCl solutions and trace metal extraction. Geochim. **Acta**, **32**, 1356-1363.

ELLIS A.J. and MAHON W.A.J., 1964 - Natural hydrothermal systems and experimental hot water/rock interactions. Geochim. **Acta**, **28**, 1323-1358.

ELOUARD P.E. and MILLOT G., 1959 - Observations sur les silicifications du Lutétien en Mauritamé et dans la vallée du Sénégal. **Bull. Serv. Carte Géol. Als.-Lorr.**, **12**, 15-19.

ERNST W.G., 1963 - Significance of phengitic micas from low-grade schists. **Amer. Min.**, **48**, 1357-1373.

EROSHCHER-SHAK V.A., 1970 - Mixed-layer biotite-chlorite formed in the course of local epigenesis in the weathering crust of a biotite gneiss. **Sediment.**, **15**, 115-121.

ESLINGER E.V. and SAVIN S.M., 1973.a - Mineralogy and oxygen isotope geochemistry of the hydrothermally altered rocks of the Ohaki-Broadlands, New Zealand geothermal area. **Amer. Journ. Sci.**, **273**, 240-269.

ESLINGER E.V. and SAVIN S.M., 1973.b - Oxygen isotope geothermometry of the burial metamorphic rocks of the Precambrian Belt Supergroup, Glacier National Park, Montana. **Bull. Geol. Soc. Amer.**, **84**, 2549-2560.

ESQUEVIN J., 1956 - Synthèse de phyllites zincifères. **Bull. Gr. Fr. Arg.**, **VIII**, 17-22.

ESQUEVIN J., 1960 - Les silicates de zinc, étude de produits de synthèse. **Ann. Agron.**, **11**, 497-556.

ESTEOULE J., 1965 - Evolution des gels alumino-siliciques en présence de solutions magnésiennes et salines concentrées. Thesis, Fac. Sci., Univ. Rennes, 79 p.

ESTEOULE J., 1969 - Contribution à la genèse des argiles dioctaédriques dans les conditions de surface. Thesis, Fac. Sci., Univ. Rennes, 116 p.

ESWARAN H. and SYS C., 1970 - An evolution of the free iron in tropical basaltic soils. **Pédologie, 1,** 62-85.

EVANS R., 1978 - Origin and significance of evaporites in basins around the Atlantic margin. **A.A.P.G. Bull., 62,** 223-234.

FAUST G.T., HATHAWAY J.C. and MILLOT G., 1959 - A restudy of stevensite and allied minerals. **Amer. Min., 44,** 342-370.

FAWCETT J.J. and YODER H.S., 1966 - Phase relationships of chlorites in the system $MgO-Al_2O_3-SiO_2-H_2O$. **Amer. Min., 51,** 353-380.

FERSMANN A., 1913 - Recherches sur les silicates de magnésie. **Mém. Acad. Sci. Saint-Pétersbourg, 32,** 377-392.

FISCHER G., 1977 - Non-equilibrium thermodynamics in metamorphism. **In** FRASER D.G. - Thermodynamics in Geology. **Reidel, Boston,** p. 381-404.

FLASCHER S.S., 1957 - Studies in the system iron oxide-silica-water at low oxygen partial pressures. **Econ. Geol., 52,** 923-943.

FLEISCHER P., 1972 - Sepiolite associated with Miocen diatomite Cruz Basin, California. **Amer. Min., 57,** 903-913.

FONTANAUD A., 1982 - Les faciès d'altération supergène des roches ultrabasiques. Etude de deux massifs de lherzolite (Pyrénées, France). Thesis, Univ. Poitiers, 103 p.

FONTES J.C., FRITZ P., GAUTHIER J. and KULBICKI G., 1967 - Minéraux argileux, éléments traces et compositions isotopiques ($^{18}O/^{16}O$ et $^{13}C/^{12}C$) dans les formations gypsifères de l'Eocène Supérieur et dans l'Oligocène de Cormeilles-en-Parisis. **Bull. Cent. Rech. Pau - SNPA, 1,** 315-366.

FORD J.H., 1978 - A chemical study of alteration at the Panguna Porphyry copper deposit, Bougainville, Papua New Guinea. **Econ. Geol.**, **73**, 703-720.

FOSTER M.D., 1951 - The importance of the exchangeable magnesium as cation exchange capacity in the study of montmorillonitic clays. **Amer. Min.**, **36**, 717-730.

FOSTER M.D., 1953 - Geochemical studies of clay minerals. II - Relation between substitution and swelling in montmorillonite. **Amer. Min.**, **38**, 994-1006.

FOSTER M.D., 1956 - Correlation of dioctahedral potassium micas on the basis of their charge relations. **U.S. Geol. Surv. Bull.**, 1036-D, 51-67.

FOSTER M.D., 1962 - Interpretation of the composition and classification of chlorites. **U.S. Geol. Surv. Bull.**, Prof. Papers 414.A.

FOSTER M.D., 1963 - The composition of vermiculites and hydrobiotites. **Clays Clay Min.**, **10**, 70-89.

FOURNIER R.O., 1965 - Montmorillonite pseudomorphic after plagioclase in a porphyry copper deposit. **Amer. Min.**, **50**, 771-777.

FOURNIER R.O., 1967 - The porphyry copper deposit exposed in the liberty open-pit mine near Ely, Nevada. Part. II : The formation of hydrothermal alteration zones. **Econ. Geol.**, **62**, 202-227.

FRANKART R. and HERBILLON A.J., 1970 - Présence et genèse d'analcime dans les sols sodiques de la Basse Ruzizi (Burundi). **Bull. Gr. Fr. Argiles**, **XXII**, 79-89.

FRANK-KAMENECKIJI V.A. and KLOCKOVA N.V.K., 1969 - Phasenumwandlungen des Sepioliths und Palygorskits bei verschiedenem Druck in hydrothermalen Bedingungen. **Geochimija, Alademija, Nauk. SSSR**, **1**, 16-21.

FREY M., 1970 - The step from diagenesis to metamorphism in pelitic rocks during alpine orogenesis. **Sediment.**, **15**, 261-279.

FREY M., 1974 - Alpine metamorphism of pelitic and marly rocks of the central Alps. **Schw. Petr. Mitt.**, 54, 489-506.

FREY M. and HUNZIKER J.C., 1973 - Progressive niedriggradige Metamorphose glaukonitfuhrender Horizonte in den helvetischen Alpen der Ostschweiz. **Contr. Min. Petr.**, 39, 185-218.

FRONDEL C., 1962 - Dana's the System of Mineralogy. 7th ed., vol. III : Silica minerals. John Wiley and Sons, New-York, 334 p.

FUCHTBAUER H. and GOLDSCHMIDT H., 1959 - Die Tonminerale der Zechstein-formation. **Beiträge für Min. Petr.**, 6, 320-345.

FUCHTBAUER H. and GOLDSCHMIDT H., 1963 - Beobachtungen zur Tonmineraldiagenese. **Proc. 1st Int. Clay Conf.**, 99-111.

FUJISHIMA K.Y., 1977 - Hydrothermal mineralogy of Keolu Hills, Oahu Hawaii. **Amer. Min.**, 42, 578-582.

FURBISH W.J., 1975 - Corrensite of deuteric origin. **Amer. Min.**, 40, 928-930.

FURBISH W.J. and SANDO T.W., 1976 - Palygorskite by direct precipitation from hydrothermal solution. **Clay Min.**, 11, 147-152.

FURNES H., 1978 - Element mobility during palagonitization of a subglacial hyaloclastite in Iceland. **Chem. Geol.**, 22, 249-264.

FURNES H. and MIH El-Anbaawy, 1980 - Chemical charges of authigenic mineral formation during palagonitization of basanite hyaloclastite gran Canaria, Canant Islands. **Neues Jahb. Min. Abh.**, 139, 279-302.

GABIS V., 1963 - Etude minéralogique et géochimique de la série sédimentaire oligocène du Velay. **Bull. Soc. Fr. Min. Crist.**, 86, 315-354.

GAERTNER H.R. and SCHELLMANN W., 1965 - Rezente sedimente in Küstenbereich der Halbinsel Kaloum, Guinea. **Tschermaks Min. Petr. Mitt.**, 10, 349-367.

378

GALAN E. and FERRO A., 1982 - Palygorskite-sepiolite clays of Lebrija. Southern Spain. **Clays Clay Min.**, 30, 191-199.

GARDNER L.R., 1972 - Origin of the Mormon Mesa caliche-clark country Nevada formed under aggrading (aerobian) conditions 4×10^5 to 2.5×10^6 years. **Bull. Geol. Soc. Amer.**, 83, 143-146.

GARRELS R.M., 1957 - Some free energy values from geological relations. **Amer. Min.**, 42, 780-791.

GARRELS R.M., 1965 - Silica : Role in the buffering of natural waters. **Science**, 148, 3666-3669.

GARRELS R.M. and CHRIST L.L., 1965 - Solutions, Minerals and Equilibria. Harper and Row, New York, 335 p.

GARRELS R.M. and HOWARD P., 1959 - Reactions of feldspar and mica with water at low temperature and pressure. **Clays Clay Min.**, 6, 68-8 .

GAUDETTE H.E., EADES J.L. and GRIM R.E., 1966 - The nature of illite. **Clays Clay Min.**, 13, 33-48.

GHEORGHITESCU D. and MEDESAN A., 1972 - Hydrothermales sepiolith von Varad (Moldova Noua-Banat). **Tsch. Min. Petr. Mitt.**, 17, 189-195.

GIGGENBACH W.H., 1981 - Carbon 13 exchange between CO_2 and CH_4 under geothermal conditions. **Geochim. Cosmochim. Acta**, 46, 159-166.

GILL W.D., KHALAF F.I. and MASSOUD M.S., 1977 - Clay minerals as an index of the degree of terrigenous rocks in the South Wales coalfield. **Sediment.**, 24, 675-691.

GILLERY F.H., 1959 - The X-ray study of synthetic Mg-Al serpentines and chlorites. **Amer. Min.**, 44, 143-149.

GIRESSE P. and ODIN G.S., 1973 - Nature minéralogique et origine des glauconies du plateau continental du Gabon et du Congo. **Sedimentol.**, 20, 457-488.

GLAESER R. and MERING J., 1967 - Effet de chauffage sur les montmorillonites saturées de cations de petit rayon. C.R. Acad. Sci., **265 D**, 833-835.

GLUSKOTER J.J., 1967 - Clay mineralogy in Illinois coals. Journ. Sed. Petr., **37**, 205-214.

GOTTARDI G., 1978 - Mineralogy and crystal chemistry of zeolites. Natural zeolites : occurrence properties and use. L. SAND and F.A. MUMPTON eds. Pergamon., 31-44.

GOUT R., KLEIN J.L. and MONCHOUX P., 1980 - Evolution minéralogique et chimique des bauxites au cours de leur genèse dans les gisements de l'Ariège (France). **Bull. Min.**, 103, 224-229.

GRANDQUIST W.T. and POLLACK S.S., 1967 - Clay mineral synthesis. II - A randomly interstratified aluminian montmorillonoid. **Amer. Min.**, **52**, 212-226.

GREENWOOD H.J., 1961 - The system $NaAlSi_2O_6$-H_2O-argon : total pressure and water pressure in metamorphism. **Journ. Geophys. Res.**, **66**, 3923-3946.

GRIFFIN G.M., 1962 - Regional clay mineral facies-products of weathering intensity and current distribution in the Northeastern Gulf of Mexico. **Bull. Geol. Soc. Amer.**, **73**, 737-768.

GRIFFIN J.J., WINDEM H. and GOLDBERG E.D., 1968 - The distribution of clay minerals in the world ocean. **Deep-sea Res.**, **15**, 433-459.

GRIM R.E., 1953 - Clay Mineralogy. McGraw-Hill, New-York, 383 p.

GRIM R.E., 1968 - Clay Mineralogy. 2nd Ed. McGraw-Hill, New-York, 560 p.

GRIM R.E. and KULBICKI G., 1961 - Montmorillonite high temperature reactions and classification. **Amer. Miner.**, **46**, 1329-1369.

GUDE A.J. and SHEPPARD R.A., 1967 - Composition and genesis of analcime in the Barstow formation, San Bernadino County, Calif. **Clays Clay Min.**, **15**, 189.

GUDE A.J. and SHEPPARD R.A., 1981 - Woolly erionite from the Rease River zeolite deposit, Lander County, Nevada and its relation to other erionites. **Clays Clay Min.**, **29**, 378-384.

GULBRANDSTEN R.A. and CRESSMAN E.R., 1960 - Analcime and albite in altered Jurassic tuff in Idaho and Wyoming. **Journ. Geol.**, **68**, 458-464.

GÜVEN N. and BURNHAM C.W., 1967 - The crystal structure of 3T muscovite. **Zeit Krist.**, **125**, 163-183.

GÜVEN N. and CARNEY L.L., 1979 - The hydrothermal transformation of sepiolite to stevensite and the effect of added chlorides and hydroxides. **Clays Clay Min.**, **27**, 253-260.

GÜVEN N., HOWER W.F. and DAVIES D.K., 1980 - Nature of authigenic illites in sandstone reservoirs. **Journ. Sed. Petr.**, **50**, 761-766.

HAJASH A., 1975 - Hydrothermal processes along the mid-ocean ridges : an experimental investigation. **Contrib. Min. Pet.**, **53**, 205-226.

HAJI-VASSILIOU A. and PUFFER J.H., 1975 - A macrocrystalline attapulgite-palygorskite occurrence in calcite veins. **Amer. Min.**, **60**, 328-330.

HANSHAW B.B. and COPLEN T.B., 1973 - Ultrafiltration by a compacted clay membrane. II - sodium ion exclusion at various ionic strengths. **Geochim. Acta**, **37**, 3211-3227.

HAMILTON E.L., 1959 - Thickness and consolidation of deep-sea sediment. **Bull. Geol. Soc. Amer.**, **70**, 1399-1424.

HAMILTON J.D., 1967 - Partially-ordered, mixed-layer mica-montmorillonite from Maitland, New South Wales. **Clay Min.**, **7**, 63-78.

HARADA K., IWAMOTO S. and KIHARA K., 1967 - Erionite, phyllipsite and gonnardite in the amygdales of altered basalt from Mazé, Niigata prefecture, Japan. **Amer. Min.**, **52**, 1785-1794.

HARDER H., 1972 - The role of magnesium in the formation of smectite minerals. **Chem. Geol.**, 10, 31-39.

HARDER H., 1974 - Illite mineral synthesis at surface temperatures. **Chem. Geol.**, 14, 241-253.

HARDER H., 1976 - Nontronite synthesis at low temperatures. **Chem. Geol.**, 18, 169-180.

HARDER H., 1978 - Synthesis of iron layer silicate minerals under natural conditions. **Clays Clay Min.**, 26, 65-72.

HARDER H., 1980 - Synthesis of glauconite at surface temperatures. **Clays Clay Min.**, 28, 217-222.

HARDER H. and FLEMING W., 1970 - Quartzsynthese bei tiefen Temperaturen. **Geochim. Acta**, 34, 295-305.

HARDIE L.A. and EUGSTER H.P., 1970 - The evolution of closed-basin brines. **Min. Soc. Amer. Spec. Pap.**, 3, 273-290.

HARRISON J.E., 1972 - Precambrian Belt Basin of Northwestern United States : Its geometry, sedimentation and copper occurrences. **Bull. Geol. Soc. Amer.**, 83, 1215-1240.

HARRISON J.E. and JOBIN D.A., 1963 - Geology of the Clark Fork quadrangle, Idaho-Montana. **U.S. Geol. Survey Bull.**, 1141-K, 38 p.

HARRISON J.L. and MURRAY H.H., 1959 - Clay mineral stability and formation during weathering. **Clays Clay Min.**, 6, 144-153.

HARRISS R.C. and PILKEY O.H., 1966 - Interstitial waters of some deep marine carbonate sediments. **Deep Sea Res.**, 13, 467-469.

HART R., 1970 - Chemical exchange between sea water and deep ocean basalts. **E.P.S.L.**, 9, 269-279.

HART S.R., LANK A.K. and KABLE E.J.D., 1974 - Sea floor basalt alteration : some chemical and isotopic effects. **Contr. Min. Petr.**, 44, 219-230.

HART S.R. and NALWALK A.J., 1970 - K, Rb, Cs and Sr relationships in submarine basalts from the Puerto Rico trench. **Geochim. Acta, 34,** 145-155.

HARWARD M.E., CASTEA D.D. and SAYEGH A.L., 1969 - Properties of vermiculites and smectites: Expansion and collapse. **Clays Clay Min., 11,** 437-447.

HASSOUBA H. and SHAW H.F., 1980 - The occurrence of palygorskite in Quaternary sediments of the coastal plain of N-W Egypt. **Clay Min., 15,** 77-84.

HAWKINS D.B., 1981 - Kinetics of glass dissolution and zeolite formation under hydrothermal conditions. **Clays Clay Min., 29,** 331-340.

HAY R.L., 1963 - Zeolite weathering in Oldewai gorge, Tanganyika. **Bull. Geol. Soc. Amer., 74,** 1281-1286.

HAY R.L., 1964 - Phillipsite of saline lakes and soils. **Amer. Min., 49,** 1366-1387.

HAY R.L., 1966 - Zeolites and zeolitic reactions in sedimentary rocks. **Geol. Soc. Amer. Sp. Paper, 85,** 130 p.

HAY R.L. and IIJIMA A., 1970 - Nature and origin of palagonite tuffs of the Honolulu group on Oahu, Hawaii. **Geol. Soc. Amer. Mem.,** 116. Coast, Hay and Anderson eds. Studies in Volcanology.

HAY R.L. and JONES B.F., 1972 - Weathering of basaltic tephra on the island of Hawaii. **Bull. Geol. Soc. Amer., 83,** 317-332.

HAY R.L. and MOIOLA R.J., 1963 - Authigenic silicate minerals in Searles Lake, California. **Sediment., 2.** 312-332.

HAY R.L. and WIGGINS B., 1980 - Pellets, ooids, sepiolite and silica in three calcretes of the South Western United States. **Sediment., 27,** 559-576.

HAYES J.N., 1963 - Clay mineralogy of Mississippian strata of southeast Iowa. **10th Nat. Conf. Clays and Clay Min.,** Pergamon, 413-425.

HAYES J.B., 1970 - Polytypism of chlorite in sedimentary rocks. **Clays Clay Min.**, **18**, 285-306.

HATHAWAY J.C. and SACHS P.L., 1965 - Sepiolite and clinoptilolite from the mid-Atlantic ridge. **Amer. Min.**, **50**, 852-867.

HAYHURST D.J. and SAND L.B., 1975 - Experimental kinetics related to alkali zeolite paragenesis. **Geol. Soc. Amer. Annual Meeting Abst.**, 1106.

HEATH G.R., 1969 - Mineralogy of Cenezoic deep-sea sediments from the equatorial Pacific Ocean. **Bull. Geol. Soc. Amer.**, **80**, 1997-2018.

HEIN J.R. and SCHOLL P.W., 1978 - Diagenesis and distribution of late Cenezoic volcanic sediments in the Southern Bering Sea. **Bull. Geol. Soc. Amer.**, **89**, 197-210.

HEIN J.R., YEH H.W. and ALEXANDER E., 1979 - Origin of iron-rich montmorillonite from the manganese nodule belt of the North Equatorial Pacific. **Clays Clay Min.**, **27**, 185-194.

HELGESON H.C., 1968 - Evaluation of irreversible reactions in geochemical processes involving minerals and aqueous solutions. I - thermodynamic relations. **Geochim. Acta**, **32**, 853-877.

HELGESON H.C., 1969 - Thermodynamics of hydrothermal systems at elevated temperatures and pressures. **Amer. Journ. Sci.**, **267**, 729-804.

HELGESON H.C., GARRELS R.M. and MACKENZIE F.T., 1969 - Evolution of irreversible reactions in geochemical processes involving mineral and aqueous solutions. II - Applications. **Geochim. Acta**, **33**, 455-481.

HELING D., 1978 - Diagenesis of illite in argillaceous sediments of the Rhine graben. **Clay Min.**, **13**, 211-220.

HEMLEY J.J., 1959 - Some mineralogical equilibria in the system $K_2O-Al_2O_3-SiO_2-H_2O$. **Amer. Journ. Sci.**, **257**, 241-270.

HEMLEY J.J. and JONES W.R., 1964 - Chemical aspects of hydrothermal alteration with emphasis on hydrogen metasomatism. **Econ. Geol.**, **59**, 538-569.

HEMLEY J.J., MEYER C. and RICHTER, 1961 - Some alteration reactions in the system $Na_2O-Al_2O_3-H_2O$. **U.S. Geol. Sur. Prof. Papers**, **4**, 338-340.

HEMLEY J.J., MONTEYA J.W., MARINENKO J.W. and LUCE R.W., 1980 - Equilibria in the system $Al_2O_3-SiO_2-H_2O$ and some general implications for alteration mineralization processes. **Econ. Geol.**, **75**, 210-228.

HEMLEY J.J. MONTEYA J.W., NIGRINI A. and VINCENT H.A., 1971 - Some alteration reactions in the system $CaO-Al_2O_3-SiO_2-H_2O$. **Soc. Min. Geol. Japan, Spec. Issue**, **2**, 58-63.

HENDRICKS S.B. and ROSS C.S., 1941 - Chemical composition and genesis of glauconite and celadonite. **Amer. Min.**, **26**, 683-708.

HERBILLON A.J., FRANKART R.F., VIELVOYE L., 1981 - An occurrence of interstratified kaolinite-smectite minerals in a red-black soil toposequence. **Clay Min.**, **16**, 195-201.

HERBILLON A.J. and MAKUMBI M.N., 1975 - Weathering of chlorite in a soil derived from a chloritoschist under humid tropical conditions. **Geoderma**, **13**, 89-104.

HESS P., 1966 - Phase equilibria of some minerals in the $K_2O-Na_2O-Al_2O_3-SiO_2-H_2O$ system at 25°C and 1 atmosphere. **Amer. Journ. Sci.**, **264**, 289-309.

HEYDEMANN A., 1964 - Untersuchungen über die Bildungsbedingungen von Quartz im Temperaturbereich zwischen 100°C und 250°C. **Beiträge zur Min. Petr.**, **10**, 242-259.

HEUVEL R.C. Van den, 1966 - The occurrence of sepiolite and attapulgite in the calcareous zone of a soil near Las Cruces, N. Mex. **Clays Clay Min**, **13**, 193-207.

HIGH L.R. and PICARD M.D., 1965 - Sedimentary petrology and origin of analcime-rich Popo Agie Member, Chugwater (Triassic) formation, West Central Wyoming. **Journ. Sed. Petr.**, **35**, 49-70.

HODA S.N. and HOOD W.C., 1972 - Laboratory alteration of trioctahedral micas. **Clays Clay Min.**, **20**, 343-358.

HOFFERT M., 1980 - Les "argiles rouges des grands fonds" dans le Pacifique Centre-Est, authigenèse, transport, diagenèse. **Sci. Géol.**, **61**, 231 p.

HOFFERT M., PERSEIL A., HEKINIAN R., CHOUKROUNE P., NEEDHAM H.D., FRANCHETEAU J. et LE PICHON X., 1978.a - Hydrothermal deposits sampled by diving saucer in transform fault "A" near 37°N on the Mid-Atlantic Ridge, Famous area. **Oceanologica Acta**, **1**, 73-86.

HOFFERT M., KARPOFF A.M., CLAUER N., SHAAF A., COURTOIS C. and PAUTOT G., 1978.b - Néoformations et altérations dans trois faciès volcano-sédimentaires du Pacifique Sud. **Oceanologica Acta**, **1**, 187-202.

HOFFMAN J. and HOWER J., 1979 - Clay mineral assemblages as low grace metamorphic geothermometers : Application to the thrust faculted disturbed belt of Montana. U.S.A. Aspects of Diagenesis. **Soc. Econ. Pal. Min.**,, Sp. Pub. Z6, 55-81.

HOGG C.S., MALDEN P.J. and MEADS A.W., 1975 - Identification of iron-containing impurities in natural kaolinites using the Mössbauer effect. **Min. Mag.**, **40**, 89-96.

HOHLING H.J., 1958 - Bemerkung zu dem "Serpentintalk" aus dem Zechstein-Anhydritprofil der Erdgasbohrung Frenswegen 3 im Emsland. **Beiträge zur Min. Petr.**, **6**, 108-111.

HONNOREZ J., 1972 - La palagonitisation - l'altération sous-marine du verre volcanique basique de Palagonia-Sicile. **Pub. Vulkaninstitut Immanuel Friedlaender**, **9**, 131 p.

HONNOREZ J., HERZEN R.P. von, BARRETT T.J., RECKER K., BENDER M.L., BORELLA P.E., HUBBERTEN H.W., JONES S.C., KARATO S., LAVERNE C., MIGDISOV A.G., MOORBY A. and SCHRADER E.L., 1981 - Hydrothermal mounds and young ocean crust of the Galapagos : Preliminary deep sea drilling results, Leg 70. **Bull. Geol. Soc. Amer.**, **92**, 457-472.

HONDA S. and MUFFLER J.P., 1970 - Hydrothermal alteration in core from research drill hold Y-1, Upper Geyser Basin, Yellowstone Park, Wyoming. **Amer. Min.**, 55, 1714-1737.

HOSTETLER P.B. and CHRIST C.L., 1968 - Studies in the system $MgO-SiO_2-CO_2-H_2O$. I - The activity product constant of chrysotile. Geochim. **Acta**, 32, 485-497.

HOWARD J.J., 1981 - Lithium and potassium saturation of illite/smectite clays from interlaminated shales and sandstones. **Clays Clay Min.**, 29, 136-142.

HOWER J., 1961 - Some factors concerning the nature and origin of glauconite. **Amer. Min.**, 47, 886-896.

HOWER J., 1967 - Order of mixed-layering in illite/montmorillonites. **Clays Clay Min.**, 15, 63-84.

HOWER J., ESLINGER E.V., HOWER M.E. and PERRY E.A., 1976 - Mechanism of burial metamorphism of argillaceous sediment : 1. Mineralogical and chemical evidence. **Geol. Soc. Amer. Bull.**, 87, 725-737.

HOWER J., HURLEY P.M., PINSON W.H. and FAIRBAIRN H.W., 1963 - The dependence of K-Ar age on the mineralogy of various particle size ranges in a shale. Geochim. **Acta**, 27, 405-410.

HOWER J. and MOWATT T.C., 1966 - The mineralogy of illites and mixed-layer illite/montmorillonites. **Amer. Min.**, 51, 825-854.

HUANG T.C. and GOODELL H.G., 1967 - Sediments of Charlotte Harbor, S.W. Florida. **Journ. Sed. Petr.**, 37, 449-474.

HUFF W.D. and TURKMENOGLU A.G., 1981 - Chemical characteristics and origin of Ordovician K-bentonites along the Cincinnati Arch. **Clays Clay Min.**, 29, 113-123.

HUMPHRIS S.E. and MARRINER G.F., 1979 - The mineralogy and geochemistry of basalt weathering, Holes 417.A and 418.A. Init. **Rep DSDP**, 51-53, pt 2, 1201-1205.

HURLEY P.M., BROOKINS D.G., PINSON W.H., HART S.R. and FIARBAIRN H.W., 1961 - K-Ar age studies of Mississippi and other river sediments. **Bull. Geol. Soc. Amer.**, **72**, 1807-1816.

HURLEY P.M., FAIRBAIRN H.W., PINSON W.H. and HOWER J., 1962 - Unmetamorphosed minerals in the Gunflint formation used to test the age of the Animikie. **J. Geol.**, **70**, 489-492.

HURLEY P.M., HUNT J.M., PINSON W.H. and FAIRBAIRN H.W., 1963 - K-Ar age values on the clay fractions in dated shales. **Geochim. Acta**, **27**, 279-284.

HUTCHEON A.T., 1966 - Thermodynamics of cation exchange on clay : Ca-K montmorillonite. **Journ. Soil Sci.**, **17**, 339-355.

HUTCHEON I., OLDERSHAW A. and GHENT E.D., 1980 - Diagenesis of Cretaceous sandstones of the Kootenay formation at Elk Valley (Southeastern British Columbia) and Mt Allan (Southwestern Alberta). **Geochim. Acta**, **44**, 1425-1435.

IIJIMA A., 1970 - Present day zeolitic diagenesis of the Neogene geosynclinal deposits in the Niigata Oil field, Japan. **Amer. Chem. Soc. 2nd Int. Zeolite Conf.**, 540-546.

IIJIMA A., 1972 - Latest Cretaceous-early Tertiary lateritic profile in northern Kitakami massif, Northeast Honsku, Japan. **J. Fac. Sci. Univ. Tokyo**, **18**, 325-370.

IIJIMA A., 1975 - Effect of pore water to clinoptilolite-analcime-albite reaction series. **J. Fac. Sci. Univ. Tokyo**, **19**, 133-147.

IIJIMA A. and HARADA K., 1969 - Authigenic zeolites in zeolitic palagonite tuffs on Oahu, Hawaii. **Amer. Min.**, **54**, 182-197.

IIJIMA A. and HAY R.L., 1968 - Analcime composition in tuffs on the Green River Formation, Wyoming. **Amer. Min.**, **53**, 184-200.

IIJIMA A. and MATSUMOTO R., 1982 - Berthierine and chamosite in coal measures of Japan. **Clays Clay Min.**, **30**, 264-274.

IIJIMA A. and TADA R., 1981 - Silica diagenesis of Neogene diatomaceous volcanoclastic sediments in Northern Japan. **Sediment.**, **28**, 185-200.

IIJIMA A. and UTADA M., 1966 - Zeolites in sedimentary rocks, with reference to the depositional environments and zonal distribution. **Sediment.**, **7**, 327-357.

IIYAMA J.T. and ROY R., 1963 - Controlled synthesis of heteropolytypic (mixed-layered) clay minerals. **Clays Clay Min.**, **10**, 4-22.

ILDEFONSE P., 1978 - Mécanismes de l'altération d'une roche gabbroïque du Massif du Pallet (Loire-Atlantique). Thesis Doct. 3ème cycle, Univ. Poitiers, 142 p.

ILDEFONSE P., 1980 - Mineral facies developed by weathering in a meta-gabbro, Loire-Atlantique, France. **Geoderma**, **24**, 257-274.

ILDEFONSE P., COPIN E. and VELDE B., 1979 - A soil vermiculite from a meta-gabbro, Loire-Atlantique, France. **Clay Min.**, **14**, 201-209.

IMAI N., OTSUKA R. and KASHIDE H., 1969 - Dehydration of palygorskite and sepiolite from the Kuguu District, Tochigi pref. central Japan. **Proc. Int. Clay Conf.**, **1**, 99-108.

INOUE A. and MINATO H., 1979 - Ca-K exchange reaction and interstratification in montmorillonite. **Clays Clay Min.**, **27**, 393-401.

ISPHORDING W.C., 1971 - Talc from Gulf Coast Miocene sediments. **Amer. Min.**, **56**, 1399-1402.

JACKSON M.L., 1959 - Frequency distribution of clay minerals in major soil groups as related to factors of soil formation. **Clays Clay Min.**, **6**, 133-143.

JACKSON M.L., TYLER S.A., WILLIS A.L., BOURBEAU G.A.,
PENNINGTON R.P., 1948 - Weathering sequences of clay
size minerals in soils and sediments. **Journ. Phys.
Colloid Chem.**, 52, 1237-1260.

JACOBS D.C. and PARRY, 1976 - A comparison of the geochemistry of biotite from some basin and range stocks. **Econ.
Geol.**, 71, 1029-1035.

JACOBS M.B., 1970 - Clay mineral investigations of Cretaceous
and Quaternary deep sea sediments of the North American
basin. **Journ. Sed. Petr.**, 40, 864-868.

JACKSON M.L., HZEUNG Y., COREY R.B., EVANS E.J. and VANDEN
HEUVEL R.C., 1952 - Weathering sequence of clay-size
minerals in soils and sediments. II. Chemical weathering of layer silicates. **Proc. Soil Soc. Amer.**, 16, 3-6.

JOHANNES W., 1969 - An experimental investigation of the
system $MgO-SiO_2-H_2O-CO_2$. **Amer. Journ. Sci.**, 267, 1083-
1104.

JOHNSON L.J., 1964 - Occurrence of regularly interstratified
chlorite-vermiculite as a weathering product of chlorite in a soil. **Amer. Min.**, 49, 556-572.

JONES B.F., 1965 - The hydrology and mineralogy of Deep
Springs Lake, Inyo County, California. **U.S. Geol. Sur.
Prof. Papers**, 502-A.

JUNG J., 1954 - Les illites du bassin Oligocène de Salins
(Cantal). **Bull. Soc. Fr. Min. Crist.**, 77, 1231-1249.

JUTEAU T., BINGOL F., NOVACK Y., WHITECHURCH H., HOFFERT M.,
WIRRMANN D. and COURTOIS C., 1978 - Preliminary results : mineralogy and geochemistry of alteration
products in leg 45 basement samples. **Initial Reports
DSDP**, 45, 613-620.

KANO K., 1979 - Deposition and diagenesis of siliceous sediments of the Onnagawa formations. **Sci. Rep. Tohoku
Univ.**, 14, 135-189.

KARLSON W., VOLLSET J., BIORLYKKE K. and JORGENSEN P.,
1979 - Changes in mineralogical composition of Tertiary

sediments from North Sea wells. Developments in Sedimentology, Proceed. Int. Clay Conf., 1978, 27, 281-289.
Elsevier.

KASTNER M., 1971 - Authigenic feldspars in carbonate rocks.
Amer. Min., 56, 1403-1409.

KASTNER M., KEENE J.B., GIESKES J.M., 1977 - Diagenesis of
siliceous cozes. I. Chemical controls on the rate of
opal-t to opal-CT transformation : an experimental
study. Geochim. Acta, 41, 1041-1060.

KAUTZ K., 1964 - Sedimentpetrographische Untersuchung zur
Diagenese in Sandsteinen der marinen Unterkreide Nord-
deutschlands. Beiträge zur Min. Petr., 9, 423-461.

KAUTZ K. and PARADA H., 1976 - Sepiolite formation in a Pan
of the Kalahari South West Africa. N. Jb. Miner. Mh.,
12, 545-559.

KELLER W.D., 1958 - Glauconitic mica in the Morrison formation in Colorado. Clays Clay Min., 5, 120-128.

KELLER W.D., 1963 - Hydrothermal kaolinitization (endelliti-
zation) of a volcanic glassy rock. Clays Clay Min., 10,
333-343.

KELLER W.D. and HANSON R.F., 1968 - Hydrothermal alteration
of a rhyolite flow breccia near San Luis Potose, Mexico, to refactory kaolin. Clays Clay Min., 16, 223-229.

KELLEY D.R. and KERR P.R., 1957 - Clay alteration and ore,
Temple Mountain, Utah. Bull. Geol. Soc. Amer., 58,
1101-1116.

KERNS R.L. and MANKIN C.J., 1967 - Compositional variation
of a vermiculite as related to particle size. Clays
Clay Min., Proc. 15th Conf., 163-177.

KERRICK D.M. and COTTON W.R., 1971 - Stability relations of
jadeite pyroxene in Franciscan metagreywackes near San
José, California. Amer. Journ. Sci., 271, 350-369.

KESLER T.L., 1970 - Hydrothermal kaolinitization in Michoa-
can, Mexico. Clays Clay Min., 18, 121-124.

KHARAKA Y.K. and BERRY F.A.F., 1973 - Simultaneous flow of water solute through geological membranes. I. Experimental investigation. **Geochim. Acta, 37,** 2577-2603.

KIMBARA K., 1973 - Clay minerals in the Miocene low-grade metamorphic rocks, Tanzawa Mountains, Kanagawa Prefecture, Central Japan. **Journ. Jap. Assoc. Min. Petr. Econ. Geol., 68,** 311-328.

KIMBARA K., SHIMODA S. and SATO O., 1971 - An interstratified mineral of chlorite and montmorillonite from the green tuff in the Yamakata District. **Journ. Jap. Assoc. Min. Petr. Econ. Geol., 66,** 99-111.

KIMBARA K. and SUDO C.T., 1973 - Chloritic clay minerals in tuffaceous sandstone of the Miocene Green Tuff formation, Yamanaka District, Ishikawa Prefecture, Japan. **Journ. Jap. Assoc. Min. Petr. Econ. Geol., 68,** 246-258.

KIRKMAN J.H., 1975 - Clay mineralogy of some tephra beds of Rotorna Area, North Island, New-Zealand. **Clay Min., 20,** 437-449.

KITTRICK J.A., 1969 - Soil minerals in the Al_2O_3-SiO_2-H_2O system and a theory of their formation. **Clays Clay Min., 17,** 157-167.

KITTRICK J.A., 1971 - Stability of montmorillonites. I. Belle Fourche and Clay Spur montmorillonites. **Soil Sci. Amer. Proc., 35,** 140-145.

KITTRICK J.A., 1973 - Mica-derived vermiculities as unstable intermediates. **Clays Clay Min., 21,** 479-488.

KLEIN C., 1974 - Greenalite, stilpnomelane minnesotaite, crocidolite and carbonates in a very low-grade metamorphic Precambrian iron-formation. **Can. Min., 12,** 475-498.

KODAMA H., 1966 - The nature of the component layers of rectorite. **Amer. Min., 51,** 1035-1055.

KODAMA H. and BRYDON J.E., 1966 - Interstratified montmorillonite-mica clays from subsoils of the Prairie Provinces, Western Canada. **Clays Clay Min., 13,** 151-173.

KODAMA H. and FOSCOLOS A.E., 1981 - Occurrence of berthieri-ne in canadian arctic desert soils. **Can. Miner., 19,** 279-283.

KOIZUMI M. and ROY R., 1959 - Synthetic montmorillonoids with variable exchange capacity. **Amer. Min., 44,** 788-805.

KOPP O.C. and FALLIS S.M., 1974 - Corrensite in the Wallington formation Lyons, Kansas. **Amer. Min., 59,** 623-624.

KORZHINSKII D.S., 1959 - Physiochemical basis of the analysis of the paragenesis of minerals. (Trans.) New-York Consultants Bureau, 143 p.

KORZHINSKII D.S., 1965 - The theory of systems with perfectly mobile components and processes of mineral formation. **Amer. Journ. Sci., 263,** 193-205.

KORZHINSKII D.S., 1970 - Theory of Metasomatic Zoning. Clarendon Press, Oxford, 158 p.

KOSSOVSKAYA A.G., 1972 - Genetic types and paragenetic associations of minerals of the corrensite groups. **Proc. Int. Clay Conf.,** 341-342.

KOSSOVSKAYA A.G. and DRITS V.A., 1970 - The variability of micaceous minerals in sedimentary rocks. **Sediment., 15,** 83-101.

KRAUSKOPF K.B., 1956 - Dissolution and precipitation of silica at low temperatures. **Geochim. Acta, 10,** 1-27.

KRAUSKOPF K.B., 1959 - The geochemistry of silica in sedimentary environments. **Soc. Econ. Pal. Min., Special Pub., 7,** 4-19.

KRUMBEIN W.C. and PETITJOHN F.J., 1938 - Manual of Sedimentary Petrography. Appleton-Century-Crofts, Inc., New-York.

KÜBLER B., 1968 - Evaluation quantitative du métamorphisme par la cristallinité de l'illite. **Bull. Centre Rech. Pau, SNEAP, 1,** 259-278.

KÜBLER B., 1970 - La composition des fractions fines et la distinction flysch-molasse dans le domaine. **Bull. Soc. Géol. France**, **12**, 599-602.

KÜBLER B., 1973 - La corrensite, indicateur possible de milieux de sédimentation et du degré de transformation d'un sédiment. **Bull. Centre Rech. Pau-SNPA**, **7**, 543-556.

KÜBLER B., MARTINI P. and VUAGNAT M., 1974 - Very low grade metamorphism in the western Alps. **Schweitz. Min. Petr. Mitt.**, **54**, 461-469.

KUJAWA F.B. and EUGSTER H.P., 1966 - Stability sequences and stability levels in unary systems. **Amer. Journ. Sci.**, **264**, 620-642.

KULBICKI G., 1959 - High temperature phases in sepiolite, attapulgite and saponite. **Amer. Min.**, **44**, 752-764.

KULKE H., 1969 - Petrographie und Diagenese des Stubens-andsteintes (mittlered Keuper) aus Tiefbohrungen im Raum Memmingen (Bayern). **Contr. Min. Petr.**, **20**, 135-163.

LAGALY G., 1979 - The layer charge of regular interstrati-fied 2:1 minerals. **Clays Clay Min.**, **27**, 1-10.

LAGALY G., FERNANDEZ-GONZALEZ M. and WEISS A., 1976 - Problems in layer-charge determination of montmorilloni-tes. **Clay Min.**, **11**, 173-188.

LAHANN R.W., 1980 - Smectite diagenesis and sandstone cement: the effect of reaction temperature. **Journ. Sed. Pet.**, **50**, 755-760.

LAHANN R.W. and ROBERSON H.E., 1980 - Dissolution of silica from montmorillonite: effect of solution chemistry. **Geochim.**, **44**, 1937-1943.

LAMBOY M., 1967 - Répartition de la "glauconie" sur le plateau continental de la Galice et des Asturies (Espagne). **Compt. Rend. Acad. Sci. Paris**, **265**, 855-857.

LAND L.S. and DUTTON S.P., 1978 - Cementation of Pennsylvanian deltari sandstone isotopic data. **J. Sed. Pet.**, **48**, 1167-1176.

LANIER G., RAAB W.J., FOLSOM R.B. and CONE S., 1978 - Alteration of equigranular monzonite, Bingham mining District, Utah. **Econ. Geol.**, **73**, 1270-1286.

LANTEAUME M. and HACCARD D.C., 1961 - Stratigraphie et variations de faciès des formations constitutives de la nappe du Flyscha Helminthoïdes des Alpes-Maritimes franco-italiennes. **Boll. Soc. Geol. Italiana**, **80**, 3-15.

LAPPARENT A.F., 1935 - Sur un constituant essentiel des terres à foulon. **Compt. Rend. Acad. Sci.**, **Paris**, **201**, 481-483.

LARSEN G. and CHILINGAR G.V., eds, 1967 - Developments in Sedimentology 8 - Diagenesis in Sediments. Elsevier, Amsterdam, 551 p.

LATOUCHE C., 1971 - Découverte d'attapulgite dans des sédiments carottés sur le dôme Cantabria (Golfe de Gascogne). **Compt. Rend. Acad. Sci.**, **Paris**, **272**, 2064-2066.

LAWRENCE J.R., DREVER J.J. and KASTNER M., 1978 - Low temperature alteration of basalts predominates at D.S.D.P., site 395. **Initial Reports of DSDP, Wash.**, **45**, 609-612.

LAWRENCE J.R., DREVER J.I., ANDERSON T.F. and BRUECKNER H.K., 1979 - Importance of alteration of volcanic material in the sediments of Deep Sea Drilling site 323: Chemistry. **Geochim.**, **43**, 573-588.

LECLAIRE L., 1968 - Détermination du degré d'oxydation d'un sédiment (boues et vases actuelles ou récentes, marines, etc.) par l'étude de l'état du fer dans ses formes minérales authigènes. **Compt. Rend. Acad. Sci.**, **Paris**, **266**, 452-454.

LEIKINE M., 1981 - Influence des faibles métamorphismes sur les variations du chimisme global des sédiments et sur les paramètres de l'interstratification des illites-smectites. **Bull. Minér.**, **104**, 47-55.

LELONG F., 1969 - Nature et genèse des produits d'altération de roches cristallines sous climat tropical humide (Guyane française). **Mém. Sci. Terre (Nancy)**, **14**, 187 p.

LEONARD R.A. and WEED S.B., 1970 - Mica weathering rates as related to mica type and composition. **Clays Clay Min.**, **18**, 187-195.

LEONE M., ALAINO R. and CALDERONE S., 1975 - Genesis of chlorite pellets from Mesozoic bedded cherts of Sicily. **Journ. Sed. Petr.**, **45**, 618-628.

LERMAN A. and MACKENZIE F.T., 1975 - Rates of neoformation of alumino-silicates and chert in shallow and deep ocean sediments. **Geol. Soc. Ame. Annual Meeting Abst.**, p. 1167.

LEVY R. and SHAINBERG I., 1972 - Calcium-magnesium exchange in montmorillonite and vermiculite. **Clays Clay Min.**, **20**, 37-46.

LEVY R., SHAINBERG I., SHALHEVET J. and ALPEROVITCH M., 1972 - Selectivity coefficients of Ca-Mg exchange for three montmorillonite soils. **Geoderma**, **8**, 133-138.

LIM C.H. and JACKSON M.L., 1980 - Polycomponent interstratified phyllosilicates in dolomite residuum and sandy till of central Wisconsin. **Soil Sci. Amer. Journ.**, **44**, 868-871

LIN F.C. and CLEMENCY C.V., 1981 - The kinetics of dissolution of muscovites at 25°C and 1 atm CO_2 partial pressure. **Geochim.**, **45**, 571-576.

LIOU J.C., 1971a - Analcime equilibria. **Lithos**, **4**, 389-402.

LIOU J.C., 1971b - P-T stabilities of laumontite, wairakite lawsonite and related minerals in the system $CaAl_2Si_2O_8\text{-}SiO_2\text{-}H_2O$. **Journ. Petr.**, **12**, 379-411.

LIOU J.C., 1974 - Mineralogy and chemistry of glassy basalts, Coastal Range ophiolites, Taiwan. **Bull. Geol. Soc. Amer.**, **85**, 1-10.

LIPPMANN F., 1956 - Clay minerals from the Röt member of the Triassic near Göttingen, Germany. **Journ. Sed. Petr.**, **26**, 125-139.

LIPPMANN F. and SAVASCIN M.Y., 1969 - Mineralogische Untersuchungen an Lösungsrückständen eines württembergischen Keupergipsvorkommens. **Tschermaks Min. Petr. Mitt., 13,** 165-190.

LISS P.S. and SPENCER C.P., 1970 - Abiological processes in the removal of silicate from sea water. **Geochim. Acta, 34,** 1073-1088.

LOMBARDI G. and SHEPPARD S.M.F., 1977 - Petrographic and isotopic studies of the altered acid volcanics of the Tolfa-cerite Area Italy: the genesis of the clays. **Clay Min., 12,** 147-162.

LONSDALE P.F., BISCHOFF J.L., BURNS V.M., KASTNER M. and SWEENEY R.E., 1980 - A high-temperature hydrothermal deposit on the seabed at a Gulf of California spreading center. **E.P.S.L., 49,** 8-20.

LOUGHNAN F.C., 1966 - Analcite in the Newcastle coal measure sediments of the Sydney Basin, Australia. **Amer. Min., 51,** 486-494.

LOVELAND P.J., 1981 - Weathering of a soil glauconite in Southern England. **Geoderma, 25,** 35-54.

LOVELL J.P.G., 1969 - Tyle formation undeformed turbidites and their lateral equivalents: mineralogy and paleogeography. **Bull. Geol. Soc. Amer., 80,** 9-22.

LOWELL J.D. and GUILBERT J.M., 1970 - Lateral and vertical alteration-mineralization zoning in porphyry ore deposits. **Econ. Geol, 65,** 373-408.

LUCAS J., PREVOT L., ATAMAN G., GUNDOGDU N., 1980 - Mineralogical and geochemical studies of the phosphatic formations in South eastern Turkey (Mazidagi-Mardin). **S.E.P.M. Special Pub., 29,** 149-152.

MACIAS-VASQUEZ F., 1981 - Formation of gibbsite in soils and saprolites of temperate-humid zones. **Clay Min., 16,** 43-52.

MACDONALD K.C., BECKER K., SPEISS F.N. and BALLARD R.D., 1980 - Hydrothermal heat flux of the black smoker vents on the East Pacific Rise. **E.P.S.L., 48,** 1-8.

MACDOWELL S.D. and ELDERS W. A. 1980 - Authigenic layer silicate minerals in Borehole Elmore 1, Salton Sea geothermal field, California, U.S.A. **Contrib. Min. Petr.**, **74**, 293-310.

MACKENZIE R.C., 1957 - The illite in some old Red Sandstone soils and sediments. **Min. Mag.**, **31**, 681-686.

MACKENZIE R.C., 1963 - Retention of exchangeable ions by montmorillonite. **Proc. 1st Int. Clay Conf.**, **1**, 183-193.

MACKENZIE F.T. and GEES R., 1971 - Quartz : Synthesis at earth-surface conditions. **Science**, **173**, 533-535.

McBRIDE M.B., 1980 - Interpretation of the variability of selectivity coefficients for exchange between ions of unequal charge on smectites. **Clays Clay Min.**, **28**, 255-261.

McLEAN S.A., ALLEN B.L. and CRAIG J.R., 1972 - The occurrence of sepiolite and attapulgite on the Southern High Plains. **Clays Clay Min.**, **20**, 143-151.

McHARDY W.J., WILSON M.J. and TAIT J.M., 1982 - Electron microscope and X-ray diffraction studies of filamentous illitic clay from sandstones of the Mapours Field. **Clay Min.**, **17**, 23-39.

McMURTRY G.M., WANG C.H. and YEH H.W., 1983 - Chemical and isotopic investigations into the origin of clay minerals from the Galapagos hydrothermal mounds field. **Geochim. Cosmochim. Acta**, **47**, 475-489.

MAES A., PEIGNEUR P. and CREMERS A., 1975 - Thermodynamics of transition metal ion exchange in montmorillonite. **Proceed. Int. Clay Conf.**, 319-329.

MAMMY J., 1970 - Extraction of interlayer-K from phlogopite specific effects of cations, role of Na and H concentrations in extraction solutions. **Clays Clay Min.**, **18**, 157-163.

MANGELSDORF P.C., WILSON T.R.S. and DANIELL E., 1969 - Potassium enrichments in interstitial waters of recent marine sediments. **Science**, **165**, 171-173.

MANHEIM F.T., 1970 - The diffusion of ions in unconsolidated sediments. **Earth Planet. Sci. Lett.**, **9**, 307-309.

MARSHALL C.E., 1964 - The Physical Chemistry and Mineralogy of Soils. John Wiley Sons, New-York, 388 p.

MARTIN VIVALDI J.L. and MACEWAN D.M.C., 1960 - Corrensite and swelling chlorite. **Clay Miner. Bull.**, **4**, 173-181.

MASSONE H.J., 1981 - Phengite : Eine experimentelle Untersuchung ihres Druck-Temperatur-Verhaltens in System K_2O $MgO-Al_2O_3-SiO_2-H_2O$. **Thesis, Univ. Bochum (CFR)**, 211 p.

MATTIGOD S.V. and KITTRICK J.A., 1979 - Aqueous solubility studies of muscovite: Apparent nonstoichiometric solute activities at equilibrium. **Soil Sci. Amer. Journ.**, **43**, 180-185.

MAUREL P., 1962 - Etude minéralogique et géochimique des formations argileuses des environs de Saint-Affrique (Aveyron). **Bull. Soc. Franç. Minér. Crist.**, **85**, 329-374.

MAXWELL D.T. and HOWER J., 1967 - High-grade diagenesis and low-grade metamorphism of illite in the Precambrian Belt series. **Amer. Min.**, **52**, 843-856.

MEADE R.H., 1966 - Factors influencing the early stages of the compaction of clays and sands - Review. **Journ. Sed. Petr.**, **36**, 1085-1101.

MEILHAC A. and TARDY Y., 1970 - Genèse et évolution des séricites, vermiculites et montmorillonites au cours de l'altération des plagioclases en pays tempérés. **Bull. Serv. Carte Géol. Als. Lorraine**, **23**, 145-161.

MELSON W.G. and THOMPSON G., 1973 - Glassy abyssal basalts, Atlantic sea floor near St Pauli Rocks: Petrography and composition of secondary clay minerals. **Bull. Geol. Soc. Amer.**, **84**, 703-716.

MERINO E., 1975 - Diagenesis in Tertiary sandstones from Kettleman North Dome, California. I: Diagenetic mineralogy. **J. Sed. Petr.**, **45**, 320-336.

MEUNIER A., 1980 - Les mécanismes de l'altération des granites et le rôle des microsystèmes. Etude des arènes du massif granitique de Parthenay (Deux-Sèvres). **Mém. Soc. Géol. France, 140,** 80 p.

MEUNIER A., 1982 - Superposition de deux altérations hydrothermales dans la syénite monzonitique du Bac de Montmeyre (sondage INAG 1, Massif Central, France). **Bull. Minéral., 105,** 386-394.

MEUNIER A. and VELDE B., 1979 - Weathering mineral facies in altered granites: the importance of local small scale equilibria. **Min. Mag., 43,** 261-268.

MEUNIER A. and VELDE B., 1982 - Phengitization, sericitization and potassium-beidellite in a hydrothermally altered granite. **Clay Min., 17,** 285-299.

MEVEL C., 1979 - Mineralogy and chemistry of secondary phases in low temperature altered basalts from Deep Sea Drilling Project legs 51, 52 and 53. **D.S.D.P. Initial Reports, 53,** 1299-1317.

MEYER C. and HEMLEY J.J., 1959 - Hydrothermal alteration in some granodiorites. **Clays Clay Min., 6,** 89-100.

MEYER C. and HEMLEY J.J., 1967 - Wall rock alteration. Geochemistry of Hydrothermal Ore Deposits Rinehondt Winston N.Y. (BARNES ed.), 166-235.

MIDGLEY H.C., 1959 - A sepiolite from Mullion, Cornwall. **Clay Min., 4,** 88-93.

MILLOT G., 1964 - Géologie des Argiles. Masson and Cie, Paris, 510 p.

MILLOT G. and BONIFAS M., 1964 - Transformations isovolumétriques dans les phénomènes de latéritisation et de bauxitisation. **Bull. Serv. Carte Géol. Als. Lorr., 8,** 3-20.

MILLOT G., LUCAS J. and PAQUET H., 1965 - Evolution géochimique par dégradation et agradation des minéraux argileux dans l'hydrosphère. Geol. **Rundschau, 55,** 1-20.

MILLS W., 1980 - Analysis of conglomerates and associated sedimentary rocks of the Daito Ridge. Deep Sea Drilling Project site 445. **D.S.D.P. Initial Reports**, LVIII, 643-658.

MITRA S.D. and PRAKASH D., 1957 - Adsorption of potassium as influenced by concentration and pH of the solution. **Clay Min. Bull.**, 3, 151-153.

MITSUI K., 1975 - Diagenetic alteration of some minerals in argillaceous sediments in Western Hokkaido, Japan. **Sci. Rep. Tohoku Univ.**, 3rd Ser., 13, 13-65.

MITSUI K. and TAGUCHI, 1977 - Silica mineral diagenesis in Neogene Tertiary shales in the Tempoku District, Hokkaido, Japan. **J. Sed. Pet.**, 47, 158-167.

MIYASHIRO A. and SHIDO F., 1970 - Progressive metamorphism in zeolite assemblages. **Lithos.**, 3, 251-260.

MIYASHIRO A., SHIDO F. and EWING M., 1969a - Diversity and origin of abyssal tholeite from the middle atlantic Ridge near 24° and 30° north latitude. **Contr. Min. Pet.**, 23, 38-52.

MIYASHIRO A., SHIDO F. and EWING M., 1969b - Composition and origin of serpentinites from the Mid-Atlantic Ridge near 24° and 30° north latitude. **Contrib. Min. Petr.**, 23, 117-127.

MIYASHIRO A., SHIDO F. and KANEHIRA K., 1979 - Metasomatic chloritization of gabbros in the Mid-Atlantic Ridge near 30°N. **Marine Geol.**, 31, 1147-1152.

MIZUTANI S., 1970 - Silica minerals in the early stages of diagenesis. **Sedimentology**, 15, 419-436.

MOIOLA R.J., 1970 - Authigenic zeolites and K-feldspar in the Esmeralda formation, Nevada. **Amer. Min.**, 55, 1681-1691.

MONCURE G.K., SURDAM R.C., MCKAGUE H.L., 1980 - Zeolite diagenesis below Pahute Mesa, Nevada test site. **Clays Clay Min.**, 29, 385-396.

MOORE W.J., 1978 - Chemical characteristics of hydrothermal alteration at Bingham, Utah. **Econ. Geol.**, **73**, 1260-1269.

MOORE W.J. and CZAMANSKE G.K., 1973 - Compositions of biotites from unaltered and altered monzonitic rocks in the Bingham Mining District, Utah. **Econ. Geol.**, **68**, 269-280.

MOORE W.J. and NASH J.T., 1974 - Alteration and fluid inclusions studies of the porphyry copper ore body at Bingham, Utah. **Econ. Geol.**, **69**, 631-645.

MOORT J.C. VAN, 1971 - A comparative study of the diagenetic alteration of clay minerals in Mesozoic shales from Papua, New Guinea and in Tertiary shales from Louisiana, U.S.A. **Clays Clay Min.**, **19**, 1-20.

MOREY G.W., FOURNIER R.O. and ROWE J.S., 1962 - The solubility of quartz in water in the temperature interval from 25°C to 300°C. **Geochim. Acta**, **26**, 1029-1043.

MORGENSTEIN M., 1967 - Authigenic cementation of deep-sea sediments west of the Society Ridge, South Pacific. **Sedimentology**, **9**, 105-118.

MOTTE M.J. and HOLLAND H.D., 1978 - Chemical exchange during hydrothermal alteration of basalt by sea water. I: Experimental results for major and minor components of sea water. **Geochim.**, **43**, 1103-1116.

MUFFLER L.J.P. and WHITE D.E., 1969 - Active metamorphism of Upper Cenezoic sediments in the Salton Sea Geothermal field and the Salton Trough, Southeastern California. **Bull. Geol. Soc. Ame.**, **80**, 157-182.

MULLER G., 1961 - Die rezenten Sedimenten in Golf von Neapel. 2: Mineral-Neu-und Umbildingen in den rezenten Sedimenten des Golfes von Neapel. **Beiträge zur Min. Petr.**, **8**, 1-20.

MULLER G. and FORSTNER Y., 1976 - Primary nontronite from the Venezuelan Guayana: additional primary occurrences (Red Sea, Lake Malani). **Amer. Min.**, **61**, 500-501.

MUMPTON F.A. and ROY R., 1956 - The influence of ionic substitution on the hydrothermal stability of montmorillonoids. **Clays Clay Min.**, 3, 337-339.

MURATA K.J. and LARSON R.R., 1975 - Diagenesis of Miocene
siliceous shales, Tremblor Range, California. **Journ.
Res. U.S. Geol. Survey**, 3, 553-566.

MURRAY J.W., 1970 - The clay mineralogy of marine sediments
in the North Atlantic at 20°C latitude. **Earth Planetary
Sci. Letters**, 10, 1, 39-40.

NADEAU P.H. and REYNOLDS R.C., 1981 - Burial and contact
metamorphism in the Mancos Shale. **Clays Clay Min.**, 29,
249-259.

NAGY B. and BRADLEY W.T., 1955 - The structural scheme of
sepiolite. **Amer. Min.**, 40, 885-892.

NAHON D., CAROZZI A.V. and PARRON C., 1980 - Lateritic
weathering as a mechanism for the generation of ferruginous ovids. **Journ. Sed. Pet.**, 50, 1287-1298.

NAHON D., CLAUER N. and DHOSTE M., 1981 - Zeolitic hydrothermal metamorphism in laterites of Western Senegal.
Chem. Geol., 34, 319-330.

NASH T.J., 1973 - Microprobe analyses of sericite, chlorite
and epidote from Jerome, Arizona. **Journ. Res. U.S.
Geol. Survey**, 1, 673-678.

NATHAN Y. and FLEXER A., 1977 - Clinoptilolite, paragenesis
and stratigraphy. **Sediment.**, 24, 845-855.

NELSON B.W. and ROY R., 1958 - Synthesis of chlorites and
their structural and chemical constitution. **Amer. Min.**,
43, 707-725.

NICHOLS C.R., 1970 - Diabase argillation at King Mountain,
Kiown Country, Okla. **Journ. Sed. Petr.**, 40, n° 3, 838-
847.

NICOT E., 1981 - Les phyllosilicates des terrains précam-
briens du Nord-Ouest du Montana (U.S.A.) clans. **Bull.
Min.**, 104, 615-624.

NIELSON R.L., 1968 - Hypogene texture and mineral zoning in a copper bearing granodiorite porphyry stock, Santa Rita, New Mexico. **Econ. Geol.**, **63**, 37-50.

NORTON D., 1978 - Sourcelines, sourceregions and pathlines for fluids in hydrothermal systems related to cooling plutons. **Econ. Geol.**, **73**, 21-28.

ODIN G.S., 1975 - Les glauconites: constitution, formation, âge. Thesis, Univ. Paris, 245 p.

ODOM I.E., 1976 - Microstructure, mineralogy and chemistry of Cambrian glauconite pellets and glauconite, Central U.S.A. **Clays Clay Min.**, **24**, 232-238.

OJAKANGAS R.W. and KELLER W.D., 1964 - Glauconitization of rhyolite sand grains. **Journ. Sed. Petr.**, **34**, 84-90.

OTALORA G., 1964 - Zeolites and related minerals in Cretaceous rocks of East-Central Puerto Rico. **Amer. Journ. Sci.**, **262**, 726-734.

OWENS J.P. and MINARD J.P., 1960 - Some characteristics of glauconite from the coastal plain formations of New Jersey. **U.S. Geol Sur. Special Papers**, 60 p.

PAPAVASSILIOU C.Th. and COSGROVE M.E., 1981 - Chemical and mineralogical changes during basalt-sea water interaction: site 223, Leg 23. D.S.D.P., North-West Indian Ocean. **Min. Mag.**, **44**, 141-146.

PAPKE K.G., 1972 - A sepiolite-rich playa deposit in Southern Nevada. **Clays Clay Min.**, **20**, 211-215.

PAQUET H., 1970 - Evolution géochimique des minéraux argileux dans les altérations et les sols des climats méditerranéens tropicaux à saisons contrastées. **Bull. Serv. Carte Géol. Als. Lorraine**, 30, 1-212.

PAQUET H. and MILLOT G., 1972 - Geochemical evolution of clay minerals in the weathered products of soils of mediterranean climate. **Proc. Int. Clay Conf.**, **Madrid,**, 199-206.

PARADIS S., VELDE B. and NICOT E., 1983 - Chloritoïd pyrophyllite-rectorite facies rocks from Brittany France. **Contrib. Min. Petr.** (in press).

PARNEIX J.C. and MEUNIER A., 1982 - Les paragenèses de remplacement des biotites utilisées comme marqueurs des conditions de température et de composition des fluides dans les altérations hydrothermale et supergène du granite de Mayet-de-Montagne (Allier, France). **Bull. Minér.**, 105, 662-672.

PARRY W.T. and REEVES C.C., 1966 - Lacustrine glauconitic mica from pluvial Lake Mound, Lynn and Terry Counties, Texas. **Amer. Min.**, 51, 229-235.

PARRY W.T. and REEVES C.C., 1968 - Sepiolite from pluvial Mound Lake, Lynn and Terry Counties, Texas. **Amer. Min.**, 53, 984-993.

PASSAGLIA E., 1970 - The crystal chemistry of chabazites. **Amer. Min.**, 55, 1278-1301.

PATTON T.C., GRANT A.R. and CHENEY E.S., 1973 - Hydrothermal alteration at the Middle Fork copper prospect, Central Cascades, Washington. **Econ. Geol.**, 68, 816-830.

PEDRO G., 1966 - Essai sur la caractérisation géochimique des roches superficielles (cycle alumino-silicique). **Compte-Rendu Acad. Sci. Paris**, 262, 1828-1831.

PEDRO G., 1968 - Distribution des principaux types d'altération chimique à la surface du globe. **Revue Géog. Phys. et de Géol. Dynam.**, X, 457-470.

PEDRO G., CARMOUZE J.P. and VELDE B., 1978 - Peloidal nontronite formation in recent sediments of Lake Chad. **Chem. Geol.**, 23, 139-149.

PERRY E.A. and HOWER J., 1970 - Burial diagenesis in Gulf Coast pelitic sediments. **Clays Clay Min.**, 18, 165-178.

PERRY E.A. and HOWER J., 1972 - Late stage dehydratation in deeply buried pelitic sediments. **Bull. Amer. Assoc. Petr. Geol.**, 56, 2013-2021.

PETERS T. and VON SALIS K., 1965 - Palygorskite als Kluft-
belag in der tortonen Molasse des Entlebuchs (schwei-
zerisches Mitteland). **Schweiz Min. Pet. Mitt.**, **45**, 123-
140.

PEVEAR D.R., WILLIAMS V.E. and MUSTOE G.E., 1980 - Kaolinite, smectite and K-rectorite in bentonites: relation to
coal rank at Tulameen. **Clays Clay Min.**, **28**, 241-250.

PEYRONE L., PAGNIANI G. and FAAGNANI G., 1965 - Tufi con
glauconite nell'alta v. Trompia (Brescia). **Rend. Soc.
Min. Italiana, 21.**

PILLIPS C.H., CAMBELL N.A. and FOUNTAIN D.S., 1974 - Hydrothermal alteration, mineralization and zoning in the
Ray deposit. **Econ. Geol.**, **69**, 1237-1250.

PIRANI R., 1963 - Sul fillosilicato dei livelli eruttivi di
Monte Bonifato di alcamo e di Monte Barbaro di Segesta
e sulla validita di uso della nomenclatura binomica:
Glauconite-celadonite. **Min. Petr. Acta**, **9**, 31-78.

PORRENGA D.H., 1966 - Clay minerals in recent sediments.
Clays Clay Min., **14**, 221-233.

PORRENGA D.H., 1976a - Glauconite and chamosite as depth
indicators in the marine environment. **Marine Geol.**, **5**,
495-501.

PORRENGA D.H., 1967b - Clay mineralogy and geochemistry of
recent marine sediments in tropical areas. Thesis,
Univ. Amsterdam.

PORRENGA D.H., 1968 - Non-marine glauconitic illite in the
lower Oligocene of Aadebrug, Belgium. **Clay Min.**, 7,
421-429.

POST J.L., 1978 - Sepiolite deposits of the Las Vegas, Nevada area. **Clays Clay Min.**, **26**, 58-64.

POWERS M.C., 1967 - Fluid release mechanisms in compacting
marine rocks and their importance in oil exploration.
Bull. Amer. Assoc. Petr. Geol., **51**, 1240-1253.

PREISINGER A., 1959 - X-ray study of the structure of sepiolite. **Clays Clay Min.**, **6**, 61-67.

PRIGOGINE I. and DEFRAY R., 1954 - Chemical Thermodynamics. Longmans, London, 543 pp.

PRITCHARD R.G., 1979 - Alteration of basalts from Deap Sea Drilling project Legs 51, 52 and 53, Holes 417A and 418A. D.S.D.P. Init. Reports, **46**, 1185-1199.

PROST R., 1975 - Etude de l'hydratation des argiles : interactions eau-minéral et mécanismes de la rétention de l'eau. Thesis, Fac. Sci. Univ. Paris, 100 pp.

PROUST D., 1976 - Etude de l'altération des amphibolites de La Roche-l'Abeille : évolutions chimiques et minéralogiques des plagioclases et des hornblendes. Thesis, Univ. Poitiers, 85 pp.

PROUST D., 1982 - Supergene alteration of metamorphic chlorite in an amphibolite from the Massif Central, France. **Int. Clay Conf. 1981, Bologne. Developments in Sedimentology** H. VAN OLPHEN & F. VENIALE eds, **35**, 357-364.

PROUST D. and VELDE B., 1978 - Beidellite crystallization from plagioclase and amphibole precursors: local and long-range equilibrium during weathering. **Clay Min.**, **13**, 199-209.

PRYOR W.A., 1975 - Biogenic sedimentation and alteration of argillaceous sediments in shallow marine environments. **Bull. Geol. Soc. Amer.**, **86**, 1244-1254.

QUIGLEY R.M. and MARTIN R.T., 1963 - Chloritized weathering products of a New England glacial till. **Clays Clay Min.**, **10**, 107-116.

RAMBERG H. and DEVORE G.W., 1951 - The distribution of Fe^{++} and Mg^{++} in coexisting olivines and pyroxenes. **Journ. Geol.**, **59**, 193-210.

RAMBOZ C., 1980 - Géochimie et étude des phases fluides de gisements et indices d'étain - tungstène du Sud du Massif Central (France). **Thesis 3ème cycle, Univ. Nancy**, 278 p.

RATTERMAN N.G. and SURDAM R.C., 1980 - Zeolite mineral reactions in a tuff in the Laney member of the Green River Formation, Wyo. **Clays Clay Min.**, **29**, 365-377.

RAVINA I. and LOW P.F., 1972 - Relation between swelling, water properties and b dimension in montmorillonite-water systems. **Clays Clay Min.**, **20**, 109-123.

RAYNER J.H., 1965 - Multivariate analysis of montmorillonite. **Clay Min.**, **6**, 59-70.

READ P.B. and EISBACHER G.H., 1974 - Regional zeolite alteration of the Sustat Group, North Central British Columbia. **Can. Min.**, **12**, 527-541.

REESMAN A.L. and KELLER W.D., 1967 - Chemical composition of illite. **Journ. Sed. Petr.**, **37**, 592-596.

REYNOLDS W.R., 1970 - Mineralogy and stratigraphy of lower Tertiary clays and claystones of Alabama. **Journ. Sed. Petr.**, **40**, 829-837.

REYNOLDS R.C. and ANDERSON D.M., 1967 - Cristobalite and clinoptilolite in bentonite of the Colville group, Northern Alaska. **Journ. Sed. Petr.**, **37**, 966-969.

REYNOLDS R.C. and HOWER J., 1970 - The nature of interlayering in mixed-layer illite-montmorillonites. **Clays Clay Min.**, **18**, 25-36.

REX R.W., 1967 - Authigenic silicates formed from basaltic glass by more than 60 million years contact with sea water, Synvania Guyot Marshall Islands. **Clays Clay Min.**, **15**, 195-203.

REX R.W. and MARTIN B.D., 1966 - Clay mineral formation in sea water by submarine weathering of K-feldspar. **Clays Clay Min.**, **14**, 235-240.

REX R.W., SYERS J.K., JACKSON M.L. and CLAYTON R.N., 1969 - Eolian origin of quartz in soils of Hawaiian Islands and in Pacific pelagic sediments. **Science**, **163**, 277-279.

RICCI J.E., 1966 - The Phase Rule and Heterogeneous Equilibrium. Dover, New-York, 505 p.

RICH C.I., 1958 - Muscovite weathering in a soil developed in the Virginia Piedmont. **Clays Clay Min.**, **5**, 203-213.

RICH C.I. and OBERSHAIN S.S., 1955 - Chemical and clay mineral properties of a red-yellow podzolic soil derived from a muscovite schist. **Soil Sci. Amer. Proc.**, **19**, 334-339.

RIMSAITE J., 1972 - Genesis of chlorite, vermiculite, serpentine, talc and secondary oxides in ultrabasic rocks. **Proceed. Int. Clay Conf.**, **Madrid**, 291-302.

RIMSTIDT J.D. and BARNES H.L., 1980 - The kinetics of silica-water reactions. **Geochim.**, **44**, 1683-1700.

RINALDI R., 1976 - Crystal chemistry and structural epitaxy of offretite-erionite from Sasbach, Kaiserstuhl. **N. Jb. Miner. Mh.**, **4**, 145-156.

ROBERSON H.E. and LAHANN R.W., 1981 - Smectite to illite conversion rates: effects of solution chemistry. **Clays Clay Min.**, **29**, 129-135.

ROBERT M., 1970-1971 - Etudes expérimentales de la désagrégation du granite et de l'évolution des micas. **Ann. Agron.**, 1970, **21**, 778-817 ; 1971, **22**, 43-93 and 155-181.

ROBERT M. and PEDRO G., 1972 - Etablissement d'un schéma de l'évolution expérimentale des micas trioctaédriques en fonction des conditions du milieu (pH, concentration). **Proc. Int. Clay Conf.**, **Madrid**, 433-448.

ROGERS L.E.R., QUIRK J.P. and NORRISH K., 1956 - Aluminous sepiolite. **Journ. Soil Sci.**, **7**, 177-183.

ROHRLICH V., PRICE N.B. and CALVERT S.E., 1969 - Chamosite in recent sediments of Loch Etive Scotland. **Journ. Sed. Petr.**, **39**, 624-631.

ROSE A.W., 1970 - Zonal relations of wallrock alteration and sulfide distribution at Porphyry Copper Deposits. **Econ. Geol.**, **65**, 920-936.

ROSS C.S. and HENDRICKS S.B., 1945 - Minerals of the montmorillonite group. **U.S. Geol. Surv. Prof. Papers, 205**.

ROY R. and ROMO L.A., 1957 - Weathering Studies. 1: New data on vermiculite. **Journ. Geol.**, **65**, 603-610.

ROY M.D. and ROY R., 1954 - Synthesis and stability of minerals in the system $MgO-Al_2O_3-SiO_2-H_2O$. **Amer. Min.**, **39**,
147-178.

ROZENSON I., BAUMINGER E.R. and HELLER-KALLAI L., 1979 -
Mossbauer spectra of iron in 1:1 phyllosilicates. **Amer.
Min.**, **64**, 893-901.

ROZENSON I., SPIRO B. and ZAK I., 1982 - Transformation of
iron-bearing kaolinite to iron-free kaolinite, goethite
and hematite. **Clays Clay Min.**, **30**, 207-214.

RUSSEL J.D. and CLARK D.R., 1978 - The effect of Fe for Si
substitution on the b-dimension of nontronite. **Clay
Min.**, **13**, 133-138.

SABATIER G., 1969 - Palygorskite from the Deep-Sea. A discussion. **Amer. Min.**, **54**, 567-568.

SAEGART W.E., SELL J.D. and KILPATRICK B.E., 1974 - Geology
and mineralization of La Caridad porphyry copper deposit, Sonora, Mexico. **Econ. Geol.**, **69**, 1060-1077.

SAND L.B. and REGIS A.J., 1966 - An unusual zeolite assemblage, Bowie, Arizona. **Geol. Soc. Amer. Special Paper**,
87.

SAND L.B., ROY R. and OSBORN E.F., 1957 - Stability relations of some minerals in the $Na_2O-Al_2O_3-SiO_2-H_2O$ system. **Econ. Geol.**, **52**, 169-179.

SAVIN S.M. and EPSTEIN S., 1970 - The oxygen and hydrogen
isotope geochemistry of ocean sediments and shales.
Geochim., **34**, 43-64.

SAWATZKI G.G., 1975 - Etude géologique et minéralogique des
flyschs à grauwackes volcaniques du synclinal de Thones
(Haute-Savoie, France). **Arch. Sci.**, **38**, 271-368.

SCHALLER W.T., 1950 - An interpretation of the composition
of high-silica sericites. **Min. Mag.**, **29**, 407-415.

SCHEIDEGGER K.F. and STAKES D.S., 1977 - Mineralogy, chemistry and crystallization sequence of clay minerals in

altered tholeotic basalts from the Peru trench. E.P.S.L., **36**, 413-422.

SCHEIDEGGER K.G. and STAKES D.S., 1979 - X-ray diffraction and chemical study of secondary minerals from Deep-Sea drilling project leg 51, Holes 417A and 417D. **Init. Rep. D.S.D.P.**, **51-53**, 1253-1263.

SCHELLMANN W., 1966 - Eroded oolites, Fe oxide = chamosite in sea sed. **Zeit Evzbergbau und Metallhütenwesen**, **19**, 302-305.

SCHELLMANN W., 1969 - Die Bildungsbedingungen sedimentärer Chamosit und Hämatit-Eisenerze am Beispiel der Lager-stätte Echte. **N. Jb. Miner. Abh.**, **111**, 1-31.

SCHLENKER B., 1971 - Petrographische Untersuchungen am Gipskeuper und Lettenkeuper von Stuttgart. **Oberrhein Geol. Abh**, **20**, 69-102.

SCHMIDT G.W., 1973 - Interstitial water composition and geo-chemistry of deep Gulf Coast shales and sandstones. **Bull. A.A.P.G.**, **57**, 321-337.

SCHMIDT V. and MAC DONALD D.A., 1979 - The role of secondary porosity in the course of sandstone diagenesis. Aspect of Diagenesis. **Soc. Econ. Palco Miner.**, **Sp. Pub.**, **26**, 443 pp.

SCHOEN R., 1964 - Clay minerals of the Silurian Clinton ironstones, New York State. **Journ. Sed. Petr.**, **34**, 855-863.

SCHOEN R. and WHITE D.E., 1965 - Hydrothermal alteration in GS-3 and GS-4 drill holes, main Terrace, Steamboat Springs, Nevada. **Econ. Geol.**, **60**, 1411-1421.

SCHOEN R. and WHITE D.E., 1966 - Hydrothermal clay minerals in granodiorite of the Main Terrace, Steamboat Springs, Nevada. **Clays Clay Min.**, **13**, 121-122.

SCHRADER E.L., ROSENDAHL B.R., FURBISH W.J. and MATTEY D.P., 1980 - Mineralogy and geochemistry of hydrothermal and pelagic sediments from the mounds hydrothermal field, Galapagos spreading center, D.S.D.P. Leg 54. **Journ. Sed. Petr.**, **50**, 917-928.

SCHWAIGHOFER B., 1980 - Pedogenetischen Palygorskit in einem Lössprofil bei Stillfried ander March (Neiderösterreich). **Clay Min.**, 15, 283-290.

SCHULTZ L.G., 1969 - Lithium and potassium absorption, dehydroxylation temperature, and structural water content of aluminous smectites. **Clays Clay Min.**, 17, 115-149.

SCHWOCHOW F.E. and HEINZE G.W., 1970 - Process of zeolite formation in the system $Na_2O-Al_2O_3-SiO_2-H_2O$. **Amer. Chem. Soc. 2nd Zeolite Conf.**, 95-100.

SEIBERTZ E. and VORTISCH W., 1979 - Zur Stratigraphie, Petrologie und genese einen Bentonite-Lage aus dem oberen Mittel-Turon (Oberkreide) des südostlichen Munsterlandes. **Geol. Rund**, 68, 649-679.

SEKI Y., 1969 - Facies series in low-grade metamorphism. **Journ. Geol. Soc. Japan**, 75, 255-266.

SEYFRIED W.E. and BISCHOFF J.L., 1979 - Low temperature basalt alteration by seawater: an experimental study at 70°C and 150°C. **Geochim.**, 43, 1937-1948.

SEYFRIED W.E. and BISCHOFF J.L., 1981 - Experimental sea water basalt interaction at 300°C, 500 bars, chemical exchange, secondary mineral formation and implications for the transport of heavy metals. **Geochim.**, 45, 135-148.

SHELTON J.W., 1964 - Authigenic kaolinite in sandstone. **Journ. Sed. Petr.**, 34, 102-111.

SHEPPARD R.A., 1970 - Zeolites in sedimentary deposits of the United States: A review. **Amer. Chem. Soc. 2nd Zeolite Conf.**, 428-459.

SHEPPARD R.A. and GUDE A.J., 1969 - Diagenesis of tuffs in the Barstow formation, Mud Hills, San Bernadino County, California. **U.S. Geol. Sur. Prof. Paper**, 634, 34 p.

SHEPPARD R.A. and GUDE A.J., 1971 - Chemical composition and physical properties of phillipsite from the Pacific and Indian Oceans. **Amer. Min.**, 55, 205-262.

SIEVER R., 1957 - The silica budget in the sedimentary cycle. **Amer. Min.**, **42**, 821-841.

SIEVER R., 1959 - Petrology and geochemistry of silica cementation in some Pennsylvanian sandstones. **Soc. Econ. Pal. Min. Special Pub.**, **7**, 55-79.

SIEVER R., 1962 - Silica solubility 0°-200°C, and the diagenesis of siliceous sediments. **Journ. Geol.**, **70**, 127-150.

SIFFERT B., 1962 - Quelques réactions de la silice en solution: La formation des argiles. **Mém. Serv. Carte Géol. Als. Lorr.**, **21**, 86 p.

SIGVALDASON G.E., 1962 - Epidote and related minerals in two deep geothermal drill holes, Reyjavick and Hveragerdi, Iceland. **U.S. Geol. Sur. Prof. Paper**, **450E**, 77-79.

SIGVALDASON G.E. and WHITE D.E., 1961 - Hydrothermal alteration of rocks in two drill holes at Steamboat Springs, Washoe County, Nevada. **U.S. Geol. Sur. Prof. Papers**, **424D**, 116-122.

SILLITOE R.H., 1973 - Geology of the Los Pelambres porphyry copper deposit, Chile. **Econ. Geol.**, **68**, 1-10.

SINGER A., 1979 - Palygorskite in sediments: Detrital, diagenetic or neoformed. A critical review. **Geol. Rund.**, **68**, 996-1008.

SINGER A. and NORRISH K., 1974 - Pedogenic palygorskite occurrences in Australia. **Amer. Min.**, **59**, 508-517.

SINGER A. and STOFFERS P., 1980 - Clay mineral diagenesis in two East African lake sediments. **Clay Min.**, **15**, 291-307.

SINGER A. and STOFFERS T., 1981 - Hydrothermal vermiculite from the Atlantic II Deep, Red Sea. **Clays Clay Min.**, **29**, 454-458.

SRÖDON J., 1980a - Synthesis of mixed layered kaolinite/smectite. **Clays Clay Min.**, **28**, 419-424.

SRÖDON J., 1980b - Precise identification of illite/smectite interstratification by X-ray powder diffraction. **Clays Clay Min.**, **28**, 401-411.

STAKES D.S. and O'NEIL J.R., 1982 - Mineralogy and stable isotope geochemistry of hydrothermally altered oceanic rocks. **E.P.S.L.**, **57**, 285-304.

STANLEY K.O. and BENSON L.V., 1979 - Early diagenesis of high plains Tertiary vitric and arkosic sandstone, Wyoming and Nebraska. **In** Aspects of Diagenesis. **Soc. Econ. Paleo. Miner.**, Sp. Pub., **26**, 401-424.

STAUDIGEL H. and HART S.R., 1983 - Alteration of basaltic glass : Mechanisms and significance for the ocean-crust-seawater budget. **Geochim. Cosmochim. Acta**, **47**, 337-350.

STAUDIGEL H., MUELENBACHS K., RICHARDSON S.H. and HART S.R., 1981 - Agents of low temperature ocean crust altera-tion. **Contrib. Min. Pet.**, **77**, 150-157.

STEINER A., 1953 - Hydrothermal rock alteration at Wairakei, New Zealand. **Econ. Geol.**, **48**, 1-13.

STEINER A., 1968 - Clay minerals in hydrothermally altered rocks at Wairakei, New Zealand. **Clays Clay Min.**, **16**, 193-213.

STONECIPHER S.A., 1976 - Origin, distribution and diagenesis of phillipsite and clinoptilolite in deep-sea sedi-ments. **Chem. Geol.**, **17**, 307-318.

STRINGHAM B. and TAYLOR A., 1950 - Nontronite at Bingham, Utah. **Amer. Min.**, **35**, 1060-1066.

STUDER H.P., 1967 - Mineral analysis of natural zeolite deposits. **Clays Clay Min.**, **15**, 186-188.

STUDER M. and BERTRAND J., 1981 - Métamorphisme de sédiments marneux en bordure de filons basiques (Haut-Atlas central, Maroc). **Schweiz Min. Petr. Mitt.**, **61**, 51-80.

SUDO T., 1963 - Interstratified minerals from Japan, their geological behaviors and origins. **Proc. 1st Int. Clay Conf.**, 113-120.

SUMMERS K.V., 1976 - The clay component of the Columbia River palagonites. **Amer. Min.**, **61**, 492-494.

SUQUET H., 1978 - Propriétés de gonflement et structure de la saponite. **Thesis, Univ. Paris**, 282 pp.

SUQUET H., IIYAMA J.T., KODAMA H. and PEZERAT H., 1977 - Synthesis and swelling properties of saponites with increasing layer charge. **Clays Clay Min.**, **25**, 231-242.

SURDAM R.C., 1966 - Analcime-wairakite mineral series. Abstr. Geol. Soc. Amer. Meeting, **Spec. Pap.**, **87**.

SURDAM R.C. and BOLES J.R., 1979 - Diagenesis of volcanic sandstones. **In** Aspects of Diagenesis. **Soc. Econ. Paleo. Miner.**, Sp. Pub., **26**, 227-242.

SURDAM R.C. and EUGSTER H.P., 1976 - Mineral reactions in the sedimentary deposits of the Lake Magadi region, Kenya. **Bull. Geol. Soc. Amer.**, **87**, 1739-1752.

SURDAM R.C. and PARKER R.D., 1972 - Authigenic alumino-silicate minerals in the tuffaceous rocks of the Green River Formation, Wyoming. **Bull. Geol. Soc. Amer.**, **83**, 689-700.

SWINDALE L.D. and POW-FOONG FAN, 1967 - Transformation of gibbsite to chlorite in ocean bottom sediments. **Science**, **157**, 799-800.

TAILBURDEEN O. and GOULDING W.D., 1983 - Charge heterogeneity in smectites. **Clays Clay Min.**, **31**, 37-42.

TARDY Y., 1969 - Géochimie des altérations. Etudes des arènes et des eaux de quelques massifs cristallins d'Europe et d'Afrique. **Mém. Ser. Carte Géol. Als. Lorr.**, **31**, 187 p.

TATEYAMA H., TOMITA K. and OBA N., 1970 - On alteration minerals in the "Green Tuff" in the Northern part of Kagoshima Prefecture, Japan. **Reports Fac. Sci. Kagoshima Univ.**, **3**, 5-15.

TAYLOR A.M. and ROY R., 1964 - Zeolite studies. II : Na-P zeolites and ion-exchanged derivatives of tetragonal Na-P. **Amer. Min.**, **49**, 656-682.

TAYLOR M.W. and SURDAM R.C., 1980 - Zeolite reactions in the tuffaceous sediments at Teels Marsh, Nevada. **Clays Clay Min.**, **29**, 341-352.

TAYLOR R.P. and FRYER B.J., 1980 - Multiple-stage hydrothermal alteration in porphyry copper systems in Northern Turkey. **Can. Journ. Earth Sci**, **17**, 901-926.

THOMPSON A.B., 1971 - Analcite-albite equilibria at low temperatures. **Amer. Journ. Sci.**, **271**, 79-92.

THOMPSON G.R. and HOWER J., 1975 - The mineralogy of glauconite. **Clays Clay Miner.**, **23**, 289-300.

THOMPSON G.R. and MELSON W.G., 1970 - Boron contents of serpentinites and metabasalts in the oceanic crust: implication for the boron cycle in oceans. **E.P.S.L.**, **8**, 61-65.

THOMPSON J.B., 1955 - The thermodynamic basis for the mineral facies concept. **Amer. Journ. Sci.**, **253**, 65-103.

THOMPSON J.P., 1970 - Geochemical reaction and open systems. **Geochim. Acta**, **34**, 529-551.

THOREZ J. and VAN LECKWIJCK W., 1967 - Les minéraux argileux et leurs altérations dans le Namurien Inférieur de Belgique. **Ann. Soc. Géol. Belgique**, **90**, 329-377.

TIEN PEI-LIN, 1973 - Palygorskite from Warren Quarry, Enderly Leicester-shire England. **Clay Min.**, **10**, 27-34.

TIMOFEEV P.P., EREMEEV V.V. and RATEEV M.A., 1977 - Palygorskite, sepiolite and other clay minerals in leg 41 oceanic sediments: mineralogy, facies and genesis. **Init. Rep. D.S.D.P.**, **41**, 1087-1101.

TOMASSON J. and KRISTMANNSDOTTIR H., 1972 - High temperature alteration mineral and thermal bines, Reykjanes, Iceland. **Contr. Min. Petr.**, **36**, 123-134.

TOMITA K., TATEYAMA H. and OBA N., 1970 - Formation of vermiculite and kaolin mineral from hornblends. **Journ. Jap. Assoc. Min. Petr. Econ. Geol.**, 64-71.

TOMITA K., YAMASHITA H. and OBA N., 1969 - An inter-stratified mineral found in altered andesite. **Journ. Jap. Assoc. Min. Petr. Econ. Geol.**, 61, 25-34.

TRAUTH N., 1977 - Argiles évaporitiques dans la sédimentation carbonatée continentale et épicontinentale tertiaire. **Sci. Géol.**, 49, 195 pp.

TRESCASES J.J., 1979 - Remplacement progressif des silicates par les hydroxydes de fer et de nickel dans les profils d'altération tropicale des roches ultrabasiques. **Sci. Géol.**, 32, 181-188.

TRIPPLEHORN D.M., 1970 - Clay mineral diagenesis in Atoka (Penn) sandstones Crawford County, Ark. **Journ. Sed. Petr.**, 40, 838-847.

TRUESDELL A.H. and CHRIST C.L., 1968 - Cation exchange in clays interpreted by regular solution theory. **Amer. Journ. Sci.**, 266, 402-412.

USDOWSKI H.E. and BARNES H.L., 1972 - Untersuchungen über das Gleichgewicht zwischen K-feldspat, Quarz und Muskovit und die Anwendung auf Fragen der Gesteinsbildung bei tieferen Temperaturen. **Contr. Min. Petr.**, 36, 207-219.

VELDE B., 1965a - Experimental determination of muscovite polymorph stabilities. **Amer. Min.**, 50, 436-449.

VELDE B., 1965b - Phengite micas: synthesis, stability and natural occurrence. **Amer. Journ.**, 262, 886-913.

VELDE B., 1968 - The effect of chemical reduction on the stability of pyrophyllite and kaolinite in pelitic rocks. **Journ. Sed. Petr.**, 38, 13-16.

VELDE B., 1969 - The compositional join muscovite-pyrophyllite at moderate temperatures and pressures. **Bull. Soc. Fr. Min. Crist.**, 92, 360-638.

VELDE B., 1971 - A discussion of the stability and natural occurrence of margarite. **Min. Mag.**, **295**, 317-323.

VELDE B., 1972 - Celadonite micas: Solid solutions and stability. **Contr. Min. Petr.**, **37**, 235-247.

VELDE B., 1973 - Phase equilibria studies in the system MgO-Al_2O_3-SiO_2-H_2O: Chlorites and associated minerals. **Min. Mag.**, **39**, 297-312.

VELDE B., 1977 - A proposed phase diagram for illite, expanding chlorite, corrensite and illite-montmorillonite mixed layered minerals. **Clays Clay Min.**, **25**, 264-270.

VELDE B., 1978 - High temperature or metamorphic vermiculites. **Contr. Miner. Petr.**, **66**, 319-323.

VELDE B. and BYSTROM-BRUZEWITZ A.M., 1972 - Transformation of natural clay minerals at elevated temperatures and pressures. **Geol. For. Forsh.**, **94**, 450-458.

VELDE B. and BRUZEWITZ A.M., 1981 - Metasomatic and non-metasomatic low grade metamorphism in Ordovician meta-bentonites in Sweden. **Geochim. Cosmochim. Acta**, **46**, 447-452.

VELDE B. and HOWER J., 1963 - Petrological significance of illite polymorphism in Paleozoic sedimentary rocks. **Amer. Min.**, **48**, 1239-1254.

VELDE B. and KORNPROBST J., 1969 - Stabilité des silicates d'alumine hydratés. **Contr. Min. Petr.**, **21**, 63-74.

VELDE B. and ODIN G.S., 1975 - Further information related to the origin of glauconite. **Clays Clay Min.**, **23**, 376-381.

VELDE B., RAOULT J.F. and LEIKINE, 1974 - Metamorphosed berthiérine pellets in Mid-Cretaceous rocks from North-Eastern Algeria. **Journ. Sed. Petr.**, **44**, 1275-1280.

VELDE B. and RUMBLE D., 1977 - Alumina content of chlorites in muscovite-bearing assemblages. Carnegie Inst. Wash. Yearbook, 76, 621-623.

VELDE B. and WEIR A., 1979 - Synthetic illite in the chemical system $K_2O-Al_2O_3-SiO_2-H_2O$ at 300°C and 2 Kb. **Proc. Sixth Int. Clay Conf.**, Elsevier, 395-404.

VELDE D., 1971 - Les lamprophyres à feldspaths alkalins et biotite : minettes et roches voisines. **Contr. Min. Petr.**, 30, 216-239.

VENIALE F. and VAN DER MAREL H.W., 1963 - An interstratified saponite-swelling chlorite mineral as a weathering product of Lizardite rock from St Margherita Staffora (Pavia Province) Italy. **Beiträge Min. Petr.**, 9, 198-245.

VENIALE F. and VAN DER MAREL H.W., 1968 - A regular talc-saponite mixed-layer mineral from Ferriere, Nare Valley (Piacenza Province), Italy. **Contr. Min. Petr.**, 17, 237-254.

VERGO N. and APRIL R.H., 1982 - Interstratified clay minerals in contact aureols, West Rock, Connecticut. **Clays Clay Min.**, 30, 237-240.

VILLAS R.N. and NORTON D., 1977 - Irreversible mass transfer between circulating hydrothermal fluids and the Mayflower stock. **Econ. Geol.**, 72, 1471-1504.

WACKERMAN J.M., 1975 - L'altération des massifs cristallins basiques en zone tropicale semi-humide. **Cah. O.R.S.T.O.M., sér. Géol.**, 7, 67-172.

WALKER T.R., WAUGH B. and GRONE A.J., 1978 - Diagenesis in first-cycle desert alluvion of Cenozoic age South Western United States and Northwestern Mexico. **Bull. G.S.A.**, 89, 19-32.

WALKER T.R., RIBBE P.H. and HONEA R.M., 1967 - Geochemistry of hornblende alteration in Pliocene red beds, Baja California, Mexico. **Bull. Geol. Soc. Amer.**, 78, 1055-1060.

WALTON A.W., 1975 - Zeolite diagenesis in Oligocene volcanic sediments, Trans Pecos, Texas. **Bull. G.S.A.**, 86, 615-624.

WATMUFF G., 1978 - Geology of the alteration-mineralization zoning in the central portion of the Yandera Porphyry copper prospect, Papua, New Guinea. **Econ. Geol.**, **73**, 829-856.

WATTS L.N., 1976 - Paleopedogenic palygorskite from the basal Permo-Triassic of North-West Scotland. **Amer. Min.**, **61**, 299-302.

WEAVER C.E., 1956 - Mineralogy of the middle Devonian Tioga K-bentonite. **Amer. Min.**, **41**, 359-362.

WEAVER C.E., 1959 - The clay petrology of sediments. **Clays Clay Min.**, **6**, 154-187.

WEAVER C.E. and BECK K.C., 1971 - Clay-water diagenesis during burial: how mud becomes gneiss. **Geol. Soc. Amer. Special Paper**, **134**, 155 p.

WEAVER C.E. and BECK K.C., 1977 - Miocene of the S.E. United States: A model for chemical sedimentation in a peri-marine environment. **Sed. Geol.**, **17**, 1-236.

WEL VAN DER, D., 1972 - Asbestos minerals from Kongsberg silver deposit. **Norsk. Geol. Tidsskrift**, **52**, 277-294.

WERMUND E.G. and MOIOLA R.J., 1966 - Opal, zeolites and clays in Eocene neritic bar sand. **Journ. Sed. Petr.**, **36**, 248-253.

WHELAN J.A., 1961 - An occurrence of saponite near Silver Bay, Minnesota. **Amer. Min.**, **46**, 430-433.

WHITNEY G., 1983 - Hydrothermal reactivity of saponite. **Clays Clay Min.**, **31**, 1-8.

WILDMAN W.E., JACKSON M.L. and WHITTING L.D., 1968 - Serpentine rock dissolution as a function of carbon dioxide pressure in aqueous solution. **Amer. Min.**, **53**, 1252-1263.

WILDMAN W.E. and WHITTING L.D., 1971 - Serpentine stability in relation to formation of iron-rich montmorillonite in some California soils. **Amer. Min.**, **56**, 587-602.

WILKINSON J.F.G. and WHETTEN J.T., 1964 - Some analcime-bearing pyroclastic and sedimentary rocks from New South Wales. **Journ. Sed. Petr.**, 34, 543-553.

WILSON M.D. and PITTMAN E.D., 1977 - Authigenic clays in sandstones: Recognition and influence on reservoir properties and paleoenvironmental analysis. **Journ. Sed. Petr.**, 47, 3-31.

WINKLER H.G.F., 1964 - Das P-T-feld der Diagenese und niedrigtemperierten Metamorphose auf Grund von Mineralreaktionen. **Beiträge zur Min. Petr.**, 10, 70-93.

WISE W.S. and EUGSTER H.P., 1964 - Celadonite: Synthesis, thermal stability and occurrence. **Amer. Min.**, 49, 1031-1083.

WISE W.S. and TSCHERNICK R.W., 1976a - The chemical compositions and origin of the zeolites offretite, erionite and levyne. **Amer. Min.**, 61, 853-863.

WISE W.S. and TSCHERNICK R.W., 1976b - Chemical composition of ferrierite. **Amer. Min.**, 61, 60-66.

WOLFF R.G., 1967 - Weathering of Woodstock granite near Baltimore, Maryland. **Amer. Journ.**, 265, 106-117.

WOLLAST R. and BROEU F. de, 1971 - Study of the behavior of dissolved silica in the estuary of the Scheldt. **Geochim. Acta**, 35, 613-620.

WOLLAST R., MACKENZIE F.T. and BRICKER O.P., 1968 - Experimental precipitation and genesis of sepiolite at earth-surface conditions. **Amer. Min.**, 53, 1645-1662.

YAALON D.H. and WEIDER M., 1976 - Pedogenic palygorskite in some arid brown (calciorthid) soils of Israel. **Clay Min.**, 11, 73-80.

YEH H.W. and SAVIN S.M., 1977 - Mechanism of burial metamorphism of argillaceous sediments: 3-0-isotope evidence. **Geol. Soc. Amer.**, 88, 1321-1330.

YODER H.S., 1952 - The $MgO-Al_2O_3-SiO_2-H_2O$ system and the related metamorphic facies. **Amer. Journ. Sci.**, Bowen vol., 569-627.

YODER H.S. and EUGSTER H.P., 1955 - Synthetic and natural muscovite. Geochim. Acta, **8**, 255-280.

YOSHIMURA T., 1971 - Interstratified clay minerals in the Miocene pyroclastic formations from Oshima-Fukushima, Hokkaido. **Sci. Rep. Niigata Univ.**, ser. **E2**, 1-26.

ZEN E.A., 1961 - The zeolite facies: an interpretation. Amer. Journ. Sci., **259**, 401-409.

ZEN E.A., 1962 - Problem of the thermodynamic status of the mixed-layer minerals. Geochim. Acta, **26**, 1055-1067.

ZEN E.A., 1969 - Free energy of formation of pyrophyllite from hydrothermal data: values, discrepancies and implications. **Amer. Min.**, **54**, 1592-1606.

ZHDANOV S.P., 1970 - Some problems of zeolite crystallization. **Amer. Chem. Soc.**, **2nd Zeolite Conf.**, 19-41.

SUBJECT INDEX